Essential Maths

Book 8C

David Rayner, Michael White

Elmwood Press

2

First published 2009 by
Elmwood Press
80 Attimore Road
Welwyn Garden City
Herts. AL8 6LP
Tel. 01707 333232

ISBN 9781 902 214 764

Numerical answers are published in a separate book

PREFACE

Essential Maths Book 8C has been written for pupils who are working towards National Curriculum Level 6. Level 5 work is consolidated and then developed further.

Broadly speaking the book is split into 6 units. There is no set path through the books but each unit of work could be used during one half-term with appropriate revision material at the end of the unit. Many topics are reviewed later in the book, in line with the National Numeracy Strategy guide.

Puzzle activities and mental arithmetic tasks can be found between the units, to be used whenever appropriate. Investigations appear regularly throughout the book. Ideas for discussing and exploring themes from the 'history of mathematics' are included between each pair of units.

The authors believe that children learn mathematics most effectively by *doing* mathematics. Many youngsters who find mathematics difficult derive much more pleasure and enjoyment from the subject when they are doing questions which help them build up their confidence. Pupils feel a greater sense of satisfaction when they work in a systematic way and when they can appreciate the purpose and the power of the mathematics they are studying.

No textbook will have the 'right' amount of material for every class. The authors believe that it is preferable to have too much material rather than too little. Opportunities for functional maths are incorporated into activities throughout the book.

Most work is broken down into two parts. 'M' exercises are aimed at all children at this level. 'E' exercises provide extension work. Pupils may move naturally onto this work after an 'M' exercise or teachers may judge that a number of students should *only* tackle an 'E' exercise.

Pupil self-assessment is a very important part of assessment for learning. Regular 'check yourself' sections appear throughout the book. Answers to these parts only are provided at the back of the book for immediate feedback.

David Rayner and Michael White

CONTENTS

Unit 1   Page
1.1 Sequences   1
1.2 Fractions   4
1.3 Properties of numbers   13
1.4 Negative numbers   20
1.5 Area and Perimeter   27
Unit 1 Mixed Review   34

Unit 2
2.1 Rounding off and estimating   44
2.2 Using Algebra   51
2.3 Fractions, decimals, percentages   60
2.4 Geometrical Reasoning   66
2.5 Construction and Locus   74
2.6 Circles   79
Unit 2 Mixed Review   87

Unit 3
3.1 Written Calculations   96
3.2 Using a calculator   106
3.3 Formulas and expressions   113
3.4 Drawing graphs   120
3.5 Reflection   129
Unit 3 Mixed Review   137

Unit 4
4.1 Describing data   147
4.2 Rotation and combined transformations   156
4.3 Interpreting and sketching real-life graphs   165
4.4 Brackets and equations   171
4.5 Fractions review   185
4.6 Handling data   190
Unit 4 Mixed Review   201

Unit 5
5.1 Ratio and proportion   210
5.2 Negative numbers review   216
5.3 Sequences – the nth term   218
5.4 Enlargement   226
5.5 Congruent shapes, tessellation   232
5.6 Drawing graphs review   236
5.7 Area review   241
Unit 5 Mixed Review   247

Unit 6
6.1 Precentages   256
6.2 Probability   263
6.3 Measures   273
6.4 Algebra Review   276
6.5 3–D Objects   283
6.6 Bearings and scale drawing   287
6.7 Decimals Review   294
6.8 Volume   297
Unit 6 Mixed Review   302

UNIT 1

1.1 Sequences

In section 1.1 you will:

- find the next term in a sequence
- find and use a rule for a sequence

Sequences are very important in mathematics. Scientists carrying out research will often try to find patterns or rules to describe the results they obtain from experiments.

Here is a sequence 3, 6, 12, 24

- A number sequence is a set of numbers in a given order.

- Each number in a sequence is called a *term*.

Exercise 1M

Find the next number in each sequence.

1 4, 9, 14, 19

2 5, 8, 11, 14

3 17, 13, 9, 5

4 32, 25, 18, 11

5 2, 4, 8, 16

6 $2, 2\frac{1}{2}, 3, 3\frac{1}{2}$

7 0.6, 0.8, 1, 1.2

8 1, 4, 8, 13

9 3, 30, 300

10 80, 79, 77, 74

11 1, 3, 9, 27

12 11, 7, 3, −1

13 100, 10, 1, 0.1

14 −5, −2, 1, 4

15 $\frac{1}{16}, \frac{1}{8}, \frac{1}{4}, \frac{1}{2}$

16 Write down each sequence and find the missing numbers.

(a) | 2 | 6 | 18 | 54 | ☐ |

(b) | 9 | 5 | ☐ | −3 | −7 |

(c) | ☐ | 8 | ☐ | ☐ | 17 | 20 |

(d) | 1 | 2 | 4 | ☐ | 11 |

17 The first term of a sequence is 7 and the *term-to-term rule* is 'add 8'. The next term is 7 'add 8' which equals 15. Write down the next five terms of the sequence.

18 The first term of a sequence is 19 and the term-to-term rule is 'subtract 3'.
    Write down the first five terms of the sequence.

19 Write down the term-to-term rule for each sequence.

(a) 11, 13, 15, 17, 19

(b) 62, 57, 52, 47

(c) 5, 10, 20, 40

(d) 81, 27, 9, 3

20 This picture shows ten piles of coins.

(a) Another row of piles is placed on the bottom.
     How many piles of coins are there now?

(b) Another two rows of piles are now added
     onto the bottom. How many piles of coins
     are there now ?

21 Write down the rule for each sequence.

(a) 4.3, 4.5, 4.7, 4.9   (b) 86, 43, 21.5   (c) 0.02, 0.2, 2, 20

(d) 4, 1, –2, –5   (e) 1.6, 0.8, 0.4, 0.2   (f) 2.01, 2.05, 2.09

22 You are given the first term and the rule of several sequences. Write down the first five terms
    of each sequence.

First term	Rule
(a) 26	add 5
(b) 5	subtract 2
(c) 6	double
(d) 8000	divide by 10

Exercise 1E

1 In a linear sequence the terms go up or go down in equal steps.
   For example 5, 9, 13, 17, … or 20, 17, 14, 11, …
   Find the missing numbers in these linear sequences.

(a) 2, ☐, 12, 17, ☐, ☐

(b) ☐, 32, ☐, 20, 14

(c) ☐, 27, ☐, 21, ☐

(d) ☐, 41, ☐, ☐, ☐, 17

2   The following are linear sequences.

(a)

The 2nd term is 7
The 3rd term is 12
What is the 6th term?

(b)

The 2nd term is 17
The 4th term is 31
What is the 6th term?

3   The rule for the number sequences below is

'double and add 1'

Find the missing numbers

(a) 3 $\longrightarrow$ 7 $\longrightarrow$ 15 $\longrightarrow$ 31 $\longrightarrow$ ☐

(b) ☐ $\longrightarrow$ 9 $\longrightarrow$ 19 $\longrightarrow$ 39

(c) ☐ $\longrightarrow$ 7 $\longrightarrow$ ☐ $\longrightarrow$ ☐

4   The rule for the sequences below is

'multiply by 3 and take away 1'

Find the missing numbers.

(a) 1 $\longrightarrow$ 2 $\longrightarrow$ 5 $\longrightarrow$ ☐

(b) ☐ $\longrightarrow$ 8 $\longrightarrow$ 23 $\longrightarrow$ ☐

(c) 4 $\longrightarrow$ ☐ $\longrightarrow$ ☐ $\longrightarrow$ ☐

5   Find the rule for each sequence. Each rule has two operations (similar to the rules in questions 3 and 4 above).

(a) 4 $\longrightarrow$ 7 $\longrightarrow$ 13 $\longrightarrow$ 25

(b) 2 $\longrightarrow$ 7 $\longrightarrow$ 22 $\longrightarrow$ 67

6   Look at this sequence $3^2 = 9$

$$33^2 = 1089$$
$$333^2 = 110\ 889$$
$$3333^2 = 11\ 108\ 889$$

Write down the value of $33\ 333^2$ and the value of $33\ 333\ 333^2$.

7   Copy and complete the following sequence.

$$2 \times 99 = 198$$
$$3 \times 99 = 297$$
$$4 \times 99 = 396$$
$$5 \times 99 = \boxed{}$$
$$\boxed{} \times 99 = \boxed{}$$

8   (a) Look at the pattern below and then continue if for a further three rows.

$$2^2 + 2 + 3 = 9$$
$$3^2 + 3 + 4 = 16$$
$$4^2 + 4 + 5 = 25$$
$$\vdots \quad \vdots \quad \vdots \quad \vdots$$

     (b) Write down the line which starts

$$12^2 + \ldots$$

     (c) Write down the line which starts

$$20^2 + \ldots$$

1.2 Fractions

In section 1.2 you will:

- convert improper fractions and mixed numbers
- add and subtract fractions
- multiply fractions

Proper and improper fractions

Proper fraction	*improper* fraction	*mixed number*
⬇	⬇	⬇
numerator is less than denominator.	numerator is larger than denominator.	contains both a whole number and a fraction.
examples: $\frac{3}{7}, \frac{17}{59}$	examples: $\frac{4}{3}, \frac{17}{5}$	examples: $4\frac{1}{2}, 7\frac{3}{4}$

(often called 'top–heavy' fractions)

Change $\frac{11}{4}$ to a mixed number.

Divide numerator by denominator. $11 \div 4 = 2$ rem. 3

Put remainder over denominator. $\frac{11}{4} = 2\frac{3}{4}$

Exercise 1M

Change the following improper fractions to mixed numbers or whole numbers only.

1 $\frac{7}{2}$ 2 $\frac{8}{3}$

3 $\frac{5}{4}$ 4 $\frac{9}{2}$ 5 $\frac{12}{2}$ 6 $\frac{13}{7}$ 7 $\frac{11}{8}$ 8 $\frac{28}{7}$

9 $\frac{12}{5}$ 10 $\frac{27}{4}$ 11 $\frac{22}{7}$ 12 $\frac{17}{9}$ 13 $\frac{23}{6}$ 14 $\frac{73}{10}$

15 Write the purple areas as both mixed numbers and improper fractions.

(a)   (b)

(c) 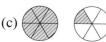   (d)

Change $3\frac{4}{7}$ to an improper fraction.

Multiply whole number by denominator. $3 \times 7 = 21$

Add the numerator. $21 + 4 = 25$

Put sum over denominator. $3\frac{4}{7} = \frac{25}{7}$

Exercise 1E

1 How many halves are there in $6\frac{1}{2}$?

2 How many quarters are there in $7\frac{3}{4}$?

In questions 3 to 17 change the mixed numbers to improper fractions.

3 $2\frac{1}{3}$ 4 $3\frac{1}{4}$ 5 $5\frac{2}{3}$ 6 $6\frac{3}{4}$ 7 $4\frac{2}{5}$

8 $7\frac{1}{8}$ 9 $5\frac{1}{5}$ 10 $4\frac{3}{7}$ 11 $5\frac{1}{3}$ 12 $2\frac{4}{5}$

13 $4\frac{7}{9}$ 14 $6\frac{7}{10}$ 15 $5\frac{3}{8}$ 16 $8\frac{1}{5}$ 17 $7\frac{4}{9}$

18 John has painted $\frac{91}{8}$ Warhammer warriors.

Kat has painted $11\frac{5}{8}$ Warhammer warriors.

Who has painted the larger amount?

19 Which fraction in this grid is *not* written as
    both an improper fraction and a mixed number?

$\frac{45}{7}$	$\frac{41}{7}$	$6\frac{6}{7}$
$5\frac{6}{7}$	$6\frac{3}{7}$	$\frac{43}{7}$
$\frac{37}{7}$	$\frac{48}{7}$	$5\frac{2}{7}$

Adding and subtracting fractions

Remember: $\frac{6}{9} = \frac{2}{3}$ ($\div 3$) $\frac{10}{15} = \frac{2}{3}$ ($\div 5$)   We say that $\frac{2}{3}$, $\frac{6}{9}$ and $\frac{10}{15}$ are *equivalent fractions*.

Fractions can be added or subtracted when they have the same denominator.

$\frac{1}{7} + \frac{3}{7} = \frac{4}{7}$ Only add the numerators, *not* the denominators.

If fractions do not have the same denominator, change them into *equivalent fractions* which do have the same denominator before adding or subtracting.

(a) $\frac{1}{12} + \frac{1}{4}$

$= \frac{1}{12} + \frac{3}{12}$

$= \frac{4}{12} = \frac{1}{3}$

(b) $\frac{9}{10} - \frac{3}{5}$

$= \frac{9}{10} - \frac{6}{10}$

$= \frac{3}{10}$

(c) $\frac{1}{3} + \frac{2}{5}$

$= \frac{5}{15} + \frac{6}{15}$

$= \frac{11}{15}$

Cancel final answer if you can

Exercise 2M

1 Find the missing number to make these fractions equivalent.

(a) $\frac{3}{8} = \frac{\square}{16}$ (b) $\frac{1}{4} = \frac{\square}{20}$ (c) $\frac{20}{48} = \frac{\square}{12}$ (d) $\frac{6}{15} = \frac{\square}{5}$

(e) $\frac{5}{9} = \frac{\square}{45}$ (f) $\frac{5}{7} = \frac{\square}{42}$ (g) $\frac{3}{11} = \frac{\square}{44}$ (h) $\frac{18}{21} = \frac{\square}{7}$

2 Write four fractions equivalent to $\frac{2}{5}$.

3 Cancel down each fraction to its simplest terms

(a) $\frac{7}{21}$ (b) $\frac{6}{24}$ (c) $\frac{18}{45}$ (d) $\frac{40}{64}$ (e) $\frac{24}{42}$

(f) $\frac{60}{144}$ (g) $\frac{20}{1000}$ (h) $\frac{34}{40}$ (i) $\frac{33}{121}$ (j) $\frac{30}{75}$

4 Each card has a fraction and a letter. Find the cards which contain equivalent fractions and arrange the letters to make the name of a capital city.

(a)

M	A	R	E	O	T
$\frac{6}{10}$	$\frac{15}{24}$	$\frac{21}{35}$	$\frac{12}{20}$	$\frac{30}{50}$	$\frac{10}{16}$

(b)

S	C	E	M	O	W	A	O
$\frac{9}{21}$	$\frac{33}{77}$	$\frac{9}{24}$	$\frac{27}{63}$	$\frac{24}{56}$	$\frac{60}{140}$	$\frac{15}{45}$	$\frac{6}{14}$

5 Work out

(a) $\frac{3}{11}+\frac{7}{11}$ (b) $\frac{2}{5}+\frac{1}{5}$ (c) $\frac{4}{15}+\frac{7}{15}$ (d) $\frac{1}{8}+\frac{2}{8}+\frac{4}{8}$

(e) $\frac{6}{7}-\frac{2}{7}$ (f) $\frac{7}{9}-\frac{5}{9}$ (g) $\frac{3}{10}+\frac{4}{10}$ (h) $\frac{1}{6}+\frac{5}{6}-\frac{3}{6}$

6 Copy and complete

(a) $\frac{3}{10}+\frac{1}{5}$

$=\frac{3}{10}+\frac{\square}{10}=\frac{\square}{10}$

(b) $\frac{5}{8}+\frac{1}{4}$

$=\frac{5}{8}+\frac{\square}{8}=\frac{\square}{8}$

(c) $\frac{7}{12}-\frac{1}{3}$

$=\frac{7}{12}-\frac{\square}{12}=\frac{\square}{12}$

7 Work out the following:

(a) $\frac{1}{6}+\frac{2}{3}$ (b) $\frac{3}{4}+\frac{1}{8}$ (c) $\frac{3}{5}-\frac{1}{10}$ (d) $\frac{5}{8}+\frac{1}{16}$

(e) $\frac{5}{6}-\frac{2}{3}$ (f) $\frac{3}{4}-\frac{3}{8}$ (g) $\frac{5}{18}+\frac{1}{9}$ (h) $\frac{1}{10}+\frac{1}{20}$

8 Christine throws away $\frac{1}{4}$ of her shoes.

She gives $\frac{1}{8}$ of her shoes to her sister.

During July she wears $\frac{1}{2}$ of her shoes.

What fraction of her shoes does she

still have but has not worn in July?

9 In an election, everyone voted for either A, B or C. If A got $\frac{1}{4}$ of the votes and B got $\frac{3}{8}$ of the votes, what fraction of the votes did C get?

Exercise 2E

1. Copy and complete these calculations

(a) $\dfrac{3}{5} - \dfrac{1}{2}$

$= \dfrac{\square}{10} - \dfrac{\square}{10}$

$=$

(b) $\dfrac{1}{2} + \dfrac{1}{7}$

$= \dfrac{\square}{14} + \dfrac{\square}{14}$

$=$

(c) $\dfrac{2}{5} - \dfrac{1}{4}$

$= \dfrac{8}{20} - \dfrac{\square}{20}$

$=$

2. Work out

(a) $\dfrac{1}{4} + \dfrac{1}{3}$

(b) $\dfrac{1}{2} + \dfrac{2}{5}$

(c) $\dfrac{1}{3} + \dfrac{2}{5}$

(d) $\dfrac{3}{4} + \dfrac{1}{5}$

(e) $\dfrac{1}{5} - \dfrac{1}{6}$

(f) $\dfrac{2}{3} - \dfrac{1}{4}$

(g) $\dfrac{7}{12} - \dfrac{1}{8}$

(h) $\dfrac{1}{2} - \dfrac{2}{11}$

(i) $\dfrac{2}{5} + \dfrac{1}{6}$

(j) $\dfrac{5}{6} - \dfrac{3}{4}$

(k) $\dfrac{7}{8} - \dfrac{3}{5}$

(l) $\dfrac{2}{7} + \dfrac{2}{5}$

3. Troy watches $\dfrac{3}{5}$ of a film then makes a cup of tea. He then watches another $\dfrac{1}{4}$ of the film. What total fraction of the film has he now watched?

4.  Trevor blows his trumpet for $\dfrac{1}{6}$ of the day and plays the drums for $\dfrac{3}{8}$ of the day. They both drive Amy to the brink of madness!
What fraction of the day does Amy spend on the brink of madness?

5. Davina reads $\dfrac{3}{8}$ of her book one day and $\dfrac{2}{5}$ the next day. What fraction of the book is still left to be read?

6. Rebecca and Chris went on a short expedition. They were given equal rations of food. The chart shows what fraction of their food they ate each day. Who had the larger fraction of food left for Thursday and by how much?

	Rebecca	Chris
Monday	$\dfrac{1}{10}$	$\dfrac{1}{6}$
Tuesday	$\dfrac{1}{3}$	$\dfrac{1}{2}$
Wednesday	$\dfrac{2}{5}$	$\dfrac{1}{5}$
Thursday	?	?

7　Copy and complete these calculations

(a) $1\frac{1}{4} + 1\frac{2}{3}$

$= \frac{5}{4} + \frac{5}{3}$

$= \frac{\square}{12} + \frac{\square}{12}$

$= \frac{\square}{12}$

$= 2\frac{\square}{12}$

(b) $2\frac{3}{5} + 1\frac{1}{2}$

$= \frac{\square}{5} + \frac{\square}{2}$

$= \frac{\square}{10} + \frac{\square}{10}$

$= \frac{\square}{10}$

$= \square\frac{\square}{10}$

(c) $3\frac{1}{3} - 1\frac{3}{4}$

$= \frac{\square}{3} - \frac{\square}{4}$

$= \frac{\square}{12} - \frac{\square}{12}$

$= \frac{\square}{12}$

$= \square\frac{\square}{12}$

8　Work out, leaving each answer as a mixed number.

(a) $1\frac{2}{5} + 2\frac{1}{3}$

(b) $2\frac{1}{2} + 2\frac{5}{8}$

(c) $1\frac{1}{3} + 2\frac{1}{4}$

(d) $3\frac{1}{2} - 1\frac{5}{6}$

(e) $4\frac{5}{6} - 2\frac{1}{2}$

(f) $3\frac{3}{4} - 1\frac{7}{8}$

Fraction of a number

Work out $\frac{4}{5}$ of 70

Find $\frac{1}{5}$ of 70 first, so $70 \div 5 = 14$

$\frac{1}{5}$ of 70 = 14, so $\frac{4}{5}$ of 70 = $14 \times 4 = 56$

$\frac{4}{5}$ of 70 = 56

Exercise 3M

Work out

1　$\frac{2}{3}$ of 15

2　$\frac{5}{6}$ of 24

3　$\frac{3}{4}$ of 16

4　$\frac{3}{8}$ of 24

5　$\frac{9}{10}$ of 60

6　$\frac{2}{5}$ of 100

7　$\frac{5}{6}$ of 36

8　$\frac{3}{5}$ of 120

9　The petrol tank of a car holds 60 litres. How much petrol is in the tank when it is $\frac{4}{5}$ full?

10  Justin works 54 hours a week and he spends $\frac{5}{6}$ of his time on the phone. How many hours is that?

11　In six years Wayne Rooney scored 144 goals and $\frac{2}{9}$ of these were headers. How many headers did he score?

12 Work out

(a) $\frac{5}{9}$ of 27 km   (b) $\frac{2}{3}$ of 63 kg   (c) $\frac{5}{7}$ of 63m   (d) $\frac{5}{6}$ of 204 kg

(e) $\frac{8}{9}$ of £108   (f) $\frac{2}{3}$ of 1275 m   (g) $\frac{1}{8}$ of 12 hours   (h) $\frac{3}{4}$ of £4.20

13 Find each missing number below.

(a) $\frac{\square}{4}$ of 32 = 24   (b) $\frac{\square}{7}$ of 21 = 9   (c) $\frac{3}{\square}$ of 20 = 12

(d) $\frac{3}{\square}$ of 14 = 6   (e) $\frac{4}{5}$ of $\square$ = 16   (f) $\frac{3}{10}$ of $\square$ = 18

14 On each bounce a ball rises to $\frac{3}{4}$ of its previous height. How high will a ball bounce if it is dropped from a height of 2 metres?

15 Noel has £60. He spends two fifths of his money on a shirt. He spends three quarters of the remaining money on some trousers. How much money has he got left?

Multiplying fractions

The pink shaded strip is $\frac{1}{5}$ of the rectangle

The black section is $\frac{1}{4}$ of $\frac{1}{5}$ of the rectangle.

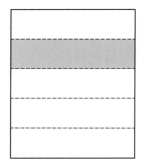
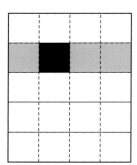

The rectangle on the right is divided into 20 equal parts so the black section is $\frac{1}{20}$ of the rectangle.

So $\frac{1}{4}$ of $\frac{1}{5}$ of the rectangle = $\frac{1}{20}$ of the rectangle

Notice that $\frac{1}{4} \times \frac{1}{5} = \frac{1}{20}$.

The word 'of' can be replaced by a multiplication.

Look at these multiplications

(a) $\frac{2}{3} \times \frac{1}{5} = \frac{2}{15}$ (b) $\frac{3}{7} \times \frac{1}{4} = \frac{3}{28}$

(c) $\frac{3}{4} \times \frac{1}{6} = \frac{\cancel{3}^1}{\cancel{24}_8} = \frac{1}{8}$ (d) $\frac{6}{7} \times \frac{2}{3} = \frac{\cancel{12}^4}{\cancel{21}_7} = \frac{4}{7}$

Multiply the numerators, multiply the denominators and then cancel down.

Exercise 3E

All fractions should be given in their simplest form.

1. Find (a) $\frac{1}{4}$ of $\frac{1}{3}$ (b) $\frac{3}{5}$ of $\frac{1}{4}$ (c) $\frac{2}{3}$ of $\frac{3}{4}$

2. Work out

   (a) $\frac{2}{5} \times \frac{3}{5}$ (b) $\frac{3}{7} \times \frac{1}{4}$ (c) $\frac{3}{8} \times \frac{2}{5}$ (d) $\frac{3}{4} \times \frac{1}{6}$

   (e) $\frac{5}{8} \times \frac{1}{2}$ (f) $\frac{5}{6} \times \frac{3}{4}$ (g) $\frac{2}{7} \times \frac{3}{4}$ (h) $\frac{1}{8} \times \frac{3}{5}$

   (i) $\frac{2}{9} \times \frac{3}{5}$ (j) $\frac{3}{11} \times \frac{1}{2}$ (k) $\frac{4}{9} \times \frac{3}{4}$ (l) $\frac{5}{12} \times \frac{8}{10}$

3. The diagram shows a square of side 1 m divided into four rectangles A, B, C and D.
   Find the areas of A, B, C and D in m².

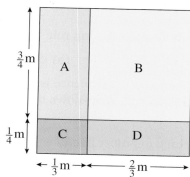

4. Work out, using cancelling.

   (a) $\frac{2}{3} \times \frac{6}{1}$ (b) $\frac{2}{5} \times \frac{20}{1}$ (c) $\frac{1}{8} \times \frac{10}{1}$ (d) $\frac{3}{7} \times 14$

   (e) $\frac{7}{10} \times 5$ (f) $\frac{5}{6} \times 4$ (g) $\frac{1}{20} \times 15$ (h) $\frac{3}{4} \times 6$

5. We can multiply mixed fractions by changing them to improper fractions ('top heavy fractions')

   For example: $2\frac{1}{2} \times \frac{3}{4} = \frac{5}{2} \times \frac{3}{4} = \frac{15}{8} = 1\frac{7}{8}$

   Work out (a) $3\frac{1}{2} \times \frac{2}{3}$ (b) $1\frac{3}{4} \times \frac{1}{5}$

6. A photograph is $3\frac{1}{4}$ inches tall and $2\frac{1}{2}$ inches wide. Calculate the area of the photograph.

7. Work out

   (a) $2\frac{1}{2} \times \frac{1}{4}$ (b) $2\frac{1}{2} \times \frac{1}{6}$ (c) $3\frac{1}{2} \times \frac{3}{10}$ (d) $1\frac{1}{2} \times \frac{2}{3}$

   (e) $3\frac{1}{4} \times \frac{1}{10}$ (f) $\frac{3}{5} \times 4\frac{1}{4}$ (g) $2\frac{1}{2} \times 1\frac{1}{2}$ (h) $3\frac{1}{2} \times 3\frac{1}{2}$

12

CHECK YOURSELF ON SECTIONS 1.1 AND 1.2

1 Finding the next number in each sequence

Find the next number in each sequence.

(a) 37, 29, 21, 13

(b) 2, 8, 32, 128

(c) 96, 48, 24, 12

(d) Find the missing numbers: $\boxed{-6}$, $\boxed{-2}$, $\boxed{}$, $\boxed{6}$, $\boxed{}$

2 Finding and using a rule for a sequence

Write down the term-to-term rule for each sequence.

(a) 3, 12, 48, 192

(b) 5, 11, 17, 23

(c) 5, 2, –1, –4

(d) The first term of a sequence is 9 and the term-to-term rule is 'multiply by 3 then subtract 1'. Write down the first four terms of the sequence.

3 Converting improper fractions and mixed numbers

Convert into mixed numbers: (a) $\frac{7}{3}$ (b) $\frac{35}{6}$

Convert into improper fractions: (c) $3\frac{4}{5}$ (d) $2\frac{3}{4}$

4 Adding and subtracting fractions

Work out (a) $\frac{1}{6} + \frac{2}{5}$ (b) $\frac{7}{8} - \frac{2}{3}$ (c) $1\frac{1}{2} + 2\frac{2}{3}$

5 Multiplying fractions

(a) Tom has 63 shots in a paintball game.
He hits with $\frac{4}{9}$ of his shots.
How many hits does he make?

(b) Find $\frac{3}{5} \times \frac{1}{2}$ (c) Find $\frac{2}{7} \times \frac{3}{4}$

1.3 Properties of numbers

In section 1.3 you will:

- use prime numbers, factors and multiples
- use square numbers
- break down numbers into prime factors
- use cube numbers and higher powers

Prime numbers, factors, multiples and square numbers

- A *prime* number is divisible by just two different numbers: by itself and by one.
  Notice that 1 is *not* a prime number.
  Here are some prime numbers: $\boxed{7}$ $\boxed{23}$ $\boxed{11}$

- The *factors* of 15 divide into 15 exactly.
  $\boxed{1 \times 15}$ $\boxed{3 \times 5}$ The factors of 15 are 1, 3, 5 and 15.

- The first four *multiples* of $\boxed{6}$ are $\boxed{6, 12, 18, 24}$
  The first four multiples of $\boxed{11}$ are $\boxed{11, 22, 33, 44}$

- The first *square number* is   1 $(1 \times 1 = 1^2)$
  The second *square number* is   4 $(2 \times 2 = 2^2)$
  The third *square number* is   9 $(3 \times 3 = 3^2)$

Exercise 1M

1. Write down the first four multiples of
   (a) 4   (b) 6   (c) 20   (d) 25

2. Which of these are prime numbers? $\boxed{21}$ $\boxed{5}$ $\boxed{49}$ $\boxed{81}$ $\boxed{13}$ $\boxed{65}$

3. Find *all* the factors of
   (a) 12   (b) 30   (c) 17   (d) 50

4. 7 is a factor of which numbers between 20 and 30?

5.
   (a) From the balls shown which two balls add up to 24?
       There are three answers.

   (b) Which two prime number balls add up to 18?
       There are two answers.

6 Write down the first ten prime numbers.

7 Which is larger and by how much? $\boxed{5^2 + 7^2}$ or $\boxed{3^2 + 8^2}$

8 The number in the square is the product of the two numbers on either side of it. Copy and complete:

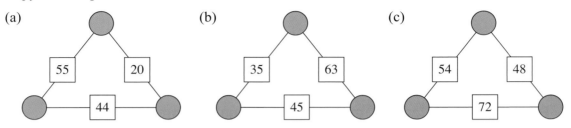

(a) 55 20 44

(b) 35 63 45

(c) 54 48 72

9 'All prime numbers are odd'. True or false?

10 Add together all the prime numbers less than 16.

Exercise 1E

1 (a) List the factors of 24.

(b) List the factors of 40.

(c) List the common factors of 24 and 40. [i.e. the numbers which are in list (a) and list (b).]

2 (a) List the factors of 28.

(b) List the factors of 36.

(c) List the common factors of 28 and 36.

(d) Write down the highest common factor of 28 and 36.

3 Find the highest common factor of

(a) 24 and 42   (b) 35 and 49

4 60 is mid-way between 2 prime numbers. What are they?

5 True or false?
'The total number of cubes in the pyramid is given by $5^2 + 4^2 + 3^2 + 2^2 + 1^2$.'

6 'All multiples of 9 are multiples of 3.' True or false?

7   Here are the first six multiples of 12 and 15

    12 : 12 24 36 48 60 72

    15 : 15 30 45 60 75 90

Write down the lowest common multiple of 12 and 15. [i.e. the lowest number which is in both lists.]

8   Copy and complete the fist five multiples of 6 and 8.

6 : 6, 12, ☐ , ☐ , ☐

8 : 8, ☐ , ☐ , ☐ , ☐

Write down the L.C.M. of 6 and 8

9   Find the lowest common multiple of:

    (a) 8 and 10   (b) 25 and 40

10   How many prime numbers have 5 as their last digit?

11   Here are the first three triangle numbers.

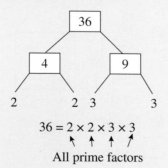

Draw similar diagrams to show the next two triangle numbers.

Show that consecutive pairs of triangle numbers add up to make square numbers.

12   'Modelkit' make kits for model planes in their factory. Martin has to check every 40th box to make sure the glue is correct. Nina checks every 50th box to make sure the paint is correct. Which is the first box that both Martin and Nina have to check?

Prime factor decomposition

Factors of a number which are also prime numbers are called prime factors. We can find these prime factors using a 'factor tree'. Here are two examples.

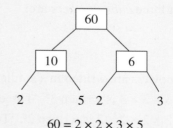

$$36 = 2 \times 2 \times 3 \times 3$$

All prime factors

$$60 = 2 \times 2 \times 3 \times 5$$

Exercise 2M

1. Copy and complete these factor trees.

(a)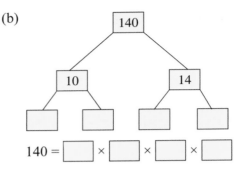

$$100 = \boxed{} \times \boxed{} \times \boxed{} \times \boxed{}$$

(b)

$$140 = \boxed{} \times \boxed{} \times \boxed{} \times \boxed{}$$

2. Draw a factor tree for 108. Remember that you only stop when you get to prime factors.

3. Draw factor trees for the following numbers.
   (a) 24　　　　(b) 72　　　　(c) 110　　　　(d) 300
   (e) 126　　　(f) 630　　　(g) 392　　　(h) 3960

4. $154 = 2 \times 7 \times 11$ and $1365 = 3 \times 5 \times 7 \times 13$. Find the highest common factor of 154 and 1365. [i.e the highest number that goes into 154 and 1365.]

5. $105 = 3 \times 5 \times 7$ and $330 = 2 \times 3 \times 5 \times 11$. Find the highest common factor of 105 and 330. [i.e the highest number that goes into 105 and 330.]

6. $975 = 3 \times 5 \times 5 \times 13$ and $550 = 2 \times 5 \times 5 \times 11$ Find the highest common factor (H.C.F) of 975 and 550.

7. Use your answers to question 1 to find the H.C.F. of 100 and 140.

8. Some prime numbers can be written as the sum of 2 square numbers, eg. $1^2 + 2^2 = 5$
   Find 4 two-digit prime numbers that can be written as the sum of two square numbers.
   [Hint: start by listing the square numbers.]

Cube numbers and higher powers

● The first three *cube numbers* are:　　$1^3 = 1 \times 1 \times 1 = 1$
　　　　　　　　　　　　　　　　　　$2^3 = 2 \times 2 \times 2 = 8$
　　　　　　　　　　　　　　　　　　$3^3 = 3 \times 3 \times 3 = 27$

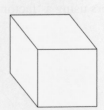

● Higher powers are written in a similar way
　$3 \times 3 \times 3 \times 3 \times 3$ is written 3^5. 'Three to the power 5'
　$2 \times 2 \times 2 \times 2 \times 2 \times 2$ is written 2^6. 'Two to the power 6'
　To work out 7^4 on a calculator, press $\boxed{7}\;\boxed{x^y}\;\boxed{4}\;\boxed{=}$

17

- Reminder: $\sqrt{81}$ is the square root of 81

  This means 'what number multiplied by itself makes 81'

  So $\sqrt{81} = 9$ because $9 \times 9 = 81$

Exercise 2E

1   Work out

(a) 4^3 (b) 5^3 (c) 6^3 (d) 10^3 (e) 7^3

2   Work out

(a) $\sqrt{16}$ (b) $\sqrt{25}$ (c) $\sqrt{64}$ (d) $\sqrt{100}$ (e) $\sqrt{49}$

3   Find how long the side of each square is:

(a) area = 36 cm²

(b) area = 9 cm²

(c) area = 144 cm²

4   Work out the following, without a calculator.

(a) 1^3 (b) 11^2 (c) $\left(\frac{1}{2}\right)^2$ (d) $\left(\frac{1}{2}\right)^3$ (e) 0.1^2

5   Copy and complete this table, using a calculator to help you obtain the answers.

We say	We write	We work out	Answer
2 to the power of 4	2^4	$2 \times 2 \times 2 \times 2$	
3 to the power of 4		$3 \times 3 \times 3 \times 3$	
	4^4		256
5 to the power of 2			
	6^5		7776
		$8 \times 8 \times 8 \times 8 \times 8$	
		$9 \times 9 \times 9$	
	3^9		
10 to the power of 2			
2 to the power of 10			

6   The numbers 10, 100, 1000 ... form the basis of the number system.

Write each of the numbers 10, 100, 1000, 10000, 100 000 and 1 million as power of 10.

7   '1 is the only cube number which is also a square number.' True or false?

8 *Without* using the square root key, use a calculator to estimate the following.
   Give your answers correct to the nearest whole number.

   (a) $\sqrt{47}$ (b) $\sqrt{125}$ (c) $\sqrt{199}$

9 Find the missing numbers so
   that the answer is always 100.

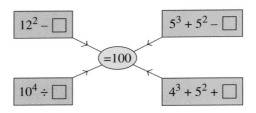

10 Read the letter which appeared recently
    in 'The Times' newspaper.
    How old was Tony at the time?

In his prime

Sir, The letters about age and numbers remind
me of an incident that occurred some years ago
when, after early retirement, I taught GCSE maths
part- time at a local college.

One of a group of mature students asked me my
age to which I replied that it was currently a prime
number and in three years' time would be a perfect
square.

Another student said I couldn't possibly be 13
to which another added that I could easily be 97.

The matter was resolved when yet another pointed
out that in three years' time my age would also be a
perfect cube. Such is the delight of numbers.

TONY HARWOOD
Chandlers Ford, Hants

Investigation – consecutive sums

- Consecutive numbers are whole numbers which appear next to each other on the number line:
  4, 5, 6, are consecutive.
  7, 10 are not consecutive.

- Using only sets of consecutive numbers it is possible to form all the numbers from 1 to 40
  except for the powers of two (1, 2, 4, 8, 16, 32).

- Copy and complete the table opposite to find the
  consecutive sums for every number from 1 to 40
  except powers of 2.
  Some target numbers can be formed in more than
  one way.

- Continue the pattern to 100. You should look at your
  results and use any patterns you can see to help you.

Target	Consecutive sum
1	Impossible
2	Impossible
3	1 + 2
4	Impossible
5	2 + 3
6	1 + 2 + 3
⋮	
40	6 + 7 + 8 + 9 + 10

Investigation – power sums

A Here is a list of the first six powers of 2.

$2^0 = 1$
$2^1 = 2$
$2^2 = 4$
$2^3 = 8$
$2^4 = 16$
$2^5 = 32$

(Yes! 2^0 really is 1. Check it on a calculator. We will discuss the power zero in a later book.)

● Using only the numbers 1, 2, 4, 8, 16 and 32 it is possible to form all the whole numbers from 1 to 32 inclusive, by adding and subtracting.

(We call them 'power *sums*' even though we sometimes subtract.)

Target	Power sum
1	1
2	2
3	4 − 1
4	4
5	4 + 1
6	2 + 4
7	1 + 2 + 4
⋮	⋮
32	32

● You may use each of 1, 2, 4, 8, 16, 32 only once.

E.g. $5 = 2 + 2 + 1$ is not allowed.

$5 = 4 + 1$ is allowed.

● Copy and complete the table above to find power sums for every number from 1 to 32.

● Can you continue the pattern to 63? 127?...

B

$3^0 = 1$
$3^1 = 3$
$3^2 = 9$
$3^3 = 27$

Here are the first four powers of 3. Using only these numbers it is possible to form all the whole numbers between 1 and 40. Copy and complete the table, again using each number only *once*.

Target	Power sum
1	1
2	3 − 1
3	3
4	1 + 3
5	9 − 3 − 1
⋮	⋮
40	?

1.4 Negative numbers

In section 1.4 you will:

- add and subtract negative numbers
- multiply and divide negative numbers

Adding and subtracting

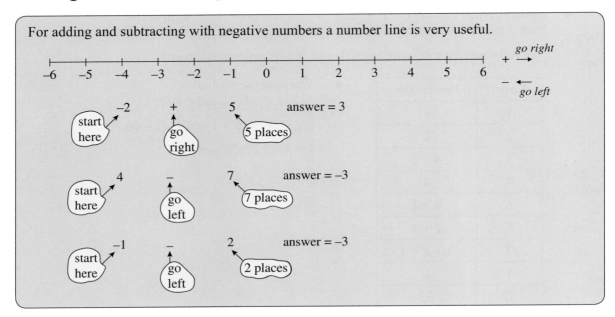

For adding and subtracting with negative numbers a number line is very useful.

Exercise 1M

1. Use a number line to work out

   (a) $3 - 4$ (b) $-3 + 5$ (c) $-2 + 7$ (d) $-3 - 1$

   (e) $1 - 6$ (f) $-4 + 6$ (g) $3 - 8$ (h) $-4 + 3$

   (i) $-3 - 2$ (j) $6 - 7$ (k) $2 - 4$ (l) $-5 + 9$

2. Work out

   (a) $5 - 10$ (b) $-4 - 4$ (c) $-3 + 1$ (d) $-2 + 2$

   (e) $7 - 11$ (f) $9 - 12$ (g) $-2 - 2$ (h) $5 - 15$

   (i) $-6 - 9$ (j) $-2 - 12$ (k) $7 - 10$ (l) $-4 + 10$

3. Copy each sentence and fill in the missing numbers.

   (a) $12, 8, 4, \boxed{}, \boxed{}$ (b) $\boxed{}, -2, 1, 4, 7$ (c) $\boxed{}, \boxed{}, -20, -10, 0$

4 Copy and complete the addition squares

(a)

+	7	−1		
		0		−1
−3			1	
2	9			
				3

(b)

+	−5	3		
−1		2		0
			10	
4				
			6	−1

Two signs together

Remember: It is possible to replace *two* signs next to each other by *one* sign as follows:

$$+ \quad + \quad = \quad +$$
$$- \quad - \quad = \quad +$$
$$- \quad + \quad = \quad -$$
$$+ \quad - \quad = \quad -$$

'add' if you have the same signs

'subtract' if you have different signs

When two signs next to each other have been replaced by one sign in this way, the calculation is completed using the number line as before.

Work out the following

(a) $-7 + (-4)$
$= -7 - 4$
$= -11$

(b) $8 + (-14)$
$= 8 - 14$
$= -6$

(c) $5 - (+9)$
$= 5 - 9$
$= -4$

(d) $6 - (-2)$
$= 6 + 2$
$= 8$

Exercise 1E

1 Work out

(a) $6 + (-3)$ (b) $3 + (-4)$ (c) $5 + (-5)$ (d) $3 + (-7)$

(e) $7 - (+2)$ (f) $4 - (+5)$ (g) $6 - (-2)$ (h) $3 - (-4)$

(i) $2 - (-4)$ (j) $5 - (-1)$ (k) $8 - (+3)$ (l) $10 - (+7)$

2 Work out

(a) $1 - (-3)$ (b) $7 - (-4)$ (c) $6 + (-8)$ (d) $4 + (-3)$

(e) $7 + (+2)$ (f) $5 - (+3)$ (g) $4 - (-6)$ (h) $3 - (-2)$

(i) $6 + (-9)$ (j) $10 + (-11)$ (k) $7 + (-10)$ (l) $-5 - (-7)$

3　At 25 000 feet on a mountain the air temperature is −23°C and because of the low air pressure water boils at 71°C (which makes it difficult to make a nice cup of tea).

What is the difference between the air temperature and the temperature of the water?

4　You can choose any 3 numbers from

−4　5　6　2　−1

Here is a calculation 　□ + □ − □ =

(a) What is the largest answer you can get?

(b) What is the smallest answer you can get?

5　Copy and complete the tables

a	9	3	8	3	2	5	4	7		
b	5	5	3	7	−2	−2			4	2
a−b	4	−2					−2	−3	−3	−1

a	−3	4	3	5	7	4	6			
b			−3	−1				5	−1	2
a−b	−3	−5			8	10	6	2	3	−2

6　Pat has −£40 in his bank account (this means he owes the bank £40).

During the next week he spends £15, £60 and £35. He pays in £30 and £75.
How much money does Pat now have in his bank account and what does this mean?

7　In a 'magic square' you get the same number when you add across each row, add down each column and add diagonally. Copy and complete the following magic squares.

(a)

0		
−1		
4	−3	

(b)

−2		−4
	−1	
		0

(c)

	−1		−3
3		9	
		−5	
−6	5	0	7

Multiplying and dividing

Remember:

When two numbers with the *same sign* are multiplied together, the answer is *positive*.

When two numbers with *different signs* are multiplied together, the answer is *negative*.

For division, the rules are the same as for multiplication.

$-3 \times (-2) = 6$ $6 \times (-4) = -24$ $-12 \div 4 = -3$

$30 \div (-3) = -10$ $-80 \div (-10) = 8$ $-2 \times (-4) \times (-2) = -16$

Exercise 2M

1 Copy and complete the multiplication square below. Some numbers inside the square are shown as an explanation.

$\times$	−5	−4	−3	−2	−1	0	+1	+2	+3	+4	+5
+5						0					
+4						0					
+3		−12				0					
+2						0				8	
+1						0					
0	0	0	0	0	0	0	0	0	0	0	0
−1						0					
−2						0		−4			
−3				6		0					
−4						0					
−5						0					

Exercise 2E

Work out

1. $6 \times (-2)$
2. -3×3
3. $8 \times (-2)$
4. $-5 \times (-3)$

5. $14 \div (-2)$
6. $12 \div (-3)$
7. $6 \div (-1)$
8. $-10 \div (-2)$

9. $-4 \div (-1)$
10. $16 \div (-8)$
11. $-20 \div (-5)$
12. $-18 \div (-6)$

13. $-25 \div 5$
14. $-30 \div (-6)$
15. $12 \div (-6)$
16. $-50 \div 10$

17. $28 \div (-4)$
18. $-36 \div 9$
19. $-24 \div (-8)$
20. $30 \div (-15)$

21. The temperature in London one night is $-3°C$ and in Toronto is $-8°C$. The temperature in Moscow is five times as cold as London. The temperature in Kiev is twice as cold as Toronto.

    Which is colder – Moscow or Kiev and by how much?

22. Find the missing numbers

    (a) $-4 \times \boxed{} = 12$
    (b) $3 \times \boxed{} = -12$
    (c) $-8 \div -4 = \boxed{}$
    (d) $5 \times \boxed{} = -5$

    (e) $\boxed{} \times (-3) = 9$
    (f) $12 \div \boxed{} = -6$
    (g) $\boxed{} \div (-3) = 2$
    (h) $\boxed{} \div 5 = -4$

    (i) $-2 \times \boxed{} = 20$
    (j) $-3 \times \boxed{} = 6$
    (k) $-2 \times \boxed{} = 4$
    (l) $(-1)^2 = \boxed{}$

23. The next number in each table is found by multiplying the two numbers before it.

    For example

-3	-2	6	-12	-72

    Copy and complete each table.

    (a)

3	-1		

    (b)

-5	3		

    (c)

-1	-2		

    (d)

3	-2		

    (e)

-2	-2		

    (f)

2		-6	

    (g)

		3	-9

    (h)

	4	-4	

    (i)

		-10	100

24. Answer true or false.

    (a) $7 \div (-7) = -1$
    (b) $(-4)^2 = -16$
    (c) $0 \times -5 = -5$

    (d) $(-3)^2 = 9$
    (e) $4 \times (-2) \times (-3) = 24$
    (f) $3 \times (-3)^2 = -18$

Practice tests

Questions on negative numbers are more difficult when the different sorts are mixed together. Do one of these tests every two weeks or so.

Test 1

1. $-8 - 8$	**2.** $-8 \times (-8)$
3. -5×3	**4.** $-5 + 3$
5. $8 - (-7)$	**6.** $20 - 2$
7. $-18 \div (-6)$	**8.** $4 + (-10)$
9. $-2 + 13$	**10.** $+8 \times (-6)$
11. $-9 + (+2)$	**12.** $-2 - (-11)$
13. $-6 \times (-1)$	**14.** $2 - 20$
15. $-14 - (-4)$	**16.** $-40 \div (-5)$
17. $5 - 11$	**18.** -3×10
19. $9 + (-5)$	**20.** $7 \div (-7)$

Test 2

1. $-10 \times (-10)$	**2.** $-10 - 10$
3. $-8 \times (+1)$	**4.** $-8 + 1$
5. $5 + (-9)$	**6.** $15 - 5$
7. $-72 \div (-8)$	**8.** $-12 - (-2)$
9. $-1 + 8$	**10.** $-5 \times (-7)$
11. $-10 + (-10)$	**12.** $-6 \times (+4)$
13. $6 - 16$	**14.** $-42 \div (+6)$
15. $-13 + (-6)$	**16.** $-8 - (-7)$
17. $5 \times (-1)$	**18.** $2 - 15$
19. $21 + (-21)$	**20.** $-16 \div (-2)$

Test 3

1. $-2 \times (+8)$	**2.** $-2 + 8$
3. $-7 - 6$	**4.** $-7 \times (-6)$
5. $+36 \div (-9)$	**6.** $-8 - (-4)$
7. $-14 + 2$	**8.** $5 \times (-4)$
9. $11 + (-5)$	**10.** $11 - 11$
11. $-9 \times (-4)$	**12.** $-6 + (-4)$
13. $3 - 10$	**14.** $-20 \div (-2)$
15. $16 + (-10)$	**16.** $-4 - (+14)$
17. $-45 \div 5$	**18.** $18 - 3$
19. $-1 \times (-1)$	**20.** $-3 - (-3)$

Test 4

1. $-4 + 4$	**2.** $-4 \times (+4)$
3. $-2 - 12$	**4.** $-2 \times (-12)$
5. $3 + (-4)$	**6.** $4 - (-10)$
7. $-22 \div 11$	**8.** $-9 + 7$
9. $-6 - (-13)$	**10.** $-3 \times (-11)$
11. $4 - 5$	**12.** $-20 - (+10)$
13. $4 \times (-7)$	**14.** $7 - (-12)$
15. $9 - 18$	**16.** $56 \div (-7)$
17. $7 - 6$	**18.** $-11 + (+2)$
19. $-2 \times (+8)$	**20.** $-8 \div (-2)$

CHECK YOURSELF ON SECTIONS 1.3 AND 1.4

1 Using prime numbers, factors and multiples

(a) Write down all the factors of 28.

(b) Add together all the prime numbers between 10 and 20.

(c) Write down the first six multiples of 15.

(d) Write down the first six multiples of 20.

(e) Write down the lowest common multiple of 15 and 20.

2 Using square numbers

(a) Work out $6^2 - 4^2$

(b) Write down the next largest square number after 100.

3 Breaking down numbers into prime factors

(a) Copy and complete this factor tree.   (b) Draw a factor tree for 150.

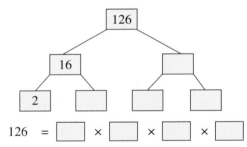

4 Using cube numbers and higher powers

(a) Which is larger and by how much? 2^5 or 3^3

(b) Work out 5 to the power 4.

(c) What number belongs in the box? $2^3 + 3^2 + \boxed{} = 4^3$

5 Adding and subtracting negative numbers

Work out

(a) $-4 - 2$ (b) $4 + (-3)$ (c) $2 - (-5)$ (d) $-4 + (-1)$ (e) $-6 - (-4)$

(f) What number belongs in the box? $-8 - \boxed{} = -5$

6   Multiplying and dividing negative numbers

Work out

(a) −7 × (−4)   (b) 20 ÷ (−2)   (c) −15 ÷ 3

(d) Write down the value of each letter:

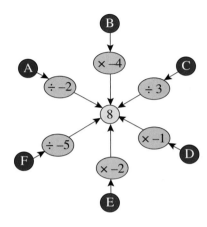

1.5 Area and Perimeter

In section 1.5 you will:

- find areas and perimeters using rectangles and triangles
- find areas of parallelograms and trapeziums

Using rectangles and triangles

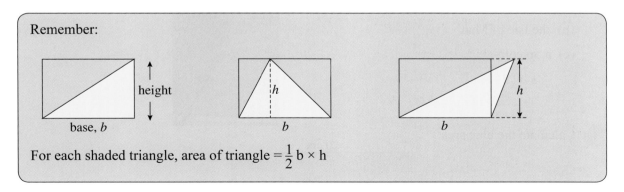

28

Exercise 1M

1 Calculate the area of each shape. The lengths are in cm.

(a)

4

7

(b)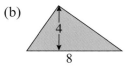

4

8

(c)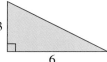

3

6

2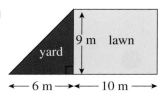

9 m   lawn

yard

←— 6 m —→←— 10 m —→

(a) Find the area of the lawn.

(b) Find the area of the yard.

(c) What is the total area of the yard and the lawn?

3 Calculate the area of each shape. The lengths are in cm.

(a)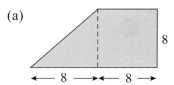

8

←— 8 —→←— 8 —→

(b)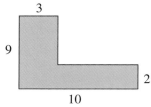

3

9

2

10

(c)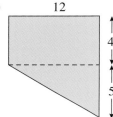

12

4

5

4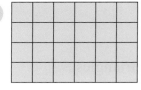

Here is a 4 × 6 rectangle made using 24 squares. What other rectangles can be made using 24 squares?

5 Suzy has enough squares to make exactly five different rectangles. How many squares does she have?

6 What metric unit would you use for the area of:

(a) a tennis court

(b) the Isle of Man

(c) a 5p coin

7 Calculate the blue area.

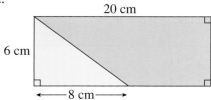

20 cm

6 cm

←— 8 cm —→

8 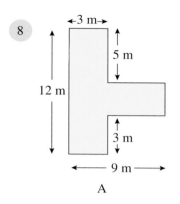 Which shape has the larger area and by how much?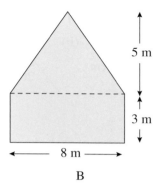

A

B

Exercise 1E

1 Calculate the area of each shape. The lengths are in cm.

(a)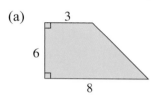

(b)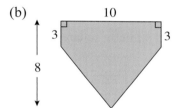

(c)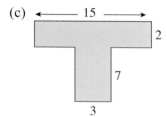

2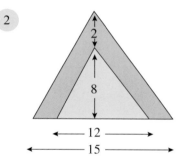

Calculate the pink area. The lengths are in cm.

3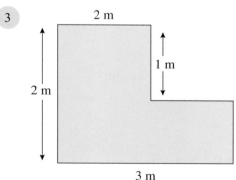

Tanya is going to tile this wall. Each tile is a square 10 cm by 10 cm. The tiles come in boxes of 25. Each box costs £18.

(a) How many tiles are needed?

(b) How much will the tiles cost?

(c) Tanya may break some of the tiles. She has to allow for an extra 10% tiles. What is the total cost of the tiles now?

4 Work out the perimeter of:

(a) a regular octagon of side 5 cm

(b) a square of area 100 cm²

5 Calculate the length of each side marked x. The area is written inside each shape.

(a)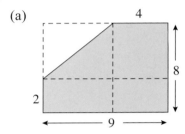

(b)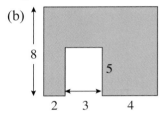

(c)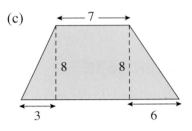

(d)

6 Find the total area of each shape. Lengths are in cm.

(a)

(b)

(c)

7 Here are some shapes made with centimetre squares.

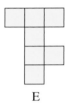

A   B   C   D

E

(a) Which shape has an area of 4 cm²?

(b) Which shape has a perimeter of 12 cm?

(c) Which two shapes have the same perimeter?

8 Draw a shape similar to those in the question above:

(a) With area 7 cm² and perimeter 14 cm.

(b) With area 11 cm² and perimeter 16 cm.

Parallelogram and trapezium

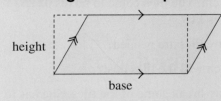

height   base

area of parallelogram = base × height

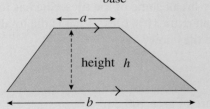

height h

area of trapezium = $\frac{1}{2}$ h (a + b)

area of trapezium = $\frac{1}{2}$ × height × sum of parallel sides

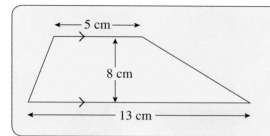

$$\text{area of trapezium} = \frac{1}{2} h (a + b)$$
$$= \frac{1}{2} \times 8 \times (5 + 13)$$
$$= 4 \times 18$$
$$= 72 \text{ cm}^2$$

Exercise 2M

Calculate the area of each shape. The lengths are in cm.

1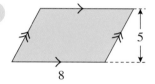

2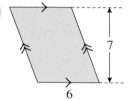

3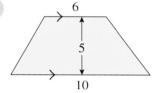

4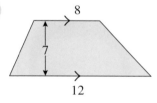

5

6 Find the pink area

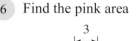
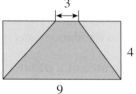

7   Sketch a trapezium with parallel sides of length 5 cm and 7 cm. The distance between the parallel sides is 4 cm. Calculate the area of the trapezium.

8   A parallelogram has a base of length 10 cm and an area of 60 cm². Calculate the height of the parallelogram.

9   The area of the parallelogram is equal to the area of the triangle. Find the height of the parallelogram.

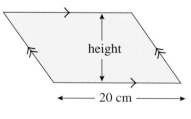

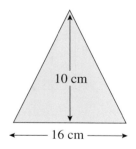

10 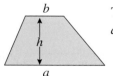 The area of the trapezium shown is 12 cm². Find a possible set of values for a, b and h.

Mixed area problems

Exercise 2E

1 Look at these shapes made with equilateral triangles.

  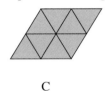 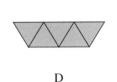

    A   B   C   D   E

(a) Which shape has the largest area?

(b) Which shape has the same area as shape A?

(c) Which shape has the same perimeter as shape C?

2 This shape has an area of 225 cm². Calculate its perimeter.

3 This delightful photo of Hannah has height 5 cm greater than its width. The area of the photo is 84 cm². Find the dimensions of the photo.

4 The area of a parallelogram is 10 cm². How long is the base of the parallelogram if its height is 20 cm?

5   4 cm   9 cm

9 cm A   +   B   5 cm   =   C

The area of square C is equal to the sum of the areas of rectangles A and B. How long is the side of square C?

6 A wall measuring 2 m by 6 m is covered with tiles which are 20 cm squares. A box of 10 tiles costs £5.95. How much will it cost to buy the tiles for this wall?

7 Here are two shapes *both* with a perimeter of 32 cm. Calculate the *area* of each shape.

A

square

B

length = 3 × width

8   The diagram shows a garden with two crossing paths. Calculate the total area of the paths.

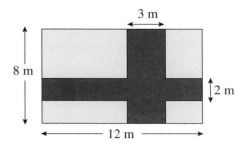

9   How many panes of glass 30 cm by 20 cm can be cut from a sheet which is 1 metre square?

10 A gardener is spreading fertilizer on his lawn (but not the pond in the middle!).
The instructions only say that 2 measures of the fertilizer will treat 10 m² of lawn. Each measure of fertilizer costs £1.50. Find the cost of the fertilizer required.

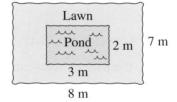

CHECK YOURSELF ON SECTION 1.5

1   Finding areas and perimeters using rectangles and triangles

Calculate the area of each shape. The lengths are in cm.

(a)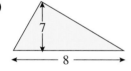

(b)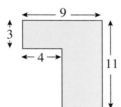

(c)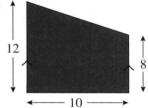

(d) A square has a perimeter of 24 cm. Find the area of the square.

2   Finding areas of parallelograms and trapeziums

Calculate the area of each shape. The lengths are in cm.

(a)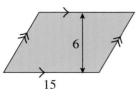

(b)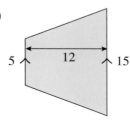

(c) Part of a wall is shown opposite. Will takes 12 minutes on average to paint 1 m². How many minutes will he take to paint the entire wall?

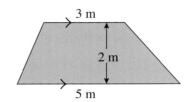

3 m

2 m

5 m

UNIT 1   MIXED REVIEW

Part one

1   Work out

(a) $-9 + 4$ (b) $-5 \times (-4)$ (c) $-7 - 9$ (d) $4 \times (-4)$ (e) $-6 \div 2$ (f) $-5 \times (-6)$

2   (a) Copy the pattern below and continue it to the line for 10^2.

$$2^2 = 1^2 + 1 + 2 = 4$$
$$3^2 = 2^2 + 2 + 3 = 9$$
$$4^2 = 3^2 + 3 + 4 = 16$$

(b) Without a calculator, use the pattern to work out:

(i) 31^2 (ii) 71^2 (iii) 101^2 (iv) 19^2

3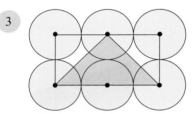

Six touching circles of radius 5 cm are shown. Calculate the area of the blue triangle.

4   Work out

(a) $\frac{1}{2} - \frac{1}{3}$ (b) $\frac{2}{5} + \frac{1}{6}$ (c) $\frac{1}{2} \times \frac{3}{4}$ (d) $\frac{2}{3} \times \frac{3}{8}$

5   A roll of wallpaper is cut into five strips. A room requires 40 strips of wallpaper. How much will it cost if one roll of wallpaper costs £9?

6   Look at these number cards

$\boxed{-3}$ $\boxed{0}$ $\boxed{+2}$ $\boxed{-5}$ $\boxed{+4}$ $\boxed{-6}$ $\boxed{+3}$

(a) Choose a card to give the answer 2.

 $\boxed{+4}$ + $\boxed{-5}$ + $\boxed{}$ = 2

(b) Choose a card to give the *lowest* possible answer.

$\boxed{-3}$ + $\boxed{}$ = $\boxed{}$

(c) Choose a card to give the *highest* possible answer.

$\boxed{-5}$ − $\boxed{}$ = $\boxed{}$

7   One day a quarter of the class is absent and 21 children are present. How many children are there in the class when no one is away?

8   The square ACDE is cut into seven pieces.

Find the area, in square units, of

(a) triangle EDI

(b) square BJIG

(c) parallelogram FGHE.

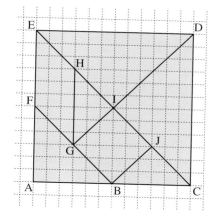

9   Work out, without a calculator:

(a) 4^2 (b) 2^3 (c) 1^5 (d) 10^3

10   Look at these numbers.

| 12 | 18 | 30 | 35 | 51 | 70 | 80 |

(a) Which numbers divide exactly by 7?

(b) Which numbers divide exactly by both 5 and 2?

(c) Which numbers are multiples of 3?

11   Write down the next number in each sequence

(a) | 3 | 9 | 15 | 21 | |

(b) | 1 | 2 | 4 | 7 | |

(c) | −40 | −20 | −10 | −5 | |

12   The floor of a room was covered with black and white square tiles of side 30 cm. The rectangular room measured 27 m by 36 m. How many tiles were there on the floor?

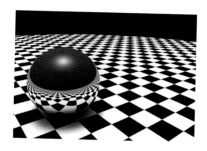

13 Copy and complete the additions.

(a)

```
    3  2  □
    2  □  1
 +  □  2  4
 ─────────
 □  1  8  9
```

(b)

```
    3  2  □
    4  □  2
 +  □  2  4
 ─────────
 □  4  3  3
```

14 A tin weighs 170 g when empty. The tin weighs 510 g when it is full of currants. How much does the tin weigh when it is a quarter full?

15 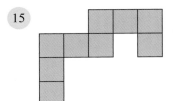 The area of this shape is 144 cm². Work out the length of the perimeter of this shape.

Part two

1 Work out

(a) $\frac{2}{3}$ of 60 (b) $\frac{3}{5}$ of 40 (c) $\frac{1}{4} + \frac{2}{3}$ (d) $1\frac{1}{2} + \frac{2}{5}$

2 The rule for the sequences below is '*double and add 3*'. Find the missing numbers.

(a) $1 \longrightarrow 5 \longrightarrow 13 \longrightarrow \square$

(b) $2 \longrightarrow \square \longrightarrow \square$

(c) $\square \longrightarrow 9 \longrightarrow \square$

3 Avram's age is a multiple of 9. Next year it will be a multiple of 8. How old is Avram?

4 Find the purple area.

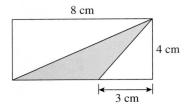

5 The number *n* has 6 factors only, including 1 and *n*. Two of its factors are 2 and 5. What is *n*?

6 Copy and complete the magic squares

(a)

6		2
	5	
8		

(b)

−4	3	−5
	−7	0

7 The Day Return train fare from Hatfield to London is £16.40. A ticket for the year costs £2875. Amelia travels to London on Monday to Friday for 45 weeks during the year. How much money does she save by buying a ticket for the whole year?

8 Postage stamps are printed on large sheets 38 cm across by 60 cm down. How many stamps are there on each sheet?

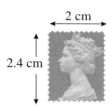

2 cm

2.4 cm

9 (a) Use a calculator to work out   (i) 350 ÷ 99

(ii) 350 ÷ 999

(iii) 350 ÷ 9999

(b) Use your answers to *predict* the answer to (i) 350 ÷ 99999, correct to 9 decimal places.

(c) Predict the answer to 350 ÷ 999999, correct to 11 decimal places.

10 Look at the pattern of paving stones and count the number of stones in the first three rings around the centre stone.

Assuming the pattern continues how many stones will there be altogether in a circular pattern of seven rings around the centre stone?

11 The pattern 24680 24680 24680 ..., is continued to form a number with one hundred digits, what is the sum of all one hundred digits?

12 Find the area of each shape. All lengths are in cm.

(a)

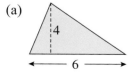

4

6

(b)

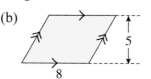

5

8

(c)

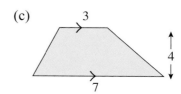

3

4

7

38

13 Copy and complete the addition square.

+		$\frac{2}{5}$
$\frac{1}{6}$	$\frac{1}{2}$	$\frac{17}{30}$
$\frac{3}{8}$		

14 Copy and complete these number walls (each box contains the sum of the two boxes beneath it).

(a)

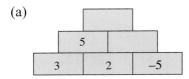

(b)

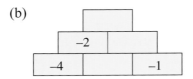

(c)

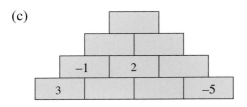

15

Mouse that roared

Fort Sumner: A mouse that had been thrown on a pile of burning leaves ran back into the house in New Mexico from which it had been ejected, setting it alight. Luciano Mares, 81, said that the mouse caught fire and ran back beneath a window, from where flames spread throughout the house. *(AP)*

Read this news item which appeared in a newspaper.

(a) Remember not to throw mice onto a pile of burning leaves.

(b) Express Luciano's age as the sum of three square numbers.

Puzzles and Problems 1

1. Villages A, B, C, D, E, F, G, H, I are joined by a network of roads.
   The lengths of the roads are in miles.

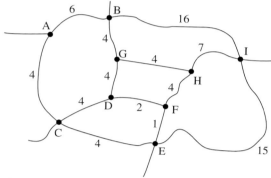

   (a) Find the shortest route from A to I.
   (b) Find the shortest route from B to E.
   (c) A family on a sight-seeing tour wish to visit all of the
       villages as they go from A to I. Find the shortest route
       passing through all the villages.

2. This network shows the roads joining towns A, B, … L.

   (a) Find the shortest route from B to K.
   (b) Find the shortest route from G to L.
   (c) Find the shortest route for a waste disposal lorry
       which has to visit every town as it travels
       from A to L.

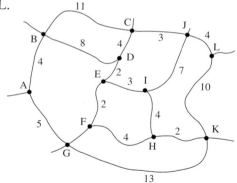

3. A class is electing five girls as captains of the following teams;
   swimming; gymnastics; netball; athletics; tennis.

   It is clearly best if the girl elected is good at the sport for
   which she is to be captain.

   Vera is good at swimming and gymnastics.
   Wilma is good at gymnastics, netball and tennis.
   Xenia is good at swimming and athletics.
   Yasmin is good at netball.
   Zara is good at netball and athletics.

   Work out the five games captains.

4 Four travellers W, X, Y, Z have to make a journey, for
which 4 tickets are available: by plane; by train;
by car; by boat.

   W prefers to go by plane or car
   X prefers to go by boat
   Y prefers to go by train or boat
   Z prefers to go by train, car or boat.

Work out who should take each ticket so that
everyone is happy with their method of transport.

5 Six actors A, B, C, D, E, F are trying to decide who should play
the six parts in a play. The parts are:
the hero (H); the princess (P); the villain (V); the reporter
(R); the tree (T); the nurse(N).

   A would like to be the princess or the reporter.
   B would like to be the hero or the villain
   C would like to be the hero or the nurse
   D would like to be the villain or the tree
   E would like to be the nurse or the tree
   F would like to be the villain, the reporter or the tree.

Work out who should play each part.
Find two different solutions.

Mental Arithmetic Practice

Ideally a teacher will read out each question twice with pupils' books closed.

Test 1

1 Add together five, four and nineteen.

2 Write the number that is eight less than
three hundred.

3 What is five hundred and forty six to the
nearest hundred?

4 What is nine multiplied by six?

5 Write the number eight thousand and six
in figures.

6 Write nought point seven as a fraction.

7 Change seven and a half metres into
centimetres.

8 What is four point six multiplied by one
thousand?

9 How many thirds are there in two whole
ones?

10 Twenty six per cent of the people in a
survey did not like cheese. What
percentage liked cheese?

11 The side of a square is five centimetres.
What is the area of the square?

12 A bus journey starts at six fifty. It lasts for
thirty five minutes. At what time does it
finish?

13 How many groups of 5 can be made from
100?

14 At mid-day the temperature is seven degrees Celsius. By midnight it has fallen twelve degrees. What is the temperature at midnight?

15 Write down a factor of twenty seven, which is greater than one.

16 What is six thousand divided by ten?

17 What number is eight squared?

18 How many seventeens are there in three hundred and forty?

19 What is the difference between 3.3 and 5.5?

20 How much does each person receive when a prize of £200 is shared between 5 people?

21 How many more than 27 is 40?

22 Twenty per cent of a number is twelve. What is the number?

23 Find the change from a £10 note if you spend £3.20.

24 How many altogether are 7, 6 and 5?

25 What is the remainder when 40 is divided by 7?

Test 2

1 What are two eighteens?

2 Add together 7, 8 and 9.

3 Divide 8 into 48.

4 Multiply 15 by 4.

5 Write $\frac{3}{4}$ as a percentage.

6 Work out 13 divided by 10 as a decimal.

7 What number is 40 less than 75?

8 Share a cost of £56 between 7 people.

9 What four coins make 67p?

10 What is the product of 60 and 3?

11 I have 2 dogs and 5 cats. What fraction of my pets are cats?

12 What is the cost of 2 C.D.s at £6.99 each?

13 Subtract the sum of 7 and 8 from 40.

14 One quarter of a number is 3.5 What is the number?

15 I have one 10p, three 5p and one 50p coin. How much money do I have?

16 Lemons cost 12p each. What is the cost of 7 lemons?

17 Apples cost 75p for five. What is the cost of one apple?

18 A bunch of grapes costs 64p. What is the change from £1?

19 How many 20p coins do I need for £2.80?

20 A shirt costs £15.95 new. I get a discount of £4. How much do I pay?

21 I share 60 sweets equally among 5 people. How many sweets does each receive?

22 The area of a square is 36 cm². How long is each side?

23 What must I spend from £20 to leave £14.50?

24 How many millimetres are there in 10 metres?

25 Write 5.30 a.m. in 24 hour clock time.

A long time ago! 1

The Eye of Horus

In Ancient Egypt, Horus was represented
as the falcon-headed god. He was the ultimate
god of mathematics.

All Egyptian fractions were unit fractions
like $\frac{1}{2}$, $\frac{1}{3}$ and $\frac{1}{8}$.

The eye of Horus represented the sacred unit
fractions. The 'eye of Horus' symbol was used
to protect from evil.

The eye of Horus.

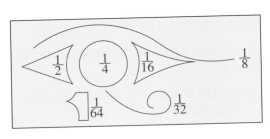

Each symbol represents the fraction shown.

By adding together different parts of the eye,
other fractions are created.

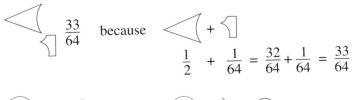

$$\frac{1}{2} + \frac{1}{64} = \frac{32}{64} + \frac{1}{64} = \frac{33}{64}$$

$$\frac{1}{4} + \frac{1}{32} = \frac{8}{32} + \frac{1}{32} = \frac{9}{32}$$

Exercise

1   Work out the value of each of these fractions.

(a)   (b)

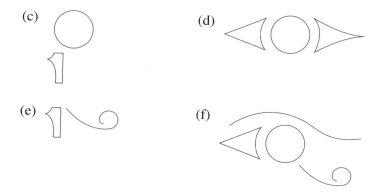

(c)

(d)

(e)

(f)

2   Use the symbols from the eye of Horus to show the following fractions.

(a) $\dfrac{1}{16}$ (b) $\dfrac{3}{16}$ (c) $\dfrac{3}{4}$ (d) $\dfrac{7}{8}$

3   (a) What is the total of all the fractions in the eye of Horus?

(b) What extra fraction is needed to make the total equal to 1?

4   **RESEARCH:**

(a) Find out more about the god Horus.

(b) Find out how the Egyptians represented the fraction $\dfrac{1}{3}$.

UNIT 2

2.1 Rounding off and estimating

In section 2.1 you will:

- round numbers to decimal places
- calculate using estimates

Rounding off

- Using a calculator, $3.19^3 = 32.461759$

  We can *round off* this number to either 1 or 2 decimal places.

- Rounding to one decimal place.

  If the figure in the 2nd decimal place is 5 *or more*, round up. Otherwise do not.

  $32.4\underset{\uparrow}{6}1759 = 32.5$ to 1 d.p.

  Also
  $17.8\underset{\uparrow}{5} = 17.9$ to 1 d.p.

- Rounding to two decimal places.

  If the figure in the 3rd decimal place is 5 *or more*, round up. Otherwise do not.

  $32.46\underset{\uparrow}{1}759 = 32.46$ to 2 d.p.

  $0.03\underset{\uparrow}{5} = 0.04$ to 2 d.p.

Exercise 1M

1. Round off these numbers to one decimal place.

    (a) 7.32   (b) 8.276   (c) 0.873   (d) 14.18

    (e) 0.462   (f) 6.832   (g) 12.629   (h) 0.949

2. Write the following numbers correct to two decimal places.

    (a) 4.368   (b) 7.062   (c) 18.333   (d) 5.073

    (e) 0.2657   (f) 28.759   (g) 0.7584   (h) 3.086

3 Work out these answers on a calculator and then round off the answers correct to two decimal places.

(a) $14.96 \div 7$ (b) $3186 \div 429$ (c) 0.63×5.4 (d) $\sqrt{19}$

(e) $\sqrt{6.8}$ (f) 0.73×0.89 (g) 2.65^2 (h) 0.56^2

(i) 3.7×0.836 (j) $15.18 \div 16$ (k) $\sqrt{(2.8 \times 4.2)}$ (l) $(13 \div 8)^2$

4 Round off these numbers to the nearest hundred.

(a) 1348 (b) 36391 (c) 609.4 (d) 18345

(e) 374.72 (f) 4444 (g) 6773 (h) 2036

Exercise 1E

1 A company makes 20 spheres. The diameter, in cm, of each sphere is listed below:

5.173	5.1761	5.168	5.1709
5.1634	5.1648	5.1762	5.167
5.1746	5.1639	5.1722	5.1753
5.1683	5.1717	5.1759	5.1628
5.172	5.1743	5.163	5.1664

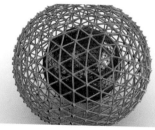

The company can only sell spheres which have a diameter of 5.17 cm when rounded off to two decimal places. How many of these spheres can the company *not* sell?

2 Work out these answers on a calculator and then round off the answers correct to one decimal place.

(a) $\sqrt{83.6}$ (b) $\dfrac{7.14}{6.3}$ (c) $\dfrac{7.4^2}{3}$ (d) $0.9 \div 0.017$

(e) $\dfrac{3.6}{0.7} + 4.6$ (f) $\dfrac{\sqrt{63}}{9}$ (g) $\dfrac{3.2 \times 1.6}{2.9}$ (h) $\dfrac{7.8}{\sqrt{47}}$

(i) $7.12 \div 4.6$ (j) $\dfrac{5.7}{0.7^2}$ (k) $(3.8 \div 1.3)^2$ (l) $\dfrac{\sqrt{(7.1 \times 2.6)}}{1.19}$

3

An estimated 50 000 people took 20 years to build the Great Wall of China. This number of people has been rounded off to the nearest thousand. What is the least number of people that may have built the Great Wall of China?

4 Jack was measured as being 1.7 m correct to one decimal place. What is Jack's smallest possible height?

46

Estimating and checking answers

(a) Look at the calculations

$4 \times 6, 4 \times 60, 40 \times 60, 40 \times 600$

$4 \times 6 = 24$
$4 \times 60 = 240$
$40 \times 60 = 2400$
$40 \times 600 = 24000$

(b) Work out a rough estimate for 382×12.

Instead of 382 use 400
Instead of 12 use 10
382×12 is roughly 400×10 which is 4000.

Exercise 2M

1 Work out

(a) 30×2 (b) 30×20 (c) 30×2000 (d) 3×200

(e) 6×70 (f) 60×700 (g) 40×9 (h) 400×90

(i) 60×60 (j) 80×300 (k) 7×5000 (l) 40×70

2 Work out a rough estimate for the following.

(a) 21×58 (b) 42×19 (c) 607×3 (d) 98.3×41

3 Do not use a calculator. Decide, by estimating, which of the three answers is closest to the exact answer. Write the calculation and the approximate answer for each question (use ≈).

	Calculation	A	B	C
(a)	97.9×11.3	90	500	1000
(b)	6.73×9.65	30	70	300
(c)	1.03×60.6	6	60	200
(d)	2.3×96	200	90	20
(e)	18.9×21.4	200	400	4000
(f)	5.14×5.99	15	10	30
(g)	811×11.72	8000	4000	800
(h)	99×98	1 million	100 000	10 000
(i)	1.09×29.6	20	30	60
(j)	$81 413 \times 10.96$	8 million	1 million	800 000
(k)	$601 \div 3.92$	50	100	150

	Calculation	A	B	C
(l)	402 ÷ 4.97	8	0.8	80
(m)	58.4 ÷ 0.98	60	300	600
(n)	0.2 × 111.3	10	20	180
(o)	217 ÷ 201.4	0.2	1	10
(p)	88.4 + 95 + 141	300	100	3000

4   Answer true or false (the sign ≈ means 'is roughly equal to').

(a) 27.8 × 3.2
     ≈ 30 × 3
     ≈ 90

(b) 904 × 23
     ≈ 900 × 20
     ≈ 18 000

(c) 4267 ÷ 38
     ≈ 4000 ÷ 40
     ≈ 100

5   Petrol costs €1.09 per litre in Spain.
    Estimate the total cost of 48 litres.

Exercise 2E

Do not use a calculator for these questions.

1   Kate pays £25 per week for her electricity. Estimate the amount she spends on electricity in one year.

2   A school buys 69 tables. Estimate the total cost if each table is priced at £18.95.

3   A 'James Bond' dvd is sold at £8.90 per copy. Estimate the total cost of 32 copies.

4   David had a three week holiday in Greece. On average he spent £58 each day. Estimate the total amount he spent during his holiday.

5   A boxer earned a fee of $8 million for a fight which lasted 1 minute 35 seconds. Estimate the money he earned per second of the fight.

6   At a fun fair, customers pay 95p for a ride on a giant spinning wheel. The operator sells 2483 tickets during the weekend and his costs for electricity and rent were £114. Estimate his profit over the weekend.

7

pot of paint	£15.95
box of tiles	£8.90
paintbrush	£2.99
piece of sandpaper	46p
2 m piece of wood	£3.12

Marie is decorating. She estimates that she needs 3 pots of paint, 4 paintbrushes, 5 pieces of wood, 12 pieces of sandpaper and 6 boxes of tiles.

(a) Estimate the total cost for her decorating.

(b) Marie has a budget of £125. Can she afford everything?

In questions 8 and 9 there are six calculations and six answers. Write down each calculation and insert the correct answer from the list given. Use estimation.

8   (a) 5.9×6.1 (b) $19.8 \div 5$ (c) 32×9.9

    (d) $0.89 + 14.7$ (e) 4.5×44 (f) $4141 \div 40$

Answers:	198, 35.99, 103.5, 15.59, 316.8, 3.96

9   (a) $102.8 \div 5$ (b) $11.2 \div 98.6$ (c) 3×0.41

    (d) 34×2.9 (e) 51×3.9 (f) $238.6 \div 4.7$

Answers:	50.76, 20.56, 1.23, 198.9, 98.6, 0.114

10   Write the decimal point in the correct place.

    (a) width of this book   1831 mm

    (b) weight of an 'average' new born baby   3124 kg

    (c) diameter of a football   3140 cm

    (d) weight of a packet of sugar   100 kg

11

Some time ago a rather aggressive shark attacked a house in England. Estimate the following.

(a) The length of the shark.

(b) The cost of repairing the damage to the house.

12 A quick way of adding lots of figures on a shopping bill is to round every number to the nearest pound.

So £2.43 becomes £2, £0.91 becomes £1, £0.24 becomes £0 and so on.

(a) Use this method to estimate the totals below:

(i)			(ii)		
WSKAS COCKTAIL *	0.85		PLN BAGUETTE		0.49
H/EATING MINCE	3.95		FOIL	*	0.65
HAWAIIAN CRN	1.85		LETTUCE ROUND		0.24
PAIN AU CHOC	0.54		JW TUNA MAYO		0.75
PAIN AU CHOC	0.54		SOYA MILK		0.47
PAIN AU CHOC	0.54		SOYA MILK		0.47
BUTTER	0.89		ORNGE MRMLDE		0.74
BUTTER	0.89		YOGHURT		0.99
EGGS	0.78		SPGHTI/HOOPS		0.26
PORK/CHICK/PIE	2.03		CHEESE		1.34
MED.MAT.CHDR.	1.21		WHISKAS	*	0.45
HOT PIES	1.47		WHISKAS	*	0.45
POT. WAFFLES	1.39		VINEGAR		0.68
WHOLE BRIE	1.01		KING EDWARDS.		0.99
MUFFINS	0.49		UHT H/FAT MILK	*	0.26
BACON RASHERS	0.65		APPLES		1.89
BEETROOT	0.99		WHISKAS	*	0.45
LOOSE CHEESE	0.99		PEACHES		0.24
			FROM. FRAIS		0.72

(b) Use a calculator to work out the exact total for part (i).
Compare the answer with your estimate above.

13 (a) In 1989 thousands of people formed a human chain right across the U.S.A., a distance of about 4300 km.
Estimate the number of people in the chain.

(b) Estimate the number of people needed to form a chain right around the equator. (Assume you have enough people volunteering to float for a while in the sea.) The distance right around the equator is about 40 000 km.

14 Estimate:

(a) the number of times your heart beats in one day (24 h),

(b) the thickness of one page in this book.

Estimating game

● This is a game for two players. On squared paper draw an answer grid with the numbers shown.

Answer grid

198	1089	99	100	360	18
180	450	22	440	155	1980
1240	200	45	62	100	550
40	620	495	279	800	55
2000	80	220	10	891	250
4950	1550	1000	3960	3069	341

● The players now take turns to choose two numbers from the question grid below and multiply them on a calculator.

Question grid

2	5	9
11	20	31
40	50	99

The number obtained is crossed out on the answer grid using the player's own colour.

● The game continues until all the numbers in the answer grid have been crossed out. The object is to get four answers in a line (horizontally, vertically or diagonally). The winner is the player with most lines of four.

● A line of *five* counts as *two* lines of four.

A line of *six* counts as *three* lines of four.

2.2 Using algebra

In section 2.2 you will:

- collect like terms

- use letters for numbers

- use rules of algebra

Basic algebra

- An algebraic *expression* is formed from letter symbols and numbers. For example $3n$, $4n + 5$ and $1 - 2x$ are all expressions. Notice that there is no equals sign in an expression.

- In an *equation,* like $2n - 1 = 15$, n is one particular unknown number.

- In the *formula* $A = LB$, A, L and B are variable quantities, related by the formula. If we know the values of L and B we can calculate the value of A.

B

L

- In the *function* $y = 2x + 7$, the value of y can be found for any chosen value of x.

$4 \times n = 4n$

$m \times n = mn$

$(m + n) \div y = \dfrac{m + n}{y}$

$m \times m = m^2$

Like terms can be added:

$2m + n + 3m + 5n = 5m + 6n$

$5n + 4 - 2n - 6 = 3n - 2$

$n^2 + 4n^2 = 5n^2$

Cancelling fractions:

$\dfrac{6 \times 2}{6} = 2 \qquad \dfrac{2 \times n}{n} = 2 \qquad \dfrac{8n}{2} = 4n$

Exercise 1M

Simplify the following expressions as far as possible by collecting like terms.

1 $6x + 2y + 3x$

2 $3m + 3m + n$

3 $4a + b + 2b + a$

4 $4m + 3n - 2m - n$

5 $7p + 5q - 3p - 4q$

6 $8x + y + 5y$

7 $a + 7 + 3a - 4$

8 $5p - 3p - 4 + p$

9 $4n + 1 - 3n - 6$

10 Which two expressions below are equivalent? (this means they give the same answer when the like terms are collected).

(a) $5m + 6n + m + 3 - 2n$ (b) $3n + 6 + 4m - 2 + 3n$ (c) $4n + 7 + 4m + 2n - 3$

11 Write down an expression for the perimeter of each shape below. Collect like terms where possible.

(a) 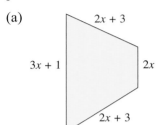   (b) 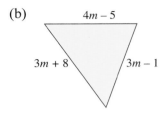   (c)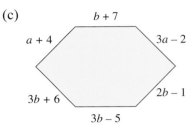

Simplify the expressions in questions ⑫ to ⑳ as far as possible.

12 $3a + b - 2a + 6b$ 13 $8 + m - 11 + m$ 14 $3x + 2 - 5x + 3$

15 $5n + 3n - 1 - 7n$ 16 $2y - 4y + 3 - 2$ 17 $9a + 4 - 6 - 7a$

18 $3 + 6q - 2 - 9q$ 19 $16 - 3n + 1 + 2n + m$ 20 $3m - 6m + 2 - 6$

21 Find three matching pairs

A $2a + 3 - a$ B $b + 3 + a + 1$ C $a + 3b + 3 - 2b$

D $b + 2a + 3 - a$ E $3 + a$ F $a + 4 + b$

Exercise 1E

1 Write down any pairs of expressions from below that are equal to each other.

$4 + 4$ 4×3 $4 + 3$ $4 - 3$

3×4 4^2 $3 - 4$ 4×4

2 Write down any pairs of expressions from below that are equal to each other.

$n - 3$ n^2 $n + 3$ $3 - n$

$3 + n$ $\frac{n}{3}$ $3 \div n$ $n \times n$

In questions ③ to ⑰ answer 'true' or 'false'.

3 $a + b = b + a$ 4 $a \times a = a^2$ 5 $7 \times n = n \times 7$ 6 $m \times m = 2m$

7 $h \times 3 = 3h$ 8 $a - b = b - a$ 9 $4n - n = 4$ 10 $n \div 6 = 6 \div n$

11 $a \div 4 = \frac{a}{4}$ 12 $\frac{6a}{2} = 3a$ 13 $a \times a \times a = a^3$ 14 $mn = nm$

15 $m \times m \times m = 3m$ 16 $(a + b) \div n = \frac{a + b}{n}$ 17 $\frac{5n}{n} = 5$

18 Here are some cards.

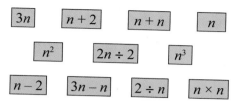

(a) Which cards will always be the same as $2n$?

(b) Which card will always be the same as $n \times n \times n$?

(c) Which card will always be the same as $\dfrac{2}{n}$?

(d) Draw a new card which will always be the same as $2n + 2n$.

19 Maurice has £$(3n + 2)$ and Jo has £$(5n + 7)$. How much more money does Jo have than Maurice?

20 Carol weighs $(3a + 1)$ kg and Lee weighs $(6a - 3)$ kg. By how much more does Lee weigh than Carol if Lee is heavier?

Using letters for numbers

Find the expressions you are left with.

(a) Start with n, multiply by 5 and then add 8.

$n \rightarrow 5n \rightarrow 5n + 8$

(b) Start with a, subract b and then add 10.

$a \rightarrow a - b \rightarrow a - b + 10$

(c) Start with p, add 3 then multiply the result by 4.

$p \rightarrow p + 3 \rightarrow 4(p + 3)$

(d) Start with m, subtract t and then square the result.

$t \rightarrow m - t \rightarrow (m - t)^2$

Notice that *brackets* are needed in parts (c) and (d).

Exercise 2M

Write down the expression you get. If any of your answers contain brackets, do not remove them.

1 Start with n, multiply by 5 then add x.

2 Start with n, add x and then multiply the result by 5.

3 Start with h, multiply by 6 and then subtract t.

4 Start with h, subtract t and then multiply the result by 6.

5 Start with b, add x and then multiply the result by 5.

6   Start with b, multiply by a and then add x.

7   Start with y, square it and then multiply the result by 3.

8   Start with n, multiply by d and then subtract 3.

9   Start with a, double it and then add A.

10   Start with h, subtract H and then multiply the result by 5.

11   Start with x, subtract 8 and then multiply the result by 5.

12   Start with x, square it and then add 2.

13   Start with y, double it and then subtract 3.

14   Start with a, add 10 and then square the result.

15   Here is a flow diagram for the expression $2(3n + 7)$

$$n \quad \xrightarrow{} \boxed{\times 3} \xrightarrow{\;3n\;} \boxed{+7} \xrightarrow{\;3n+7\;} \boxed{\times 2} \xrightarrow{\;2(3n+7)\;}$$

Find the expression for each of the following flow charts:

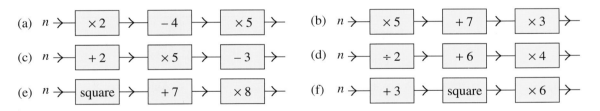

(a) $n \rightarrow \boxed{\times 2} \rightarrow \boxed{-4} \rightarrow \boxed{\times 5} \rightarrow$ (b) $n \rightarrow \boxed{\times 5} \rightarrow \boxed{+7} \rightarrow \boxed{\times 3} \rightarrow$

(c) $n \rightarrow \boxed{+2} \rightarrow \boxed{\times 5} \rightarrow \boxed{-3} \rightarrow$ (d) $n \rightarrow \boxed{\div 2} \rightarrow \boxed{+6} \rightarrow \boxed{\times 4} \rightarrow$

(e) $n \rightarrow \boxed{\text{square}} \rightarrow \boxed{+7} \rightarrow \boxed{\times 8} \rightarrow$ (f) $n \rightarrow \boxed{+3} \rightarrow \boxed{\text{square}} \rightarrow \boxed{\times 6} \rightarrow$

16   Draw the flow diagram for the following expressions.

(a) $2n + 7$ (b) $3(5n - 3)$ (c) $\dfrac{6n + 1}{5}$

(d) $n^2 - 3$ (e) $(n + 5)^2$ (f) $3(n^2 - 1)$

17   Ricky is bowling. There are 10 pins standing. On her first throw she knocks down m pins and on her second throw she knocks down n pins. How many pins are still standing?

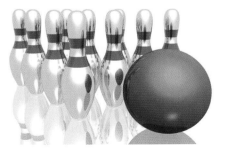

18   Terry has 90 pence. His father gives him another t pence and then he spends h pence. How much money does he now have?

19 Faye used to earn £*d* per week. She then had a rise of £9 per week. How much will she now earn in 7 weeks?

20

Monday to Friday	£6 per hour
Saturday	£7 per hour
Sunday	£9 per hour

The rate of pay at Pollock's fish store is shown in this table.

(a) Ed works for *n* hours on Wednesday. How much does he earn?

(b) Beatrice works for *p* hours on Friday and *q* hours on Sunday. How much does she earn?

(c) Sam works for *m* hours on each day of the weekend. How much does he earn in total?

Exercise 2E

1   Phil has 3 bags of coins.
Each bag has *n* coins inside.

Write an expression to show the total number of coins in Phil's 3 bags after the following.

(a) Phil took 4 coins out of *one* bag.

(b) Phil took 1 coin out of *each* bag.

(c) Phil took 3 coins out of each of *two* of the bags and *none* out of the other bag.

(d) Phil took 5 coins out of one bag and 2 coins out of each of the other two bags.

2   A small bag of peanuts contains *y* nuts and a large bag contains 5 times as many. If a boy buys a large bag and then eats 9 nuts, how many are left in his bag?

3   A tile weighs *t* kg. How much do *n* tiles weigh?

4   Alex has a large number of cards. Altogether there are 4*n* + 12 cards.

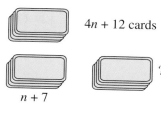

4*n* + 12 cards

(a) Alex sorts the cards into two piles. One pile has *n* + 7 cards. Write an expression for the number of cards in the second pile.

n + 7   ?

(b) Now Alex takes all the cards and puts them in two equal piles. How many cards are in each pile?

(c) Finally Alex puts the cards into two piles as shown. There are 18 cards in the first pile. How many cards are in the second pile?

first pile   second pile

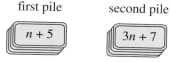

n + 5   3*n* + 7

5 In number walls each brick is made by adding the two bricks underneath it.

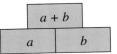

Draw the walls below and fill in the missing expressions.

(a)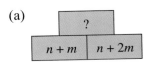

(b)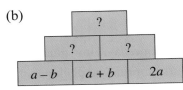

(c)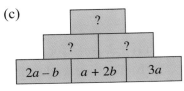

(d)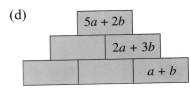

(e)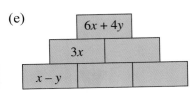

(f)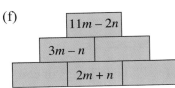

Investigation – Number squares

1 Draw your own addition square like the one shown here.

	1	2	3	4	5	6	7	8	9
1	2	3	4	5	6	7	8	9	10
2	3	4	5	6	7	8	9	10	11
3	4	5	6	7	8	9	10	11	12
4	5	6	7	8	9	10	11	12	13
5	6	7	8	9	10	11	12	13	14
6	7	8	9	10	11	12	13	14	15
7	8	9	10	11	12	13	14	15	16
8	9	10	11	12	13	14	15	16	17
9	10	11	12	13	14	15	16	17	18

2 Here are some 2 by 2 squares taken from the main square.

4	5
5	6

9	10
10	11

14	15
15	16

Add up the four numbers in each square. What do you notice?

③ In this 2 by 2 square the smallest number is 8.
Draw the square and fill in the missing numbers.

8	?
?	?

④ In another 2 by 2 square the *largest* number is 8. Draw the square and fill in the missing numbers.

⑤ In a 2 by 2 square the four numbers add up to 44. Draw the square and fill in the numbers.

⑥ Here is a 3 by 3 square taken from the main square.
Add up the nine numbers in the square. What do you notice?

4	5	6
5	6	7
6	7	8

⑦ Add up the four *corner* numbers in a 3 by 3 square. Copy and complete this sentence: 'In a 3 by 3 square the sum of the four corner numbers is _____ times the middle number.'

⑧ (a) Here is a 2 by 2 square.
The top left number is x.

x	

The other three main numbers are shown

x	$x+1$
$x+1$	$x+2$

(b) Draw the three squares shown and use x's to write down the other 3 numbers in each square.

	x

	x

x	

⑨ This is harder. Draw the square shown and use x's to fill in the other 8 numbers.

x		

⑩ Draw this square and then use x's to write down the other 3 *corner* numbers.

		x

11) We do not always use *x*. What are the 4 corner numbers in this square?

	N	

12) A large 'T' can be drawn inside the number square so that all 5 numbers in the T are inside the square.

1	2	3	4	5	6	7	8
9	10	11	12	13	14	15	16
17	18	19	20	21	22	23	24
25	26	27	28	29	30	31	32
33	34	35	36	37	38	39	40
41	42	43	44	45	46	47	48
49	50	51	52	53	54	55	56
57	58	59	60	61	62	63	64

The T can be moved around but it must stay upright. The 'T-number' is the number in the middle of the top row. So this is T18.

17	18	19		
	26			
	34			

(a) What is the smallest possible T-number?

(b) Work out the total of the numbers in T21

(c) Work out, as *quickly* as you can (Total of numbers in T37) – (Total of numbers in T36)

(d) Fill in the numbers for T75

	75	

(e) Uses *x*'s to write the numbers for T*x*

	x	

CHECK YOURSELF ON SECTIONS 2.1 AND 2.2

1 Rounding numbers to decimal places

Round off each number to one decimal place (1 d.p.) or to two decimal places (2 d.p.)

(a) 6.17 (1 d.p.)   (b) 23.854 (2 d.p.)   (c) 0.362 (2 d.p.)   (d) 0.236 (1 d.p.)

Use a calculator to work out each answer correct to two decimal places.

(e) 3.59×2.8 (f) 3.28^2 (g) $18 \times \sqrt{43}$

2 Calculating using estimates

Work out a rough estimate for the following:

(a) 19.7×41.2 (b) $804 \div 3.98$ (c) 6.09^2

(d) The label on a jar of jelly beans claims to contain 118 jelly beans. Estimate how many jelly beans there are in 21 jars.

3 Collecting like terms

Simplify by collecting like terms.

(a) $5m + 3n - 3m + 4$ (b) $3x - 2x + 4y - y$ (c) $6 + 3p + 2p - 10$

(d) Find the matching pair

A $2m + 3n - m$ B $2n - m + n$ C $n + m + n + n$

4 Using letters for numbers

(a) Max earns £m each week. How much does he earn in p weeks?

(b) Janice is three times older than Alf. Mary is 5 years younger than Janice. How old is Mary if Alf is n years old?

(c) Ralph is 'bulking' up at the gym. Each week he puts on q kilograms. If he weighs 70 kg at the start of February, how much will he weigh four weeks later?

5   Using rules of algebra

(a) Which cards below are the same as $4n$?

$n \times 4$ $2n + 2n$ $4 + n$ $5n - n$ $n \div 4$

(b) $m - 5 = 5 - m$ True or false?

(c) $p^2 = 2p$ Is this always true?

(d) David has $(6n + 18)$ dvds.
Rosie has $(2n + 5)$ dvds.
David gives Rosie half of his dvds.
Write an expression for the number of dvds Rosie now has.

2.3 Fractions, decimals, percentages

In section 2.3 you will:

- change fractions to decimals and vice versa
- change fractions to recurring decimals
- change to a percentage and vice versa

Changing fractions to decimals and vice versa

Fractions to decimals – convert denominator to 10, 100, etc.

$$\frac{3}{20} = \frac{15}{100} = 0.15 \qquad\qquad \frac{9}{25} = \frac{36}{100} = 0.36$$

If too 'tricky', divide the two numbers.

$$\frac{5}{8} = 5 \div 8 \qquad 8)\overline{5.{}^5 0^2 0^4 0}^{\,0.625} \qquad \text{so } \frac{5}{8} = 0.625$$

Decimals to fractions – always cancel the fraction if possible.

$$0.6 = \frac{6}{10} = \frac{3}{5} \qquad\qquad 0.35 = \frac{35}{100} = \frac{7}{20}$$

Exercise 1M

1   Without using a calculator, change the following fractions to decimals. Afterwards divide with a calculator to check your answer.

(a) $\frac{1}{5}$ (b) $\frac{7}{10}$ (c) $\frac{4}{5}$ (d) $\frac{9}{20}$ (e) $\frac{7}{25}$

(f) $\frac{13}{20}$ (g) $\frac{3}{4}$ (h) $\frac{6}{8}$ (i) $\frac{35}{500}$ (j) $\frac{7}{8}$

2   Use a calculator to convert the fractions to decimals. Write in order of size, smallest first.

(a) $\frac{7}{8}$, 0.85, $\frac{9}{10}$ (b) $\frac{13}{20}$, 0.645, $\frac{31}{50}$

(c) $\frac{3}{4}$, 0.715, $\frac{29}{40}$ (d) $\frac{3}{16}$, 0.18, $\frac{1}{5}$

3   0.56 of the people on a crowded beach are female. What fraction of the people are male?

4   Change the following decimals to fractions, cancelling when possible.

(a) 0.6   (b) 0.7   (c) 0.07   (d) 0.08   (e) 0.003

(f) 0.004   (g) 0.06   (h) 0.24   (i) 0.42   (j) 0.25

(k) 0.015   (l) 0.85   (m) 0.025   (n) 0.57   (o) 0.325

5   Change these mixed numbers to decimals.

(a) $3\frac{2}{5}$ (b) $5\frac{1}{2}$ (c) $2\frac{3}{4}$ (d) $2\frac{7}{8}$ (e) $6\frac{3}{100}$

Recurring decimals

Some fractions give rise to decimals which repeat themselves forever. We call these recurring decimals, and use the notation below to save us from writing out the number until our ink runs out!

(a) 0.555...   We write $0.\dot{5}$

(b) 0.434343...   We write $0.\dot{4}\dot{3}$

(c) 0.5265265...   We write $0.\dot{5}2\dot{6}$

(a) Change $\frac{1}{3}$ to a decimal

$$3\overline{)1.^{1}0^{1}0^{1}0^{1}0^{1}0...}\quad\begin{array}{c}0.\,3\,3\,3\,3\,3...\end{array}$$

The calculation is never going to end.

We write $\frac{1}{3} = 0.\dot{3}$. We say 'nought point three recurring'.

(b) Change $\frac{3}{11}$ to a decimal.

$$11\overline{)3.^{3}0^{8}0^{3}0^{8}0^{3}0^{8}0...}\quad\begin{array}{c}0.\,2\,7\,2\,7\,2\,7...\end{array}$$

This time a *pair* of figures recurs.

We write $\frac{3}{11} = 0.\dot{2}\dot{7}$

(c) Change $\frac{1}{7}$ to a decimal.

$$7\overline{)1.^{1}0^{3}0^{2}0^{6}0^{4}0^{5}0^{1}0^{3}00...}\quad\begin{array}{c}0.\,1\,4\,2\,8\,5\,7\,1\,42...\end{array}$$

The sequence '142857' recurs.

We write $\frac{1}{7} = 0.\dot{1}4285\dot{7}$

Exercise 1E

Change the following fractions to decimals.

1 $\frac{5}{9}$ 2 $\frac{2}{3}$ 3 $\frac{1}{6}$ 4 $\frac{3}{7}$ 5 $\frac{7}{9}$

6 $\frac{5}{7}$ 7 $\frac{2}{11}$ 8 $\frac{4}{9}$ 9 $\frac{7}{11}$ 10 $\frac{5}{6}$

11 (a) Work out each of the following as a decimal: $\frac{1}{7}, \frac{2}{7}, \frac{3}{7}, \frac{4}{7}, \frac{5}{7}, \frac{6}{7}$.

(b) What do you notice about the answers?

Changing to a percentage and vice versa

To change a fraction or a decimal to a percentage, multiply by 100

(a) To change $\frac{2}{5}$ to a percentage, multiply by 100.

$$\frac{2}{5} \times \frac{100}{1} = \frac{200}{5}$$
$$= 40\%$$

(b) To change $\frac{1}{8}$ to a percentage, multiply by 100.

$$\frac{1}{8} \times \frac{100}{1} = \frac{100}{8}$$
$$= 12\frac{1}{2}\%$$

(c) To change $\frac{3}{7}$ to a percentage, multiply by 100.

$$\frac{3}{7} \times \frac{100}{1} = \frac{300}{7}$$
$$= 42.857...\%$$
$$= 43\%, \text{ to the nearest whole number.}$$

(d) To change 0.37 to a percentage, multiply by 100.

$$0.37 \times 100 = 37\%$$

Exercise 2M

1   Change these fractions to percentages.

(a) $\frac{1}{4}$ (b) $\frac{3}{5}$ (c) $\frac{9}{10}$ (d) $\frac{73}{100}$ (e) $\frac{3}{8}$

(f) $\frac{7}{20}$ (g) $\frac{8}{25}$ (h) $\frac{7}{8}$ (i) $\frac{3}{4}$ (j) $\frac{19}{20}$

2   A group of people were asked if they had been to the fair in the last year. $\frac{3}{25}$ of these people said 'yes'. What *percentage* of these people said 'no'?

3   Change these decimals to percentages.

(a) 0.16   (b) 0.57   (c) 0.09   (d) 0.78   (e) 1.6

4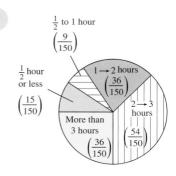

The chart opposite shows the T.V. viewing habits of 150 people in a survey. What percentage watch

(a) $\frac{1}{2}$ hour or less

(b) more than 3 hours

(c) $2 \rightarrow 3$ hours.

5   The chart opposite shows the favourite foods of 80 people.

What percentage prefer

(a) Italian,   (b) Asian,

(c) French,   (d) Anything but Chinese?

(e) Marcus plans to open a restaurant specialising in one type of food shown. He will only choose a type of food if *more than* 20% of the people prefer it.
What type of food might Marcus serve in his restaurant?

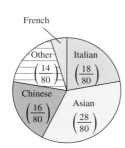

6   Here are four childrens' test results. Change them to percentages.

Clive	Abbie	Molly	Ron
$\dfrac{17}{20}$	$\dfrac{42}{60}$	$\dfrac{27}{40}$	$\dfrac{49}{140}$

7   Change these percentages to decimals.

(a) 29%   (b) 47%   (c) 1%   (d) 98%   (e) 7.5%

8

The table below shows what we throw away and the scope for recycling. Change each percentage to a fraction, cancelling down when possible.

Food waste	Plastic	Glass	Paper and card	Metals	Textiles	Other
24%	10%	8%	26%	4%	3%	25%

9   Copy and complete the table.

	fraction	decimal	percentage
(a)		0.09	
(b)			36%
(c)		0.28	
(d)	$\dfrac{11}{20}$		
(e)			7%

Exercise 2E

1   The letters shown on the right are each given a number as either a fraction, a decimal or a percentage.

In (a), (b), (c) below the numbers 1, 2, 3, …..give the positions of the letters in a sentence. So 1 is the first letter, 2 is the second letter and so on.

Find the letter whose value is the same as the number given, and write it in the correct position.

For example in part (a) number 1 is $\frac{3}{5}$.

Since $\frac{3}{5} = 0.6$, letter R goes in the first box.

Find the sentence in each part.

A 24%	N 0.9
E 0.05	O 0.625
F 0.32	R 0.6
G $\frac{3}{20}$	S $\frac{7}{20}$
H 0.36	T 0.02
I 3%	U $\frac{3}{25}$
L 0.49	V 0.1%
M $\frac{3}{4}$	Y 99%

(a)   1   2   3   4   5   6   7   8   9   10   11   12

| R | | | | | | | | | | | |

1. $\frac{3}{5}$ 2. 0.24   3. 2%   4. 0.03   5. $\frac{5}{8}$ 6. 0.35

7. $\frac{6}{25}$ 8. 60%   9. $\frac{1}{20}$ 10. 32%   11. 0.12   12. $\frac{9}{10}$

(b) 1. 15%   2. $62\frac{1}{2}$ %   3. 49%   4. $\frac{8}{25}$ 5. $\frac{3}{100}$ 6. 35%

7. 0.75   8. 0.99   9. 0.15   10. 0.24   11. 75%   12. 5%

(c) 1. $(0.6)^2$ 2. 0.2 + 0.04   3. $\frac{1}{2}$ of 0.98   4. 32%   5. $\frac{5}{8}$ 6. $\frac{8}{25}$

7. 0.2 ÷ 10   8. 5%   9. 90%   10. $\frac{15}{500}$ 11. 50% of $\frac{7}{10}$ 12. $\frac{64}{200}$

13. 3 ÷ 100   14. $\frac{1}{1000}$ 15. $(0.2)^2 + (0.1)^2$

2   Make up a sentence of your own using the letters given in question 1 . Write clues and try it out on a friend.

3   24% of the grid below is shaded (Of the 100 squares on the grid exactly 24 are shaded).

Draw a grid like this one and draw a number of your own choice. For example if you chose '16' make sure you shade in 16 out of the 100 squares. Try to make both figures the same size!

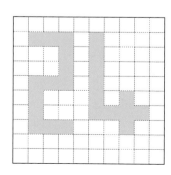

2.4 Geometrical Reasoning

In section 2.4 you will:

- calculate angles with parallel lines
- prove angle rules
- calculate angles in a quadrilateral
- solve mixed angle problems

Angle facts reminder

On a straight line

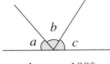

$a + b + c = 180°$

In a triangle

$a + b + c = 180°$

At a point

$m + n + p = 360°$

Angles and parallel lines

In this diagram all the arrow lines are parallel.

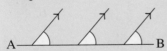

The arrows all make the same angle with the line AB. These angles are called **corresponding** angles.

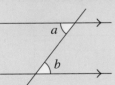

angle a = angle b
These are called *alternate* angles.

Many people think of corresponding angles as 'F' angles.

Many people think of alternate angles as 'Z' angles.

Find the angles marked with letters.

(a)

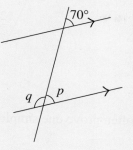

(b)

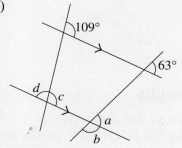

$p = 70°$ (corresponding angles)
$q = 110°$ (angles on a straight line)

$a = 63°$ (corresponding angles)
$b = 117°$ (angles on a straight line)
$c = 109°$ (corresponding angles)
$d = 71°$ (angles on a straight line)

Exercise 1M

Find the angles marked with letters.

1

2

3
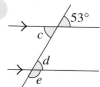

4
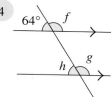

5
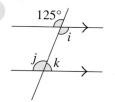

6
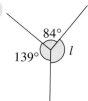

7
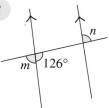

8
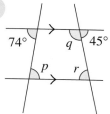

9
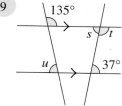

10
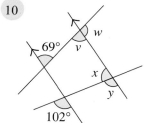

11
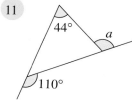

12
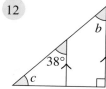

68

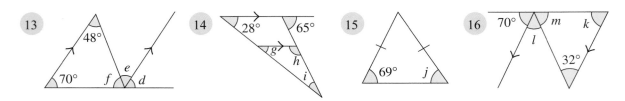

13   48°, 70°, e, f, d

14   28°, 65°, g, h, i

15   69°, j

16   70°, m, k, l, 32°

Proving results

We need to prove that angle rules are true for every possible shape. We often prove one simple result and then use that result to prove further results (and so on).

> When straight lines intersect, opposite angles are equal.
>
> By definition, the angle on one whole turn is 360°.
>
> $$a + b + a + b = 360°$$
>
> so $$a + b = 180°$$
>
>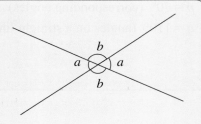
>
> This proves that the sum of the angles on a straight line is 180°.

Exercise 1E

1. Copy and complete this proof for the sum of the angles in a triangle.

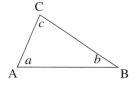   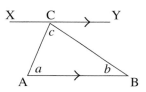   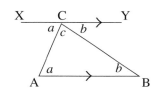

Here is $\triangle ABC$.   Draw line XCY parallel to AB. $A\hat{B}C = Y\hat{C}B$ (alternate angles)
$B\hat{A}C = \boxed{}$ (alternate angles)
$a + b + c = \boxed{}$ (angles on a straight line)
angles in a triangle: $a + b + c = 180°$

2. Copy and complete this proof for the sum of the angles in a quadrilateral.

   Draw any quadrilateral ABCD with diagonal BD.
   Now $a + b + c = \boxed{}$ (angles in a $\triangle$)
   and $d + e + f = \boxed{}$ (angles in a $\triangle$)
   $\therefore a + b + c + d + e + f = \boxed{}$

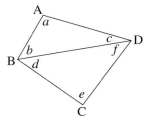

This shows that the sum of the angles in a quadrilateral is 360°.

3 To prove that the exterior angle of a triangle is equal to the sum of the two interior opposite angles.

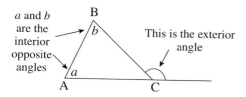

a and *b* are the interior opposite angles

This is the exterior angle

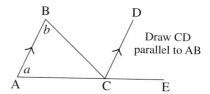

Draw CD parallel to AB

Copy and complete the proof:

$B\hat{A}C = D\hat{C}E$ (corresponding angles) ('F' angles)

$A\hat{B}C = \boxed{}$ (alternate angles) ('Z' angles)

$\therefore \boxed{} = \boxed{} + \boxed{}$

4 Explain why opposite angles of a parallelogram are equal.
[Use alternate and corresponding angles.]

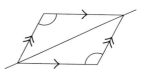

Angles in a quadrilateral

Question ② in the previous Exercise 1E proved that:

The angles in a quadrilateral add up to 360°

This is illustrated below:

Draw a quadrilateral of any shape on a piece of paper or card and cut it out. Mark the four angles *a*, *b*, *c*, and *d* and tear them off.

Arrange the four angles about a point.

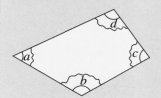

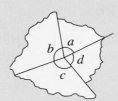

70

Exercise 2M

Find the angles marked with letters.

1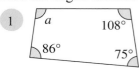

2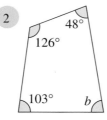

3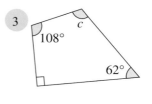

4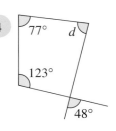

5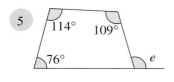

6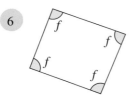

7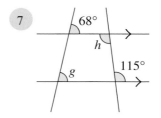

8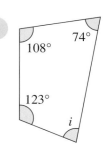

9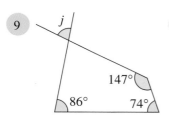

10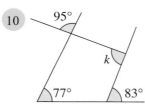

11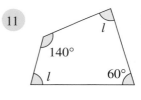

12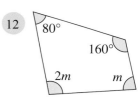

Mixed Questions

Exercise 2E

Find the angles marked with letters.

1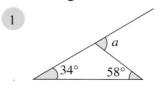

2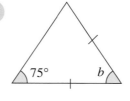

3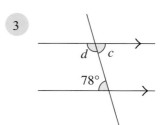

71

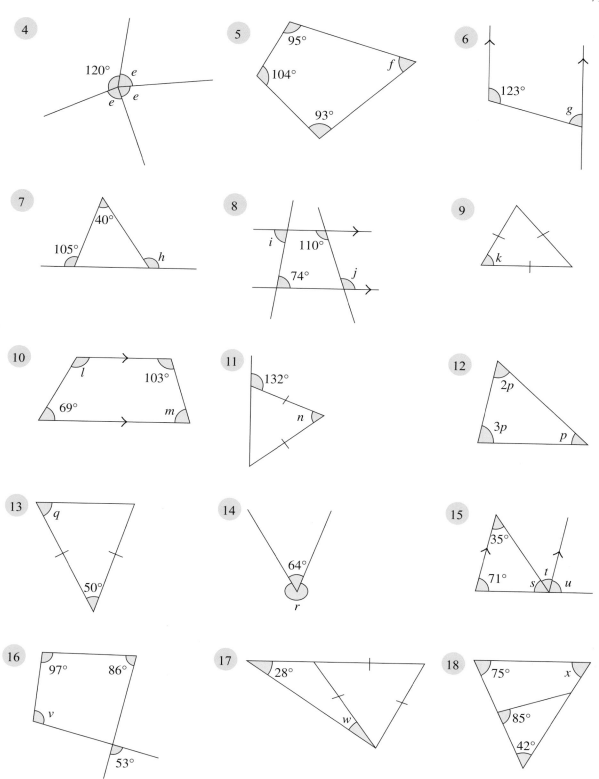

72

19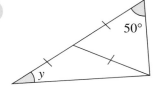

20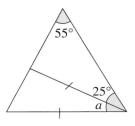

21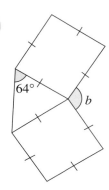

CHECK YOURSELF ON SECTIONS 2.3 AND 2.4

1   Changing fractions to decimals and vice versa

Copy and complete this table:

Fraction	$\frac{3}{5}$	$\frac{7}{20}$		$\frac{3}{8}$		
Decimal			0.03		0.12	0.8

2   Changing fractions to recurring decimals

(a) Change $\frac{8}{9}$ to a recurring decimal.

(b) Change $\frac{5}{11}$ to a recurring decimal.

3   Changing to a percentage and vice versa

(a) Change 34% into a decimal.

(b) Change $\frac{11}{25}$ into a percentage.

(c) '65% = $\frac{13}{20}$'. True or false?

(d) Fran scores $\frac{18}{25}$ in an exam and Roy scores 74% in the same exam. Who scores the higher percentage and by how much?

4   Calculating angles with parallel lines

Find the angles marked with letters.

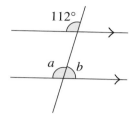

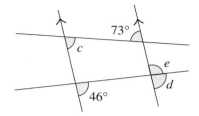

5   Proving angle rules

Use this diagram to prove that the angles in a triangle add up to 180°.

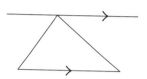

6   Calculating angles in a quadrilateral

Find the angles marked with letters.

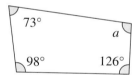

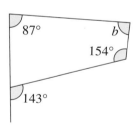

7   Solving mixed angle problems

Find the angles worked with letters.

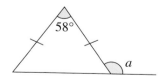

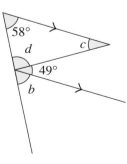

2.5 Construction and Locus

In section 2.5 you will:

- construct triangles
- describe a locus
- draw standard constructions

Constructing triangles

Two sides and the included angle given.

Two angles and a side given.

Three sides given.

6 cm
58°
4 cm

35°   70°
6 cm

7 cm   5 cm
6 cm

Construct using ruler and protractor only.

Construct using ruler and compasses only.

Exercise 1M

Construct each shape and measure the side or angle x.

1

7 cm   5 cm
x
5 cm

2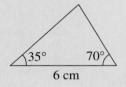

6 cm   4.5 cm
x
7.5 cm

3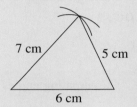

75°
7 cm x
40°

4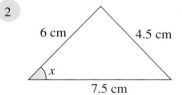

7.5 cm
x
36°
5.5 cm

5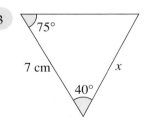

5 cm x
63°
6.5 cm

6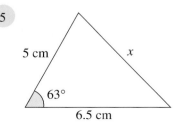

x
42°   105°
4.5 cm

7 Sally and Pete are sister and brother. There are two bedrooms in their house as shown below.

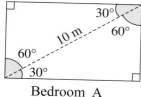

Bedroom A

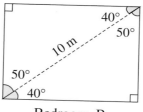

Bedroom B

They each want the bedroom with the larger area. Like all brothers and sisters they agree in a very friendly manner by tossing a coin. Sally wins. Which bedroom does she choose? (You need to construct each bedroom using a scale of 1 cm to 1 m then work out each area with a calculator.) How much larger is the area of Sally's bedroom compared to Pete's bedroom?

Locus

The *locus* of a point is the path traced out by the point as it moves.

(a) An athlete runs around a track.
   The locus looks like this

(b) Alan throws a ball to Ben.

The locus is the curve

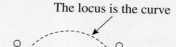

Exercise 1E

1 Mark two points A and B, 5 cm apart. Draw crosses at six points which are an equal distance from A and B. The crosses form the locus of points which are an equal distance [equidistant] from A and B.

   A   B

2 Mark a point C with a dot. Draw crosses at ten points which are all 5 cm from C. The crosses form the locus of points which are 5 cm from C. Join up the crosses with a pair of compasses. Describe the locus.

3 With a dot, mark the bottom right corner of the page you are on. Draw crosses at six points which are the same distance from the two edges of the page.

   Describe the locus of the crosses you have drawn.

4    (a) Describe the locus of the tip of the minute hand as the time goes from 10:10 to 11:10.

(b) Describe the locus of the tip of the *hour* hand as the time goes from 2 o'clock to 8 o'clock.

5   On a clock the time goes from 9:00 to 9:05. Describe the locus of the tip of the *seconds* hand.

6   A bicycle moves forward on level ground in a straight line. Sketch the locus of the valve on one of the wheels.

7   Here is a spiral shape. Write simple instructions describing how to draw the spiral so that another person would be able to draw it.

8   Work with a partner.

(a) Each person draws a fairly simple shape without showing it to their partner. Now write instructions so that your partner can draw the shape.

(b) Each person follows the written instructions to draw their partner's shape.

Standard constructions (using compasses)

Exercise 2M

You are given examples of standard constructions marked A, B, C.

You are then asked to draw your own constructions using *only* a pencil, a straight edge and a pair of compasses.

A   Perpendicular bisector of a line segment AB.

With centres A and B draw two arcs.

The perpendicular bisector is shown as a broken line.

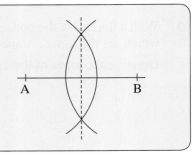

1   Draw a horizontal line AB of length 6 cm. Construct the perpendicular bisector of AB.

2   Draw a vertical line CD of length 8 cm. Construct the perpendicular bisector of CD.

3   (a) Use a protractor and ruler to draw the right-angled
       triangle ABC as shown. For greater accuracy draw
       lines slightly longer than 8 cm and 6 cm and *then*
       mark the points A, B and C.

    (b) *Construct* the perpendicular bisector of AB.

    (c) Construct the perpendicular bisector of AC.

    (d) If done accurately, your two lines from (b) and (c)
       should cross exactly on the line BC.

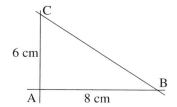

B   Perpendicular from point P to a line

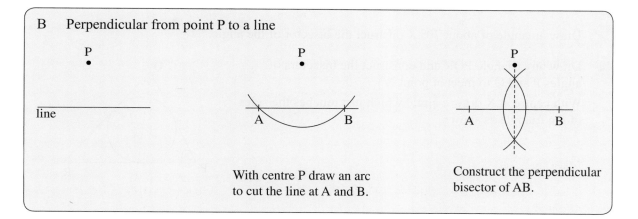

With centre P draw an arc
to cut the line at A and B.

Construct the perpendicular
bisector of AB.

---

4   Draw a line and a point P about 4 cm from the line. Construct the line which passes through P
    which is perpendicular to the line.

5   Draw another line and a point Q about 3 cm from the line. Construct the line which passes
    through Q which is perpendicular to the line.

C   Perpendicular from a point P on a line.

    With centre P draw arcs to cut the line at A and B.
    Now bisect AB as done earlier in (A).

---

6   Draw a line and a point R on the line. Construct the perpendicular from the point R.

7   Draw another line and a point S on the line. Construct the perpendicular from the point S.

78

Exercise 2E

Bisector of an angle

With centre A draw arc PQ.

With centres at P and Q draw two more arcs.

The angle bisector is then drawn.

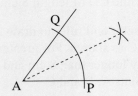

① Draw an angle of about 50°. Construct the bisector of the angle.

② Draw an angle of about 120°. Construct the bisector of the angle.

③ Draw an angle of about 70°. Construct the bisector of the angle.

④ Draw any triangle PQR and construct the bisectors of angles P and Q to meet at point X.

With centre at X draw a circle which just touches the sides of the triangle as shown.

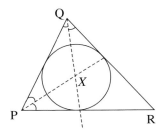

⑤ Draw a completely different triangle and repeat question ④.

⑥ Use a ruler and compasses only to construct an angle of 45°.

⑦ (a) Use a ruler and compasses only to construct triangle ABC as shown.

    (b) Construct the perpendicular bisector of AC.

    (c) Construct the angle bisector of angle A.

    (d) Let the two bisectors meet at point X. Measure the length AX.

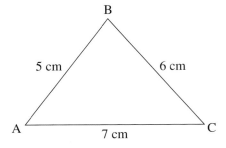

2.6 Circles

In section 2.6 you will:

- find the circumference of a circle
- find the area of a circle

Radius, diameter and circumference

Look at the following diagrams.

- The radius is half the diameter.
- The diameter is twice the radius.
- The length of the perimeter of a circle is called its *circumference*.

Exercise 1M   (Oral or written exercise)

For each of the circles shown below, write down

(a) the radius   (b) the diameter

Remember to give the units in your answers!

Activity

Find 8 circular objects (tins, plates, buckets, wheels etc.) For each object, measure the diameter and the circumference and write the results in a table. Use a flexible tape measure for the circumference or wrap a piece of string around the object and then measure the string with a ruler. For each pair of readings, work out the ratio (*circumference ÷ diameter*).

You should find that the number in the $\frac{c}{d}$ column is about the same each time.

Work out the mean value of the 8 numbers in the $\frac{c}{d}$ column.

Object	Circumference c	diameter d	$\frac{c}{d}$
Tin of tuna	28.6 cm	8.8 cm	3.25
...			
...			

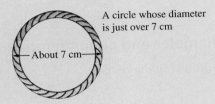

A circle whose diameter is just over 7 cm

About 7 cm

A piece of string 22 cm long will make:

— 22 cm —

If you divide the circumference of a circle by its diameter the number you obtain is always just over three.

This means $\qquad$ $\dfrac{\text{circumference}}{\text{diameter}} \approx 3$

Circumference $\approx 3 \times$ diameter

This provides a fairly good *estimate* for the circumference of any circle.

Pi

For any circle, the exact value of the ratio $\left(\dfrac{\text{circumference}}{\text{diameter}} \right)$ is a number denoted by the Greek letter π.

Since $\dfrac{\text{circumference}}{\text{diameter}} = \pi$, we can write

circumference $= \pi \times$ diameter

Learn this formula.

Most calculators have a $\boxed{\pi}$ button, which will give the value of π correct to at least 7 significant figures: 3.141593.

Find the circumference of the circle.

Radius = 4 cm, so diameter = 8 cm

Circumference = $\pi \times 8$

$\quad\quad\quad\quad = 25.13274123 \ldots$ cm

$\quad\quad\quad\quad = 25.1$ cm correct to one decimal place

Exercise 2M

Make a table and complete it for questions ① to ⑫. Make sure you write the correct units. For the calculated circumference give answers correct to one decimal place.

Number	Radius r	Diameter d	Estimated circumference	Calculated circumference
1	2 cm			
2				

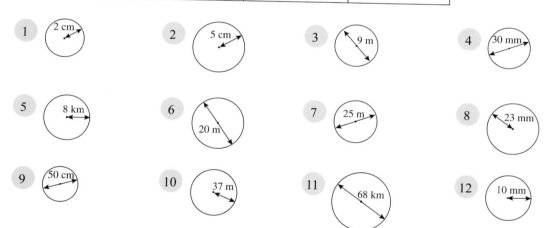

1 ⟨2 cm⟩ 2 ⟨5 cm⟩ 3 ⟨9 m⟩ 4 ⟨30 mm⟩

5 ⟨8 km⟩ 6 ⟨20 m⟩ 7 ⟨25 m⟩ 8 ⟨23 mm⟩

9 ⟨50 cm⟩ 10 ⟨37 m⟩ 11 ⟨68 km⟩ 12 ⟨10 mm⟩

13 A circular mirror has diameter 50 cm. Work out its circumference, correct to one decimal place.

14 The head of a drawing pin is circular with radius 3.6 mm. Find its circumference.

15  The knuckle of a bride's ring finger has width 19 mm. Find the internal circumference of the ring which will just fit.

16 Which has the longer perimeter and by how much: an equilateral triangle of side 10 cm or a circle of diameter 10 cm?

17 In 1897 politicians in Indiana, USA displayed a complete lack of mathematical understanding when they passed a local law stating that the value of pi was to be taken as 4.

(a) Calculate the circumference of a circle of radius 3.5 cm in Indiana.

(b) Calculate the circumference of the same circle everywhere else in the world.

P.S. The law was soon discarded!

Perimeters

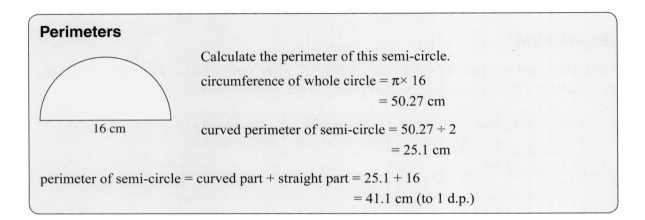

Calculate the perimeter of this semi-circle.

circumference of whole circle = π× 16

= 50.27 cm

curved perimeter of semi-circle = 50.27 ÷ 2

= 25.1 cm

perimeter of semi-circle = curved part + straight part = 25.1 + 16

= 41.1 cm (to 1 d.p.)

Exercise 2E

Calculate the perimeter of each shape.

All shapes are either semi-circles or quarter circles.

Give answers correct to 1 decimal place.

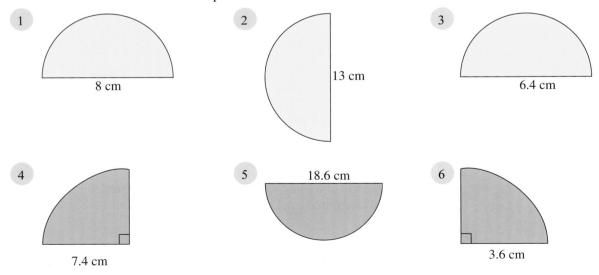

1   8 cm

2   13 cm

3   6.4 cm

4   7.4 cm

5   18.6 cm

6   3.6 cm

7 A semi-circle is attached to a rectangle as shown to make a window. What is the perimeter of the frame required for this window?

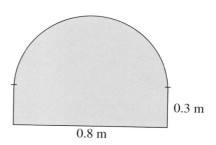

0.3 m

0.8 m

Area of a circle

(a) The circle below is divided into 12 equal sectors

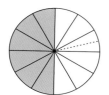

(b) The sectors are cut and arranged to make a shape which is nearly a rectangle. (one sector is cut in half).

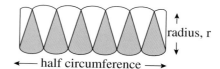

radius, r

half circumference

(c) The approximate area can be found as follows:

length of rectangle ≈ half circumference of circle

$$\approx \frac{\pi \times 2r}{2}$$

$$\approx \pi r$$

width of rectangle ≈ r

∴ area of rectangle ≈ $\pi r \times r$

$$\approx \pi r^2$$

If larger and larger numbers of sectors were used, this approximation would become more and more accurate.

This is a demonstration of an important result.

Area of a circle = πr^2 *Learn* this formula.

Note: πr^2 means $\pi(r^2)$. i.e. π multiplied by r^2

Find the area of each shape.

(a)

26 cm

radius = 13 cm

area = πr^2

= 530.9 cm² (1 d.p.)

On a calculator, press:

(b)

←3.2 cm→

The shape is a quarter circle

area = $\dfrac{\pi(3.2)^2}{4}$

= 8.0 cm² (1 d.p.)

On a calculator, press.

Exercise 3M

Calculate the area of each circle and give your answer correct to one decimal place.

1

11 mm

2

12 cm

3

20 m

4

24 cm

5

20 km

6

80 cm

7

22 mm

8

13 cm

9

30 m

10

30 cm

11

25 m

12

64 km

13 The dart board shown has a diameter of 53 cm. Calculate the area of the dart board.

14 Work out the area of a circular lawn which has a radius of 4.2 m.

15 The top of a mixing bowl is a circle with diameter 33 cm. Find the area of this circle.

Exercise 3E

Work out the area of each shape and give your answers correct to one decimal place.

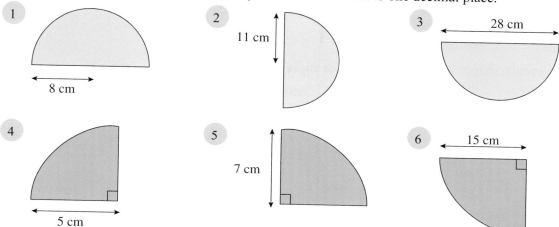

1   8 cm

2   11 cm

3   28 cm

4   5 cm

5   7 cm

6   15 cm

7   A carton of 'Verdone' weedkiller contains enough weedkiller to treat an area of 100 m². A circular lawn at Hampton Court has a radius of 16.5 m. How many cartons of weedkiller are needed to treat this lawn?

8   In this stained glass window the circle has diameter 3 m and the outer square is of side 4.5 m. Calculate the area which is outside the circle.

9   The diameters of 1p, 5p, and 10p coins are 2 cm, 1.8 cm and 2.4 cm respectively. Calculate the total area of the top faces of the five coins used to make 18p.

10   Find the shaded area.

Lengths are in cm.

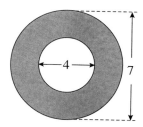

CHECK YOURSELF ON SECTIONS 2.5 AND 2.6

1   Constructing triangles

Construct each shape and measure the side or angle x.

(a)

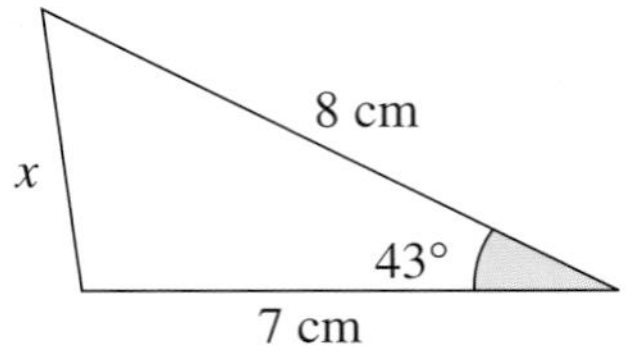

8 cm

x

43°

7 cm

(b)

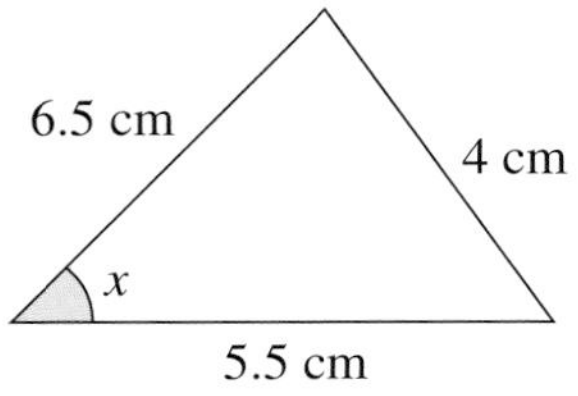

6.5 cm

4 cm

x

5.5 cm

2   Describing a locus

(a) Draw a point and label it P.
Draw the locus of all points which are 4 cm from P.

(b) Draw a 6 cm line and label it AB.
Draw crosses at six points which are 2 cm
from the line AB. Draw the whole locus of
points which are 2 cm from the line AB.

3   Drawing standard constructions

(a) Draw a vertical line of length 7 cm. Construct the perpendicular bisector of this line.

(b) Use a protractor to draw an angle of 80°. Construct the bisector of this angle.

4   Finding the circumference of a circle

(a)

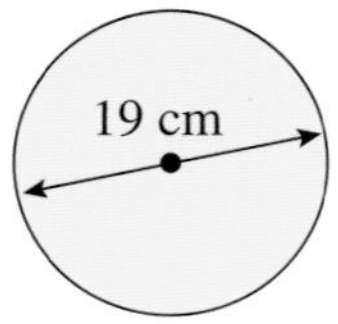

19 cm

Find the circumference of this circle, correct to 1 decimal place.

(b) A car tyre has a radius of 37 cm. How long is its circumference in cm, correct
to 1 decimal place?

5 Finding the area of a circle

The diameter of the top of the larger drum is 34 cm and the radius of the top of the smaller drum is 8.5 cm.

(a) Find the area of the top of the smaller drum.

(b) Find the area of the top of the larger drum.

(c) How many smaller drums would you need to have the same top surface area as one larger drum?

UNIT 2 MIXED REVIEW

Part one

1 George Washington's father planted a tree when his son was born. George Washington died in 1799 aged 67. How old was the tree in 2008?

2 A CD is sold at £10.95 each. Estimate the total cost of 485 CD's.

3 Answer 'true' or 'false'

(a) $3 \times n = 3 + n$

(b) $a \times 5 = 5a$

(c) $a + b + a = 2a + b$

(d) $n + 2n = 2n^2$

(e) $n \div 3 = \frac{n}{3}$

(f) $n \times n = n^2$

4 Find the angles marked with letters

(a)
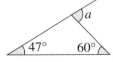

(b)
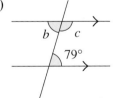

(c)
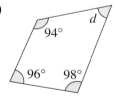

5 Which of these numbers is the largest?

$\frac{7}{25}$ 26% $\frac{1}{4}$ 0.29

6 (a) How long does it take the minute hand of a clock to move 360°?

(b) How long does it take the hour hand to move 90°?

(c) How long does it take the seconds hand to move 720°?

7. Jenny is on holiday. She spends *n* hours each day on the beach. How many hours does she spend on the beach during seven days? (your answer should be an expression containing *n*)

8. Simplify each expression by collecting like terms:

   (a) $3m + 5n - 2m + 2n$ (b) $6p + 3 + 2p - 1$ (c) $4w - w + 5q + 2w$

9. Construct an accurate copy of each triangle and find the length *x* and the angle *y*.

   (a)

   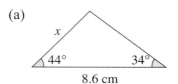

   (b)

   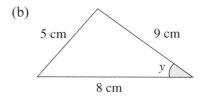

10. Norman works out $198 \div 4.03$ and gets the answer 4.91 correct to two decimal places. Use estimation to decide if Norman is likely to be correct.

11. I am a 3 digit number. The product of my digits is 2. I am an odd number, greater than 200. What number am I?

12.

    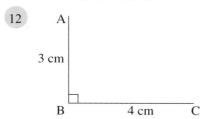

    Copy this diagram. An ant crawls from B so that it is always the same distance from AB as BC. It stops when it is 3 cm from BC.

    Draw the path taken by the ant.

13. Britney has £20. She spends £17 on a shirt. What percentage of her money does she spend?

14.

    Dennis is very sad. He used to have a diameter of 15 cm but after a heavy wash, he now only has a radius of 5 cm.

    Calculate, to one decimal place, by how much his circumference has decreased.

15. Vinny has a terrible diet. On average he eats 21 burgers each week. Estimate how many burgers he eats in one year.

Part two

1. Find two matching expressions:

   A $\boxed{a + 2 + 3b - b}$ B $\boxed{3a + 2 - a + 2b}$ C $\boxed{2 + b + a + b}$

2. Every day he plays, a snooker player uses 20 g of chalk on his cue. He plays 300 days a year. How much chalk will he use if he plays for 20 years? Give the answer in kg.

3. 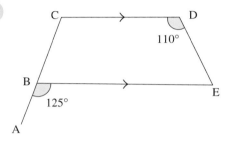 Find the value of:

   (a) $B\hat{C}D$

   (b) $B\hat{E}D$

4. Find the area of the yellow circle, giving your answer to one decimal place.

   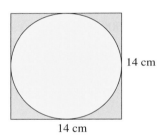

   14 cm

   14 cm

5. (a) Write an expression for the cost of n packets at 20 p each.
   (b) Write an expression for the cost of n stamps at 10 p each.

6. (a) *Construct* the perpendicular bisector of AB.   (b) *Construct* the bisector of the angle A.

   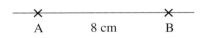

   A   8 cm   B

   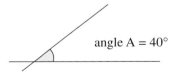

   angle A = 40°

7. Find three numbers which add up to 10 and multiply to give 30.

    $+$ $\quad$ $+$ $\quad$ = 10    $\times$ $\quad$ $\times$ $\quad$ = 30

8. Here are six calculations and six answers. Write down each calculation and insert the correct answer from the list below. Use estimation.

   (a) $79.6 \div 4$ (b) $145 \div 150$ (c) $288.2 \div 6$

   (d) $52.2 + 47.6$ (e) $10.4 \div 97$ (f) $416 \div 1.97$

   $\boxed{\text{Answers: } 0.97,\ 99.8,\ 19.9,\ 0.11,\ 211.2,\ 48.0}$

9

24 m

16 m | lawn

pond | 10 m

A box of seed costs £8.75 and will cover 50 m². How much will it cost to seed the entire lawn shown opposite?

10 The numbers 1 to 12 are arranged on the star so that the sum of the numbers along each line is the same.

Copy and complete the star.

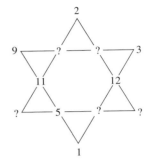

11 As part of an advertising campaign, the message '*Exercise is good for you*' is taped individually right around 500 000 tennis balls, each of diameter 6.5 cm. Find the total cost of the tape for the campaign, given that a 33 m roll of tape costs 96p. (Give your answer to the nearest pound)

12 The radius of this circle is 7 cm. Calculate the area of the region shaded pink. Give your answer correct to 1 decimal place.

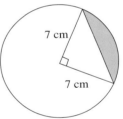

7 cm

7 cm

13

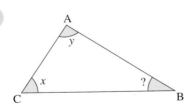

Write down an expression for the size of $A\hat{B}C$. (your answer will have the letters x and y in it)

14 17% of 18-year-olds have a tattoo.
$\frac{4}{25}$ of 19-year-olds have a tattoo.
0.18 of 20-year-olds have a tattoo.

Which age group has the highest percentage of people with tattoos?
Would you ever want a tattoo? Why?

15 John has two bags of toffees, each containing n toffees. He also has a tube of mints containing m mints.

He gives his sister 3 toffees from each bag and he eats y mints.

Write down an expression for the *total* number of toffees and mints that John now has.

Puzzles and Problems 2

Cross numbers without clues

Here are cross number puzzles with a difference. There are no clues, only answers, and you have to find where the answers go.

(a) Copy out the cross number pattern.
(b) Fit all the given numbers into the correct spaces. Work logically and tick off the numbers from lists as you write them in the squares.

1

2 digits	3 digits	4 digits	5 digits
23	146	2708	25404
26	235	2715	25814
42	245		37586
57	337		
59	539		
87	695		

2

2 digits	3 digits	4 digits	5 digits
18	244	2163	36918
21	247	4133	46514
31	248	4213	54374
33	332	4215	54704
47	333	4283	87234
63	334	4317	
64	608	4394	
77			

3

2 digits	3 digits	4 digits	5 digits	7 digits
36	145	2286	16145	4235824
52	185	5235	66145	
56	245	5248	66152	
63	246	5249	66272	
65	374	5452	91671	
77	437	6241		
90	646			
	896			

4

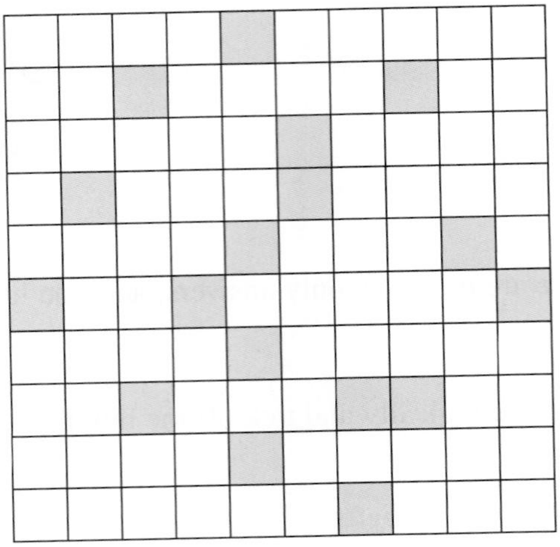

2 digits	3 digits	4 digits	5 digits
14	123	1325	14251
22	231	1478	29163
26	341	1687	29613
43	439	1976	29872
65	531	2523	34182
70	670	4798	54875
81		5601	63712
82		5611	67358
		5621	82146
		6109	84359
		8171	97273

6 digits	7 digits
145026	9354234
740136	
983514	

5

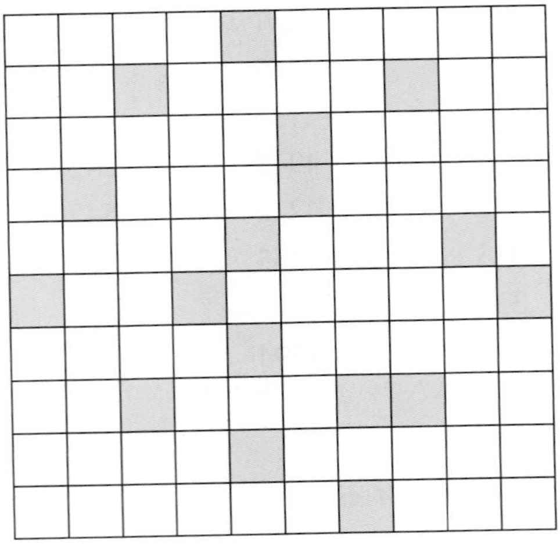

2 digits	3 digits	4 digits	5 digits
15	137	2513	29666
19	206	3048	31873
21	276	3214	40657
22	546	3244	43104
28	592	3437	43158
31	783	3514	54732
77		3517	60783
90		3544	62114
		4122	80751
		4127	82614
		6934	93654

6 digits	7 digits
235785	9733764
235815	
452705	

A long time ago! 2

Binary numbers

Decimal numbers use 10 digits:
0, 1, 2, 3, 4, 5, 6, 7, 8, 9

Binary numbers use only 2 digits: 0 and 1
A binary number uses powers of 2 to give its value.

$2^0 = 1$ $2^1 = 2$ $2^2 = 4$ $2^3 = 8$

What is the decimal value of the binary number 1101?

1 1 0 1   = 8 + 4 + 0 + 1 = 13

units
2
4
8

A switch can be 'on' or 'off'. The digit 1 can be used for 'on' and the digit 0 for 'off' so circuits could be built using binary numbers.

George Boole in the 19th century developed a 'true' or 'false' logic system called Boolean algebra.

Without binary numbers, there might never have been any computers then where would we be?

The first mention of binary numbers was more than two thousand years ago by an Indian called Pingala.

Exercise

1   Look at the example above then change these binary numbers into decimal numbers.

(a) 101   (b) 11   (c) 110   (d) 1001
(e) 10   (f) 1010   (g) 1100   (h) 1111

2   What is the decimal value of the binary number 10000?

3   Write 32 as a binary number.

4   Write 64 as a binary number.

5. Write the following numbers in binary form.

(a) 17   (b) 24   (c) 4   (d) 14   (e) 44

6. Add these binary numbers to get a binary answer.

(a)   101   (b)   1011   (c)   1010
    + 11   + 1001   + 1111
    _____   _____   _____

Mental Arithmetic Practice

Ideally a teacher will read out each question twice, with pupils' books closed.

Test 1

1. What is the perimeter of a square with sides 8 cm?

2. Write one fifth as a percentage.

3. What number is half way between 4.2 and 4.8?

4. I have six 20p, one 5p and one 2p coin. How much do I have?

5. A poster costs three pounds. Andrew saves sixty pence per week. How many weeks will it be before he can buy it?

6. Screws cost 8 pence each. What is the cost of 25 screws?

7. Hooks cost 70 pence for five. What is the cost of 1 hook?

8. A pair of earrings costs £1.23. What is the change from £2?

9. How many 5p coins do I need for 85p?

10. A drill costs £34 new. I get a discount of £8.50. How much do I pay?

11. A T.V. programme starts at 9.50 and ends at 10.40. How long is the programme?

12. I travel at 60m.p.h. for 4 hours. How far do I travel?

13. Work out ten per cent of £65.

14. Susie has 3 red pens and 4 black pens. What fraction of her pens are black?

15. Jacqui make a phone call from 18.40 until 19.21. How long is the call in minutes?

16. What five coins make 62p?

17. Write the number fifty thousand and six in figures.

18. The product of two numbers is thirty nine. One of the numbers is three. What is the other?

19. Change four and a half metres into centimetres.

20. Subtract 18 from 150.

21. Write three fifths as a decimal.

22. Increase forty pounds by 25 percent.

23. I buy three magazines at 99p each. What change do I get from £10?

24. How many lengths of 8 cm can be cut from 50 cm?

25. How many minutes are there in $2\frac{3}{4}$ hours?

Test 2

1 What are 37 twos?

2 What is the smaller angle between the hands of a clock at 8 o'clock?

3 Two angles of a triangle are 55° and 30°. What is the third angle?

4 What is 50% of £44?

5 How many 5p coins are needed to make £10?

6 A car costing £8500 is reduced by £120. What is the new price?

7 What number is twice as big as sixty-nine?

8 On a tray fourteen out of fifty peaches are rotten. What percentage is that?

9 Add together 11, 18 and 9.

10 A C.D. costs £13.55. Find the change from a £20 note.

11 What five coins make 51p?

12 What is $\frac{2}{3}$ of £186?

13 Write one twentieth as a decimal.

14 How many minutes are there between 8.15 p.m. and 10.20 p.m.?

15 A pools prize of six million pounds is shared equally between one hundred people. How much does each person receive?

16 If June 14th is a Tuesday, what day of the week is June 23rd?

17 True or false: 1 kg is about 2 pounds?

18 How many millimetres are there in 3.5 metres?

19 A daily newspaper costs 25p from Monday to Saturday and 45p on Sunday. What is the total cost for the seven days?

20 What $\frac{3}{4}$ as a decimal.

21 A clock ticks once every second. How many times does it tick between six o'clock and seven o'clock?

22 Add eleven to nine times eight

23 A rectangular piece of wood measures 15 cm by 10 cm. What is its area?

24 An egg box holds six eggs. How many boxes are needed for 100 eggs?

25 How many 19p stamps can I buy for a pound?

UNIT 3

3.1 Written Calculations

In section 3.1 you will:

- review paper and pencil calculations
- read scales and use place value
- multiply decimal numbers
- divide decimal numbers

Paper and pencil calculations

(a) $56 + 711 + 8$

$$
\begin{array}{r}
5\ 6 \\
7\ 1\ 1 \\
+\quad 8 \\
\hline
7\ 7\ 5 \\
\scriptstyle 1
\end{array}
$$

(b) $383 - 57$

$$
\begin{array}{r}
3\,^7 8\,^1 3 \\
-\quad 5\ 7 \\
\hline
3\ 2\ 6
\end{array}
$$

(c) 214×7

$$
\begin{array}{r}
2\ 1\ 4 \\
\times\quad 7 \\
\hline
1\ 4\ 9\ 8 \\
\scriptstyle 2
\end{array}
$$

(d) $1518 \div 6$

$$
\begin{array}{r}
2\ 5\ 3 \\
6\overline{)1\ 5\,^3 1\,^3 8}
\end{array}
$$

(e) $\quad 34 \times 200$
$= 34 \times 2 \times 100$
$= 6800$

(f) $406 \div 14$

$$
\begin{array}{r}
2\ 9 \\
14\overline{)4\ 0\,^{12} 6}
\end{array}
$$

Exercise 1M

Work out, without a calculator

1. $847 + 325$
2. $7140 + 396$
3. $294 - 157$
4. $6293 - 1734$
5. 35×4
6. 73×6
7. 214×8
8. 315×7
9. 23×100
10. 315×10
11. 17×1000
12. 43×20
13. 26×300
14. 124×200
15. $5184 + 2787$
16. $5615 - 3916$
17. 316×5
18. $56000 \div 20$
19. $868 \div 7$
20. 173×8
21. $14490 \div 6$
22. 52×400
23. $576 \div 16$
24. 73×30
25. $1128 \div 24$
26. $4464 \div 36$
27. 17×300
28. $4000 - 264$

29 An astronaut spends 67 hours on the moon. How many minutes did the astronaut spend on the moon?

30 A factory has made 4416 baseball caps. An equal number of caps are to be delivered to 12 stores. How many caps does each store receive?

(a) $5.6 + 12.32$

$$5.60 \leftarrow \text{add zero}$$
$$+ 12.32$$
$$\overline{17.92}$$

[Line up the decimal points]

(b) 5.26×10

$$= 52.6$$

Move the digits one place to the left.

(c) $28.1 \div 100$

$$= 0.281$$

Move the digits two places to the right.

(d) 0.38×1000

$$= 380$$

(e) $79.2 \div 6$

$$\begin{array}{r} 13.2 \\ 6)\overline{7^19.^12} \end{array}$$

(f) $17 - 5.4$

$$\begin{array}{r} {}^6\,{}^1 \\ 1\cancel{7}.\cancel{0} \\ - 5.4 \\ \hline 11.6 \end{array}$$

Exercise 1E

Work out, without a calculator

1 5.62×10

2 $59 \div 10$

3 $647 \div 100$

4 $8.3 \div 10$

5 $219 \div 1000$

6 $19.2 - 5.8$

7 $11 + 5.2$

8 $98.7 \div 7$

9 $0.38 - 0.252$

10 $73.2 \div 100$

11 5.1×100

12 $5.48 \div 4$

13 $8.52 \div 4$

14 $234 + 23.4$

15 $0.612 \div 6$

16 $7.1 + 16$

17 $0.72 - 0.065$

18 $5.7 \div 100$

19 $0.83 - 0.059$

20 0.06×1000

21 Which is larger $0.832 - 0.75$ or $0.047 - 0.034$ and by how much?

22 Ordinary pencils cost 35p but a special 'knotted' pencil costs £1.50.
Cherie buys eleven ordinary pencils and five knotted pencils.
How much change does she get from £20?

23 How many of the 'knotted pencils in question 3 could you buy with £100?

24

Photocopy prices	
A4 sheet 6.9p per sheet	
A3 sheet 12.4p per sheet	

Amy copies 1000 A4 sheets and 100 A3 sheets.
Use the prices in the table to find the total cost.

25 Copy and complete.

(a) $0.38 \times \boxed{} = 38$

(b) $\boxed{} + 1.4 = 7.63$

(c) $4.76 \div \boxed{} = 0.476$

(d) $\boxed{} - 0.35 = 0.08$

Scale reading and place value

Exercise 2M

For each of the scales work out the measurement shown by each arrow.

1   cm   6 — a ——— b — 10

2   kg   2 —— a —— b — 3

3   kg   10 — a ——— b — 50

4   m   0.6 — a ——— b — 0.7

5   m   0.5 — a ——— b — 1.0

6   kg   9 — a ——— b — 13

7   g   40 — a ——— b — 60

8   kg   0.21 — a ——— b — 0.22

9   cm   2 — a ——— b — 3

10   litres
4
← b
← a
0

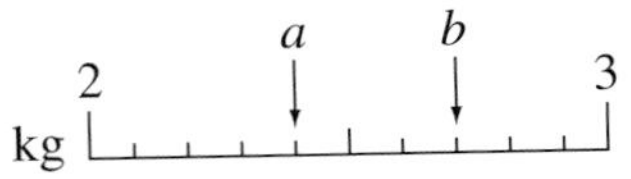

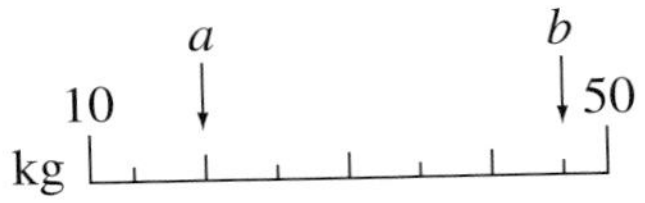

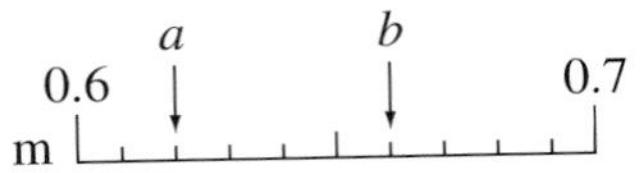

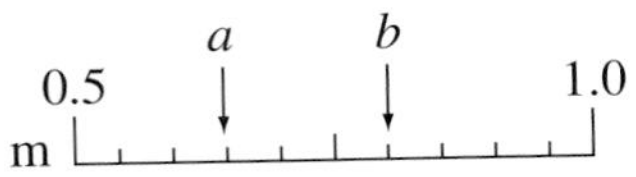

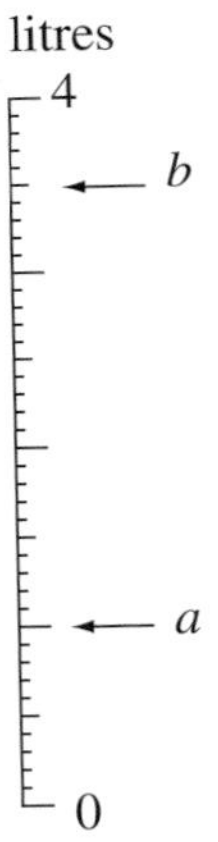

11   ml
500
← b
← a
100

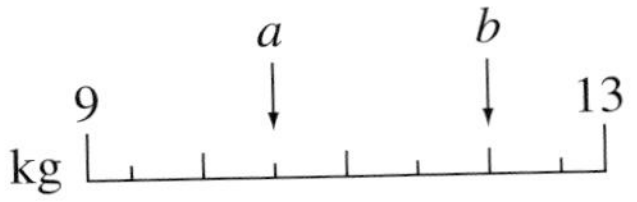

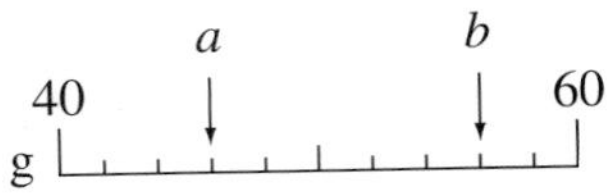

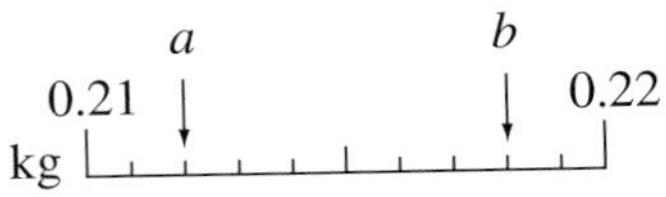

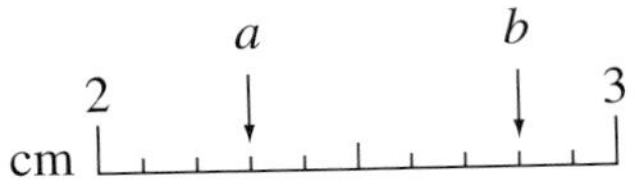

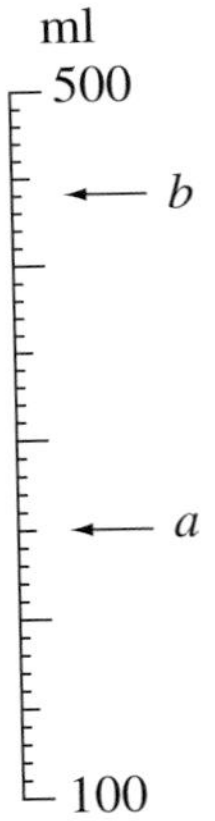

12   litres
4
← b
← a
0

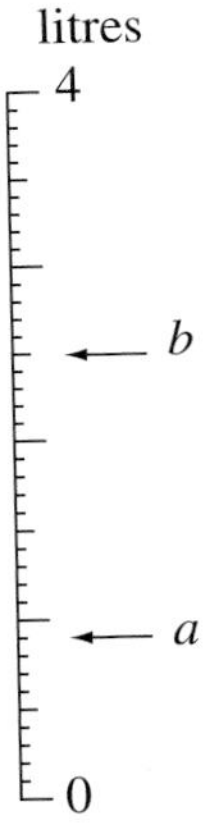

13   Newtons
2
← b
← a
1

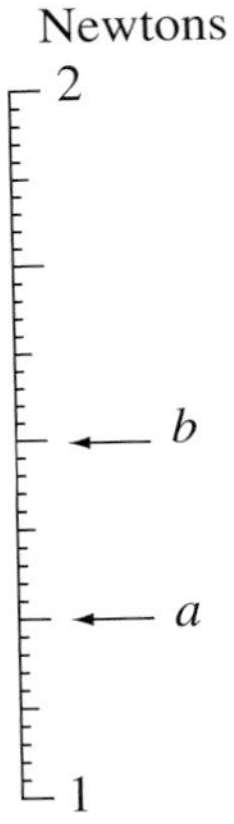

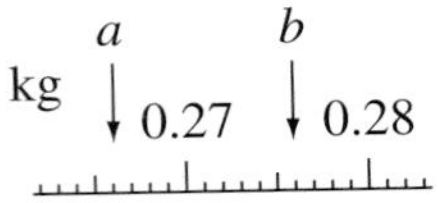

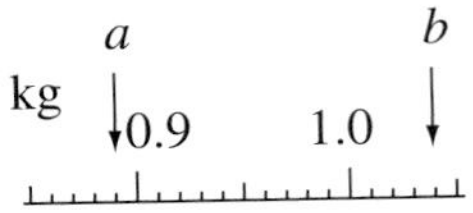

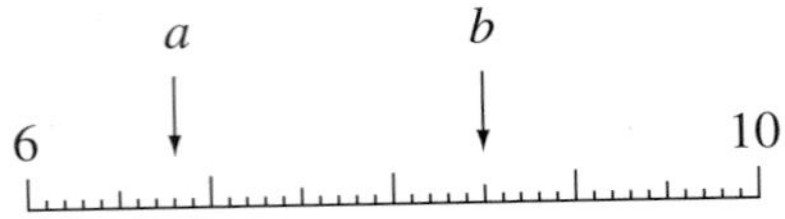

14   kg   a | 1   b | 2

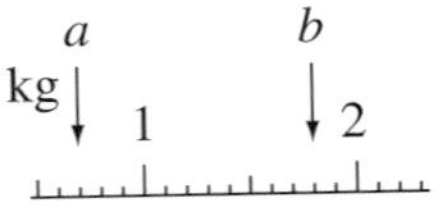

15   kg   a ↓ 0.27   b ↓ 0.28

16   kg   a ↓ 0.9   1.0   b ↓

17   6   a ——— b — 10

18   0   a ——— b — 4000

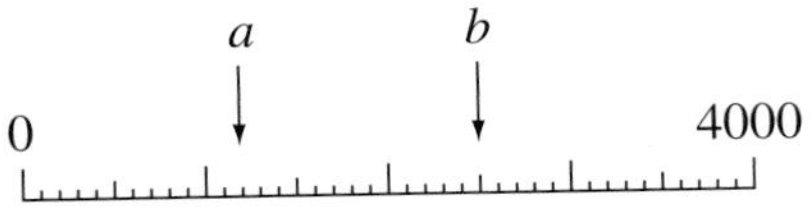

19 Copy the line and locate the numbers.

2.03 2.05 1.95 1.97 2.07

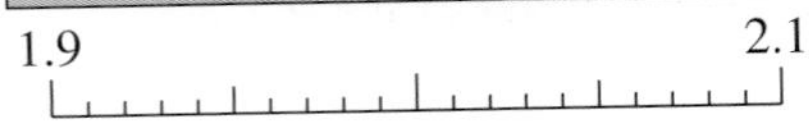

1.9 ——————————— 2.1

20 Copy the line and locate the numbers.

1.98 1.935 1.915 1.94

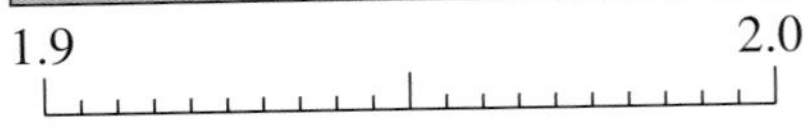

1.9 ——————————— 2.0

Write 1.41, 1.4, 1.141, 1 in ascending order.

Write in column.	Put in zeros.	Arrange in order.
1.41	1.410	1
1.4	1.400	1.141
1.141	1.141	1.4
1	1.000	1.41

Exercise 2E

1. (a) What is 0.01 more than 3.28?
   (b) What is 0.001 more than 0.625?
   (c) What is 0.001 less than 0.587?

2. Copy each sequence and fill in the spaces.
   (a) 2.67, 2.68, 2.69, ☐, ☐   (b) 1.52, 1.51, 1.5, ☐, ☐   (c) 3.6, 3.8, 4, ☐, ☐

3. Write each statement with either >, < or = in the space.
   (a) 0.032 ☐ 0.004   (b) 0.728 ☐ 0.73   (c) 0.005 ☐ 0.0006   (d) 0.09 ☐ 0.1

4. Two aliens weigh 83.216 kg and 83.23 kg.

   Which is the larger weight?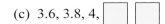

5. Arrange in order of size, smallest first.
   (a) 0.73, 0.718, 0.7   (b) 0.405, 0.5, 0.41
   (c) 0.3, 0.035, 0.029   (d) 0.06, 0.058, 0.0511
   (e) 0.92, 0.94, 0.9   (f) 0.63, 0.063, 0.306
   (g) 0.2, 0.198, 0.19   (h) 0.084, 0.812, 0.81

6. Write the number half way between:
   (a) 0.4 and 0.5   (b) 0.1 and 0.2   (c) 0.2 and 0.8

7. What has to be added or subtracted to change:
   (a) 3.24 to 3.26   (b) 0.714 to 0.712   (c) 0.142 to 0.152

8.

   Six people have to get out of a maze. Each time taken to get out of the maze is shown below.

Carl	12.73 mins	Sam	12.6 mins
Julie	12.8 mins	Ben	13.08 mins
Arwen	13.14 mins	Melinda	12.75 mins

   If they all started at the same time, write down the order in which they got out of the maze.

Multiplying decimal numbers

- 5×0.3 is the same as $5 \times \frac{3}{10}$. Work out $(5 \times 3) \div 10 = 15 \div 10 = 1.5$

  4.2×0.2 is the same as $4.2 \times \frac{2}{10}$.

  Work out $(4.2 \times 2) \div 10 = 8.4 \div 10 = 0.84$

  21.4×0.05 is the same as $21.4 \times \frac{5}{100}$. Work out $(21.4 \times 5) \div 100 = 107 \div 100 = 1.07$

- Quick method:

> When we multiply two decimal numbers together, the answer has the same number of figures to the right of the decimal point as the total number of figures to the right of the decimal point in the question.

(a) 6×0.01

$(6 \times 1 = 6)$

So $6 \times 0.01 = 0.06$

(b) 0.3×0.4

$(3 \times 4 = 12)$

So $0.3 \times 0.4 = 0.12$

(c) 0.7×0.05

$(7 \times 5 = 35)$

so $0.7 \times 0.05 = 0.035$

Exercise 3M

Work out

1. 3×0.1
2. 26×0.1
3. 7×0.01
4. 15×0.01
5. 0.7×0.1
6. 63×0.01
7. 0.5×0.1
8. 5.2×0.01
9. 0.4×0.2
10. 0.6×0.3
11. 0.8×0.2
12. 0.4×0.03
13. 0.7×3
14. 0.7×0.02
15. 0.9×0.5
16. 6×0.04
17. 15×0.03
18. 0.4×0.04
19. 0.001×0.6
20. 33×0.02

21. Work out the area of each shape

(a)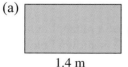
0.6 m
1.4 m

(b)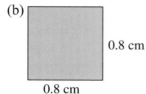
0.8 cm
0.8 cm

(c)
0.6 cm
1.2 cm

22. Phone cable costs £0.55 per metre. Calculate the cost of 2.6 m of cable.

23. Work out

(a) 0.3^2

(b) 0.5^2

(c) 0.9^2

(d) 1.2^2

24 Copy and complete

(a) $6 \times 0.2 = \boxed{}$ (b) $0.4 \times \boxed{} = 0.04$ (c) $1.5 \times \boxed{} = 150$

Exercise 3E

Work out

1 1.2×0.3 **2** 3.2×0.2 **3** 1.4×0.4 **4** 2.1×0.5

5 3.61×0.3 **6** 2.1×0.6 **7** 0.31×0.7 **8** 0.42×0.02

9 Copy and complete the multiplication square.

×	0.1	0.02		8
0.2			0.1	
2.1				
				24
10				

10 6.2×2.1 is approximately $6 \times 2 = 12$

6.2×2.1 gives the answer 13.02

The actual answer is close to the approximate answer so is probably correct.

Work out, after finding an approximate answer first.

(a) 5.3×32 (b) 2.3×1.2 (c) 3.8×17 (d) 7.9×4.1

(e) 6.2×4.2 (f) 35.1×0.9 (g) 0.32×5.8 (h) 1.9×1.8

11

You are given that £1 = \$1.95 and £1 = €1.25

(a) How many euros do you get for £40?

(b) How many dollars do you get for £75?

(c) Ben buys a radio in France for €125. The radio is 10% more expensive to buy in the USA. How many dollars will the radio cost in the USA?

12 The length of a rectangle is 1.5 m and its perimeter is 4 m. Find the area of the rectangle.

Dividing decimal numbers

Dividing by 0.1 and 0.01

- $1 \div 0.1 = 1 \div \frac{1}{10} \dots$ How many $\frac{1}{10}$s are there in 1?   Answer: 10

  $7 \div 0.1 = 7 \div \frac{1}{10} \dots$ How many $\frac{1}{10}$s are there in 7?   Answer: 70

  $5.2 \div 0.1 = 5.2 \div \frac{1}{10} \dots$ How many $\frac{1}{10}$s are there in 5.2?   Answer: 52

  $1 \div 0.01 = 1 \div \frac{1}{100} \dots$ How many $\frac{1}{100}$s are there in 1?   Answer: 100

  $13 \div 0.01 = 13 \div \frac{1}{100} \dots$ How many $\frac{1}{100}$s are there in 13?   Answer: 1300

- We see that:

  dividing by 0.1 is the same as multiplying by 10,

  dividing by 0.01 is the same as multiplying by 100.

$$3 \div 0.1 = 3 \times 10 = 30$$

$$14 \div 0.1 = 14 \times 10 = 140$$

$$0.4 \div 0.1 = 0.4 \times 10 = 4$$

$$7 \div 0.01 = 7 \times 100 = 700$$

$$52 \div 0.01 = 52 \times 100 = 5200$$

$$0.7 \div 0.01 = 0.7 \times 100 = 70$$

Exercise 4M

1. $5 \div 0.1$ 2. $9 \div 0.1$ 3. $11 \div 0.1$ 4. $6 \div 0.1$

5. $32 \div 0.1$ 6. $0.7 \div 0.1$ 7. $0.9 \div 0.1$ 8. $1.3 \div 0.1$

9. $3 \div 0.01$ 10. $11 \div 0.01$ 11. $4 \div 0.01$ 12. $0.3 \div 0.01$

13. $0.8 \div 0.01$ 14. $57 \div 0.01$ 15. $1.9 \div 0.01$ 16. $0.42 \div 0.01$

17. Find the missing numbers

    (a) $12 \div 0.1 = \boxed{}$ (b) $7 \div \boxed{} = 70$ (c) $3 \div \boxed{} = 300$

    (d) $\boxed{} \div 0.1 = 20$ (e) $1.2 \div 0.01 = \boxed{}$ (f) $1.7 \div \boxed{} = 17$

18. What numbers belong in each empty box?

    (a) $4.8 \xrightarrow{\div} \square \longrightarrow 48 \xrightarrow{\div} \square \longrightarrow 0.48 \xrightarrow{\div} \square \longrightarrow 480 \xrightarrow{\div} \square \longrightarrow 4800$

    (b) $390 \xrightarrow{\div} \square \longrightarrow 3.9 \xrightarrow{\div} \square \longrightarrow 39 \xrightarrow{\div} \square \longrightarrow 0.39 \xrightarrow{\div} \square \longrightarrow 39$

    (c) $0.4 \xrightarrow{\div} \square \longrightarrow 4 \xrightarrow{\div} \square \longrightarrow 400 \xrightarrow{\div} \square \longrightarrow 40 \xrightarrow{\div} \square \longrightarrow 0.04$

19. (a) Write 1 penny in pounds as a decimal.
    (b) How many 1ps are there in £8.05?

20. How many 0.1 metre pieces of wood can be cut from a 1.6 metre length of wood?

To divide by any decimal number we transform the calculation into a division by a *whole number*.

Examples $3.6 \div 0.2 = 36 \div 2 = 18$ [Multiply 3.6 and 0.2 by 10.]

    $1.5 \div 0.03 = 150 \div 3 = 50$ [Multiply 1.5 and 0.03 by 100.]

Since both numbers are multiplied by 10 or 100 the answer is not changed.

Exercise 4E

Work out, without a calculator

1    $1.46 \div 0.2$ 2 $2.52 \div 0.4$ 3 $0.942 \div 0.3$ 4 $0.712 \div 0.2$

5    $0.375 \div 0.5$ 6 $6.54 \div 0.2$ 7 $0.0585 \div 0.09$ 8 $5.04 \div 0.7$

9    $0.2846 \div 0.2$ 10 $0.42 \div 0.03$ 11 $7.041 \div 0.01$ 12 $0.993 \div 0.3$

13    $7.52 \div 0.4$ 14 $8.4 \div 0.02$ 15 $0.1638 \div 0.001$ 16 $32 \div 0.4$

17    $17.4 \div 0.2$ 18 $4.006 \div 0.002$ 19 $54 \div 0.3$ 20 $0.1685 \div 0.005$

21   A bottle of milk contains 1 litre. How many glasses can be filled from this bottle if each glass holds 0.2 litres?

22   A supermarket sells 200 g bags of red currants. An average red currant weighs 0.8 g. How many red currants are there in a 200 g bag?

23          $86.45 \div 35 = 2.47$

Use the calculation above to work out:

(a) $864.5 \div 35$ (b) $0.8645 \div 35$ (c) $8.645 \div 3.5$

Exercise 5M

Hidden words

(a) Start in the top left box in the first grid on the next page.

(b) Work out the answer to the calculation in the box.

(c) Find the answer in the top corner of another box.

(d) Write down the letter in that box.

(e) Repeat steps (b), (c) and (d) until you arrive back at the top left box. What is the message?

1

6.4	66	274	985	12
	L	N	E	S
5×15	$2^3 + 3^3$	20% of 50	15×100	$756 \div 9$
422	75	1.68	10	2.4
N	S	R	C	I
10^3	$150 - 67$	8×22	$8.7 \div 10$	$37 + 385$
3.85	176	0.87	1000	83
U	E	H	F	O
0.16×10	$421 - 147$	$5 + 1.4$	$8.4 \div 5$	$385 \div 7$
55	1500	1.6	35	84
L	I	N	I	S
$1000 - 15$	$\frac{2}{3}$ of 99	0.4×6	25% of 48	$5.32 - 1.47$

2

612	0.8	0.77	0.2	0.62
	T	W	V	T
$1.8 + 8.2$	5% of 400	$2^3 \times 6$	5×69	20% of 65
32	10	13	18	250
C	B	R	E	U
$50\,000 \div 200$	$\frac{2}{5}$ of 450	0.6×2.6	80% of 80	$0.9^2 - 0.1^2$
1.56	0.6	180	0.15	64
E	R	E	S	S
$\frac{3}{8}$ of 48	$\frac{1}{2}$ of 0.3	$(0.2)^2$	0.32×10^2	$806 - 194$
0.04	0.27	20	48	345
A	O	D	N	E
10% of 2	$770 \div 1000$	$0.3 - 0.03$	3.1×0.2	$4.2 \div 7$

3

45 $\frac{1}{2}+\frac{1}{4}$	4 H 2^4	371 C $10 \div 1000$	21 A $62.5 \div 100$	0.51 S $21 - 5 \times 4$
896 M $1^2 + 2^2 + 3^3$	0.06 E $51 \div 100$	0.05 L $25 \div 10$	0.01 E $5 \times (5-2)^2$	34 Y 5.1×100
0.625 T $\frac{2}{3} \times \frac{1}{5}$	1 O $6000 \div 20$	$\frac{3}{4}$ M $4 + 5 \times 6$	$\frac{3}{8}$ S 0.3×0.2	32 I 53×7
510 C $\frac{3}{5}$ of 35	16 A $\frac{1}{2} - \frac{1}{8}$	2.5 Y $8 + 888$	300 N $\frac{1}{4} - 0.2$	$\frac{2}{15}$ C $20 \div (12 - 7)$

CHECK YOURSELF ON SECTION 3.1

1   Reviewing paper and pencil calculations

Work out, without a calculator

(a) $3864 - 796$

(b) 38×74

(c) $486 \div 18$

(d) $79 \div 100$

(e) $13.08 \div 6$

(f) $0.3 - 0.18$

2   Reading scales and using place value

(a) Read the measurement shown by each arrow and write down the difference between them.

(b) What number is half way between 1.3 and 1.4?

(c)

During one day snail A travels 6.18 m and snail B manages 6.094 m. Which snail travels the furthest?

3 Multiplying decimal numbers

Work out

(a) 0.3×0.1

(b) 0.06×0.8

(c) 1.2×0.07

(d) One metre of ribbon costs £0.89. How much will 3 metres of ribbon cost?

4 Dividing decimal numbers

Work out

(a) $7 \div 0.1$

(b) $1.4 \div 0.01$

(c) $0.256 \div 0.4$

(d) A glass holds 0.15 litres. How many times can the glass be filled from a 1.2 litre bottle?

3.2 Using a calculator

In section 3.2 you will:

- use the order of operations with and without a calculator
- use fractions on a calculator
- use brackets on a calculator
- use negative numbers on a calculator

Order of operations

Some people use the word 'BIDMAS' to help them remember the correct order of operations.

Here are four examples

Brackets
Indices
Divide
Multiply
Add
Subtract

- $8 + 6 \div 6 = 8 + 1 = 9$

- $20 - 8 \times 2 = 20 - 16 = 4$

- $(13 - 7) \div (6 - 4) = 6 \div 2 = 3$

- $20 - 8 \div (5 + 3) = 20 - 8 \div 8 = 19$

Exercise 1M

Work out, without a calculator. Show every step in your working.

1. $6 + 3 \times 4$

2. $8 - 2 \times 3$

3. $(9 - 2) \times 4$

4. $16 \div 4 - 1$

5. $17 + 12 \div 3$

6. $7 + 16 \div 8$

7. $12 + 4 \times 10$

8. $36 - 11 \times 3$

9. $27 \div (13 - 4)$

10. $(17 + 5) \times 3$

11. $9 + 9 \times 9$

12. $36 - 6 - 20$

13. $8 + 3 \times 3 - 5$

14. $18 - (8 \times 1) + 4$

15. $2 + 16 \div (5 + 3)$

16. $(6 \times 5) \div (12 \div 2)$

17. $80 - (44 \div 2)$

18. $(50 \times 4) \div (201 - 199)$

19. $8 + 24 \div 6 - 2$

20. $40 \div 8 - 12 \div 3$

21. $3 \times (4 \times 2 - 3)$

22. $\dfrac{17 + 3}{2}$

23. $\dfrac{45}{12 + 3}$

24. $\dfrac{45 + 5}{8 - 6}$

25. Work out 4×5^2 [Remember: work out 5^2 and then multiply by 4]

26. Work out

   (a) $8 + 4^2$
   (d) $5^2 + 7^2$

   (b) $20 - 3^2$
   (e) $(2 + 2)^2$

   (c) $6^2 - 10$
   (f) $4 \times (4^2 - 1)$

   (g) $(12 - 8)^2 \div 2$

   (h) $(6^2 + 8^2) \div 50$

   (i) $56 \div 7 - 2^2$

   (j) $\dfrac{8^2 - 4}{20}$

   (k) $\dfrac{5^2}{4 + 1}$

   (l) $\dfrac{(2 + 3)^2 + 15}{10}$

Exercise 1E

Copy each question and write brackets so that each calculation gives the correct answer.

1. $4 + 2 \times 3 = 18$

2. $6 + 3 \times 4 = 36$

3. $2 \times 3 + 5 = 16$

4. $3 \times 10 - 5 = 15$

5. $20 - 8 \times 3 = 36$

6. $28 \div 2 + 5 = 4$

7. $13 + 7 \div 5 = 4$

8. $9 + 1 \times 8 - 6 = 20$

9. $7 + 4 \times 5 = 55$

10. $16 - 3 + 3^2 = 4$

11. $8 + 3 + 9 \div 2 = 10$

12. $7 + 2 \times 8 - 7 = 9$

13. $9 - 3^2 + 3 = 3$

14. $8 + 3 - 5 \times 0 = 0$

15. $8 + 2^2 \times 10 - 3^2 = 12$

In questions 16 to 24 find the missing signs $(+, -, \times, \div)$. There are no brackets.

16. $9 \quad 3 \quad 3 = 18$

17. $7 \quad 3 \quad 11 = 32$

18. $6 \quad 12 \quad 3 = 10$

19. $11 \quad 4 \quad 4 = 10$

20. $15 \quad 4 \quad 5 = 35$

21. $8 \quad 3 \quad 6 = 30$

22. $7 \quad 6 \quad 2 = 10$

23. $8 \quad 4 \quad 4 \quad 4 = 18$

24. $9 \quad 2 \quad 2 \quad 5 = 10$

Exercise 2M

Use a calculator and give the answer correct to two decimal places.

1. 3.4×1.23
2. $20.4 - 5.7412$
3. 0.341^2
4. $0.17 + 2.89 - 1.514$
5. $3.2^2 - 2.8$
6. $4.6 \times 1.9 + 8.05$
7. $0.54 \times 0.87 - 0.1$
8. $8.7 \div 2.73$
9. $12.5 - 0.516 + 1.2$
10. $\dfrac{8.9}{7.4}$
11. $\dfrac{20.2}{5.6} + 8.2$
12. $\dfrac{8.65}{6} - 0.12$

In questions 13 to 30 remember 'B I D M A S'.

13. $2.6 + 2.7 \times 1.9$
14. $8.01 + 0.8 \times 3.2$
15. $7.93 + 5 \div 12$
16. $8.6 \div 0.7 - 5.55$
17. $8 \div 0.55 + 2.33$
18. $8.06 + 1.4 \times 1.5$
19. $3.5 + \dfrac{8.5}{1.34}$
20. $1.53^2 + 2.53$
21. $6.4 + \dfrac{1.7}{0.85}$
22. $8.65 + 30 \div 8.2$
23. $5.44 + 1.37^2$
24. $6.4^2 \div 19$
25. $0.751 - 0.14 \times 0.9$
26. 2.3^3
27. $10 + 10 \times 10$
28. $8.9 + \dfrac{19.6}{15}$
29. $\dfrac{2.7 + 5.65}{3.3}$
30. $\dfrac{11.2 - 5.67}{1.9}$

31. Matt sends 529 texts during June. Each text costs 11p. He has to pay £14 for his June phone calls. What is his total June bill for texts and phone calls?

32. If a farmer sells a cow, he makes a profit of £110. If he cannot sell a cow, he loses £45. If the farmer sells a pig, he makes a profit of £33 but loses £18 if he cannot sell the pig. One year the farmer has 45 cows and manages to sell 34 of them. He has 59 pigs and is able to sell 41 of them. Calculate the farmer's total profit.

Fractions on a calculator

The $\boxed{a\frac{b}{c}}$ key is used for fractions.

To enter $\frac{3}{4}$, press $\boxed{3}$ $\boxed{a\frac{b}{c}}$ $\boxed{4}$. You see $\boxed{3 \lrcorner 4}$

To enter $5\frac{1}{3}$, press $\boxed{5}$ $\boxed{a\frac{b}{c}}$ $\boxed{1}$ $\boxed{a\frac{b}{c}}$ $\boxed{3}$. You see $\boxed{5 \lrcorner 1 \lrcorner 3}$

Exercise 2E

Work out

1. $\frac{2}{3} + \frac{1}{4}$

2. $\frac{5}{6} + \frac{1}{3}$

3. $\frac{8}{9} + \frac{1}{3}$

4. $\frac{4}{15} + \frac{1}{2}$

5. $\frac{3}{5} - \frac{1}{2}$

6. $\frac{7}{8} - \frac{1}{16}$

7. $\frac{5}{7} - \frac{1}{2}$

8. $\frac{5}{6} - \frac{1}{5}$

9. $\frac{9}{10} + \frac{1}{20}$

10. $\frac{11}{12} - \frac{3}{4}$

11. $\frac{4}{9} \times \frac{1}{2}$

12. $\frac{3}{11} \times \frac{1}{4}$

13. $2\frac{1}{4} + \frac{2}{3}$

14. $3\frac{2}{3} - 1\frac{1}{2}$

15. $4\frac{1}{2} + \frac{5}{8}$

16. $\frac{1}{6} + 3\frac{3}{4}$

17. $3\frac{1}{5} \times 1\frac{1}{2}$

18. $4\frac{1}{2} \div \frac{3}{4}$

19. $3\frac{1}{2} \div \frac{2}{5}$

20. $21 \div 5\frac{1}{4}$

21. Which question gives a different answer?

A $\boxed{2\frac{1}{4} + 1\frac{1}{3}}$ B $\boxed{3\frac{2}{3} - \frac{1}{2}}$ C $\boxed{5\frac{1}{3} - 1\frac{3}{4}}$

22. A shop sells carrots in $\frac{2}{5}$ kg bags and $1\frac{1}{2}$ kg bags.
Hal needs to buy *exactly* $2\frac{7}{10}$ kg carrots.
How many of each bag must he buy?

Using brackets on a calculator

(a) $8.5 - (1.2 \times 3.6)$

$\boxed{8.5}$ $\boxed{-}$ $\boxed{(}$ $\boxed{1.2}$ $\boxed{\times}$

$\boxed{3.6}$ $\boxed{)}$ $\boxed{=}$

Answer = 4.18 to 2 d.p.

(b) $\dfrac{9.62}{(8.14 - 0.27)}$

$\boxed{9.62}$ $\boxed{\div}$ $\boxed{(}$ $\boxed{8.14}$ $\boxed{-}$

$\boxed{0.27}$ $\boxed{)}$ $\boxed{=}$

Answer = 1.22 to 2 d.p.

Do not forget to press the $\boxed{=}$ button at the end to give the final answer.

Exercise 3M

Work out and give the answer correct to 2 decimal places.

1. $11.52 - (3.14 \times 2.6)$

2. $12.5 + (3.8 \div 6)$

3. $(5.27 + 8.2) \div 2.7$

4. $9.6 + (8.7 \div 11)$

5. $(9.5 \div 7) - 0.44$

6. $13.7 - (8.2 \times 1.31)$

7. $6.31 - \left(\frac{8.2}{1.9}\right)$

8. $\left(\frac{7.65}{1.5}\right) - 3.06$

9. $\dfrac{3.63}{(3.9 + 0.121)}$

10 $(2.26 + 3.15 + 8.99) \div 1.45$ **11** $5.89 \times (1.8 - 0.633)$ **12** $17.8 \div (5.8 - 4.95)$

13 $(11.2 \div 7) \times 2.43$ **14** $(3.65 + 1.4 - 2.34) \times 2.6$ **15** $35 - (8.7 \times 2.65)$

16 $\dfrac{(9.37 + 8.222)}{2.47}$ **17** $\dfrac{11.23}{(9.7 - 6.66)}$ **18** $\dfrac{(114 - 95.6)}{14}$

19 $2.7^2 - 1.56$ **20** $0.73^2 \times 5.2$ **21** $6.6 + 4.1^2$

22 $(1.5 + 2.61)^2$ **23** $(8.2 - 6.93)^2$ **24** $(2.4 \times 0.15)^2$

25 $8.9 - (1.35)^2$ **26** $(2.7^2 - 3.3) \div 5$ **27** $2.1^2 + 3.11^2$

28 $\left(\dfrac{4.5}{8}\right) + \left(\dfrac{4.7}{7}\right)$ **29** $3.2^2 - \left(\dfrac{4.2}{3.7}\right)$ **30** $\dfrac{2.6^2}{(1.4 + 1.91)}$

Hint:

Use the $\boxed{x^2}$ key

Using fractions and brackets

Work out: $\left(\dfrac{2}{3} - \dfrac{1}{4}\right) \times \dfrac{6}{7}$

Press the keys

| (| 2 | $a\frac{b}{c}$ | 3 | − | 1 | $a\frac{b}{c}$ | 4 |) | × | 6 | $a\frac{b}{c}$ | 7 | = |

Answer $= \dfrac{5}{14}$

Exercise 3E

Work out

1 $\left(\dfrac{3}{5} + \dfrac{1}{8}\right) \times \dfrac{1}{2}$ **2** $\left(\dfrac{5}{6} - \dfrac{1}{9}\right) \times \dfrac{3}{4}$ **3** $\dfrac{3}{8} \times \left(\dfrac{2}{3} + \dfrac{1}{5}\right)$

4 $\left(1\dfrac{2}{3} + \dfrac{1}{4}\right) \div \dfrac{2}{3}$ **5** $\dfrac{5}{8} \div \left(\dfrac{1}{3} + \dfrac{1}{2}\right)$ **6** $2\dfrac{3}{4} \times \left(\dfrac{2}{5} + \dfrac{1}{10}\right)$

7 Copy and complete.

(a)

+		$\dfrac{3}{5}$		$1\dfrac{3}{4}$
	$\dfrac{5}{8}$	$\dfrac{5}{6}$		
$\dfrac{1}{4}$				
$2\dfrac{1}{2}$	$2\dfrac{5}{8}$			
		$\dfrac{11}{15}$		

(b)

+			$\dfrac{5}{8}$	$2\dfrac{1}{5}$
$\dfrac{4}{5}$	$\dfrac{2}{5}$			
			$\dfrac{5}{24}$	
	$\dfrac{1}{8}$	$\dfrac{1}{6}$		
$1\dfrac{1}{2}$				

8   Work out

(a) $\left(\dfrac{4}{5} - \dfrac{1}{2}\right)^2$

(b) $\left(\dfrac{1}{3} - \dfrac{1}{4}\right) \times \dfrac{6}{7}$

(c) $\left(1\dfrac{2}{3}\right)^2 - \dfrac{5}{9}$

(d) $\dfrac{5}{8} \div 1\dfrac{7}{8} - \dfrac{1}{15}$

(e) $\dfrac{\left(2\dfrac{3}{5} - 1\dfrac{3}{4}\right)}{\left(\dfrac{1}{5} - \dfrac{1}{6}\right)}$

(f) $\dfrac{14}{15} \times \dfrac{3}{7} - \dfrac{7}{10} + \dfrac{1}{15}$

Negative numbers on a calculator

On a calculator the $\boxed{(-)}$ button is used for negative numbers.

(a) $-5.2 + 7.81$
Press the keys

$\boxed{(-)}\ \boxed{5.2}\ \boxed{+}\ \boxed{7.81}\ \boxed{=}$

Answer = 2.61

(b) $7.5 \div (-0.04)$

$\boxed{7.5}\ \boxed{\div}\ \boxed{(-)}\ \boxed{0.04}\ \boxed{=}$

Answer = -187.5

Notice that we do not *need* the brackets buttons. You may use them if you prefer.

Exercise 4M

Work out the following. Give the answer correct to one decimal place where appropriate.

1   -7×3

2   $-5 \times (-2)$

3   $8 \div (-4)$

4   $10 \times (-4)$

5   $-2 \times (-2)$

6   $-12 \div 3$

7   $-5 \times (-4)$

8   $-8 - 11$

9   $-7 + 2$

10   $-9 + 30$

11   $-20 \div 4$

12   $-16 - 15$

13   $-3.4 \times (-2.5)$

14   -0.5×6.8

15   $12.5 - (-2.5)$

16   $-1.1 \times (-1.1)$

17   $-8 \div (-0.25)$

18   $-6.8 \div 0.1$

19   $\dfrac{-8 \times (-3)}{4}$

20   $\dfrac{12}{(3 \times (-2))}$

21   $\dfrac{20}{(-2)} + 8$

22   $-11.4 + 1.71$

23   $-9.2 - 7.4 + 15.2$

24   $-4.74 - (-13.08)$

25   Answer true or false:

(a) $(-22)^2 = 484$

(b) $-3^2 = 9$

(c) $-5.1^2 = 26.01$

(d) $-20 \div -2.5 = 8$

(e) $8 - 9.5^2 = -82.25$

(f) $\dfrac{8 - (-3.2)}{-0.1} = -112$

26   Copy and complete:

(a) $4.6 - \boxed{} = 11.61$

(b) $-8.4 \times \boxed{} = 27.72$

(c) $6.3 + \boxed{} = -14.29$

(d) $\dfrac{-16.34}{\boxed{}} = -4.3$

27 Work out, giving answers to one decimal place.

(a) $\dfrac{(-8.23) \times (-1.24)}{3.6}$

(b) $\dfrac{5.1 \times (-1.42)}{(-1.7)}$

(c) $-6.2 + (-8.4)$

(d) $-7.2 + \left(\dfrac{4.3}{1.5}\right)$

(e) $-8.7 \times \left(\dfrac{7.2}{11}\right)$

(f) $(-7.2 + 4)^2$

Calculator words

- When you hold a calculator display upside down some numbers appear to form words: spells "Gosh"

spells "Old"
(ignoring the decimal point)

Exercise 4E

Translate this passage using a calculator and the clues below: "__1__!"

shouted Olag out of the window of his __2__. "I need

some __3__ / __4__ for my dinner. Do you __5__ them?" "__6__ did"

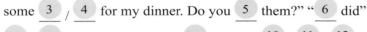

__7__ / __8__ "I even took off the __9__ for free. __10__ / __11__ / __12__ they

were. The problem is that all the __13__ were eaten in the __14__,

mostly by __15__. __16__ / __17__ such a __18__ / __19__ lately. __20__ and __21__ are always

__22__ because of the amount of __23__ they drink every night" "__24__ well,

he is the __25__ I suppose" Olag grumbled "roast __26__ again tonight then…"

Clues to passage

1 $(2.37 + 2.53) \div 0.7^2$

2 $(3 \div 40) + 0.0011$

3 $\dfrac{3}{8} - (39.2 \div 10000)$

4 $5 \times 12 \times 100 - 7$

5 $(90 \times 80) + (107 \times 5)$

6 $\sqrt{0.01} \times 10$

7 $(68 + 1.23) \div 200$

8 $101^2 - (5 \times 13) - 2$

9 $750^2 + (296\,900 \div 20)$

10 $2^2 \times 5^2 \times 6 + 16.3 + 1.7$

11 $(70\,000 \div 2) + (3 \times 2)$

12 $11\,986 \div 2$

13 $(600^2 - 6640) \div 10$

14 $200^2 - 685$

15 $(0.5^2 \times 0.6)$

16 $\sqrt{289} \times 2$

17 $836.4 \div 17 + 1.8$

18 $30^2 + 18$

19 64.6×125

20 $(63\,508 \times 5) - 3$

21 $\sqrt{(1160 - 4)}$

22 1.3803×0.25

23 $(32 \times 1000) + 8$

24 $2^2 \times 10$

25 $(5^2 \times 2^2 \times 55) + 8$

26 $7000 \times 10^2 \times 10^2 - 9563966$

3.3 Formulas and expressions

In section 3.3 you will:

- substitute numbers into a range of formula
- work out values of expressions.

Substituting into a formula

(a) In the formula $s = ut$,

  s is for distance

  u is for speed

  t is for time taken

When $u = 9$ and $t = 10$, $s = ut = 9 \times 10 = 90$

(b) The mass m of a person of height h is given by the formula

  $m = 90h + 13$

  When $h = 1.7$,

  $m = 90h + 13 = 90 \times 1.7 + 13$

  $m = 166$

Exercise 1M

In questions 1 to 10 you are given a formula. Find the value of the letter required in each case.

1 $m = 4p + 6$

  Find m when $p = 3$

2 $x = 7y + 3$

  Find x when $y = 5$

3 $a = \dfrac{b}{6} + 2$

  Find a when $b = 18$

4 $c = \dfrac{d}{4} - 5$

  Find c when $d = 20$

5 $q = 9w + 4$

  Find q when $w = 7$

6 $m = 2n - 8$

  Find m when $n = 10$

7 $y = \dfrac{x}{8} - 3$

  Find y when $x = 48$

8 $v = 4(3w - 4)$

  Find v when $w = 9$

9 $a = 5(2b + 1)$

  Find a when $b = 6$

10 $g = \dfrac{6h + 4}{2}$

  Find g when $h = 5$

114

11 When the wind velocity is v, the cost of damage, £C, is given by the formula
$C = 500\,v + 20\,000$

Find the cost of damage when $v = 100$.

12 $p = \dfrac{9m + 3}{10}$

Find p when $m = 3$

13 $y = 6(4x - 3)$

Find y when $x = 7$

14 $a = b^2 + 17$

Find a when $b = 5$

15 The area of a triangle is given by $A = \frac{1}{2}$ bh.

Find A when $b = 16$ and $h = 7$.

16 The perimeter of a hexagon is given by the formula $p = 3x + 2y + w$.

Find p when $x = 5$, $y = 4$ and $w = 9$.

Exercise 1E

1 Here are some polygons.

Number of sides:	3	4	5
Sum of angles:	180°	360°	540°

The sum of the angles in a polygon with n sides is given by the formula, $\{$ sum of angles = $(n - 2) \times 180°$ $\}$

(a) Find the sum of the angles in a hexagon (6 sides).
(b) Find the sum of the angles in a polygon with 102 sides.
(c) Show that the formula gives the correct answer for the sum of the angles in a pentagon (5 sides).

2 Using the formula $y = 70 + 3x$, find the value of y when

(a) $x = 6$ (b) $x = 100$ (c) $x = 0.1$

3 In the formulas below t is given in terms of n and a. Find the value of t in each case.

(a) $t = 5a + 2n$; $a = 3$, $n = 4$

(b) $t = 6a + 3n - 10$; $a = 2$, $n = 1$

(c) $t = an + 7$; $a = 5$, $n = 2$

4 Below are several different formulas for y in terms of x.
Find the value of y in each case.

(a) $y = 4x - 9$, $\qquad x = 2.5$

(b) $y = \dfrac{3x + 1}{2}$, $\qquad x = 3$

(c) $y = 6(5x + 3)$, $\qquad x = 1$

5 Suppose you add the numbers from 1 to 50: $1 + 2 + 3 + \ldots + 49 + 50$.

The answer is $\dfrac{50 \times 51}{2} = 1275$.

If you add the numbers from 1 to any number n the answer is given by

the formula $\qquad \text{sum} = \dfrac{n(n + 1)}{2}$.

(a) Use the formula to find the sum of the numbers from 1 to 10.
(i.e. $1 + 2 + 3 + \ldots + 9 + 10$).
(b) Check your answer by adding the numbers in the normal way.
(c) Use the formula to find the sum of the numbers from 1 to 99.

6 Using the formula $m = 35 + 2n$, find the value of m when
(a) $n = -2$ $\qquad$ (b) $n = -10$ $\qquad$ (c) $n = \dfrac{1}{2}$

7 Using the formula $h = 6(15 - y)$, find the value of h when
(a) $y = -5$ $\qquad$ (b) $y = 10$ $\qquad$ (c) $y = -10$

8 The area A of a red circle is given
by the formula $A = 3r^2$.
Find the total area of 75 red circles if
the value of r for each circle is 5.

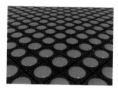

9 The total surface area A of the solid cuboid
shown is given by the formula
$A = 2bc + 2ab + 2ac$
Find the value of A when $a = 2$, $b = 3$, $c = 4$.

10 In the polygons below, diagonals are drawn from one vertex.

$n = 4$ sides
$d = 1$ diagonal

$n = 5$ sides
$d = 2$ diagonals

$n = 6$ sides
$d = 3$ diagonals

Find a formula connecting the number of diagonals and the number of sides. Write '$d = \ldots\ldots$'.

Expressions

An expression does *not* have an equals sign. For example: $3x - 7$; $2a + b$; $5y - 10$.
These are all expressions.

Below are three expressions involving a, b, c and d.
Find the value of each expression given that $a = 3$, $b = 2$, $c = 5$, $d = -1$

(i)　　$5a + 7$

　　$= 5 \times 3 + 7$

　　$= 15 + 7$

　　$= 22$

(ii)　　$2b + d$

　　$= 2 \times 2 + (-1)$

　　$= 4 - 1$

　　$= 3$

(iii)　　$ab + 5c$

　　$= (3 \times 2) + (5 \times 5)$

　　$= 6 + 25$

　　$= 31$

Notice that the working goes *down* the page, not across. This helps to avoid errors.

Exercise 2M

In questions ① to ⑩ find the value of each expression

1. $3x + 2$　if　$x = 5$

2. $4x - 3$　if　$x = 2$

3. $6x - 5$　if　$x = 2$

4. $8y + 7$　if　$y = 4$

5. $23 + p$　if　$p = 8$

6. $13 - m$　if　$m = 6$

7. $6 + 4n$　if　$n = 3$

8. $12 + 3q$　if　$q = 7$

9. $32 - 5y$　if　$y = 4$

10. $40 - 8x$　if　$x = 3$

11. Which of the cards below have a value of 9 when $n = 3$?

$(6 - n)^2$　　　$8n - 14$　　　n^2　　　$3 + 2n$

$(2n - 1)^2$　　　　　　$17 - 3n$

12. Find the value of these expressions when $x = 4$.

　(a) $\dfrac{x + 8}{x}$　　　(b) $\dfrac{x + 5}{x - 3}$　　　(c) $\dfrac{1}{x} + \dfrac{3}{x}$

13. Find the value of these expressions when $n = 6$.

　(a) $6n + 2$　　　(b) $50 - n^2$　　　(c) $4(2n - 7)$

14. Find the value of these expressions when $m = 0$.

　(a) $m^2 + 3$　　　(b) $\dfrac{5m}{2}$　　　(c) $18 - 3m$

Exercise 2E

In questions ① to ⑫ find the value of the expressions given that $x = 4$
$y = -2$

① $x + 3$	② $3(x + 2)$	③ x^2
④ $2(x - 2)$	⑤ $x + y$	⑥ $3y$
⑦ $2y + 1$	⑧ $x^2 - 9$	⑨ $\dfrac{x + 2}{x - 1}$
⑩ $8 - y$	⑪ y^2	⑫ $\dfrac{2 + y}{y}$

⑬ Given that $p = 40$ and $n = -10$, find the value of each of the following expressions.

(a) $2p + n$ (b) n^2 (c) $p - n$

(d) $n^2 - 2p$ (e) np (f) $p(p + 3n)$

⑭ For each statement, answer 'true' or 'false'

(a) $6 \times m = m \times 6$ (b) $2 \div n = n \div 2$ (c) $m + m = m^2$

(d) $a - b = -b + a$ (e) $3t - t = 2t$ (f) $n \times n \times n = n^3$

⑮ If $w = -9$, which expression has the larger value?

$\boxed{w^2 + w}$ or $\boxed{7w + w}$

In questions ⑯ to ㉟ find the value of the expressions given that $a = 6$
$b = 5$
$c = 1$
$d = -3$

⑯ $4a - c$	⑰ $3b + a$	⑱ $b + d$
⑲ $4c - b$	⑳ $5b + c$	㉑ $a - d$
㉒ $7b + 8$	㉓ $a + b + d$	㉔ $c - 5$
㉕ $4a + d$	㉖ $a^2 + b^2$	㉗ $ab + c$
㉘ d^2	㉙ $3a + b + d$	㉚ $d^2 + 8$
㉛ $3d + c$	㉜ $d + 4b$	㉝ $4(a - c)$
㉞ $bc - d$	㉟ $b(b + c)$	

Race game

START

| $w-3$ | $1-3x$ | x | $2(3-x)$ | $4-p$ | $a+2$ | $c+1$ | $4-x$ | $2y$ |

| $2(a-3)$ | | | | | | | | $5-p$ |

Players take turns to roll a dice.

The number rolled gives the value of the letter in the expression on each square

The value of the expression determines how many squares the player moves (forward for a positive number, backwards for a negative number).

For example, if you are on the square '$x-3$' and you throw a 5 you move forward 2 places.

The winner is the first player to move around the circuit. [You can also play 'first player to make 3 circuits' or any other number.]

Teachers note: The diagram may be photocopied and enlarged to fill an A4 sheet. This makes the game easier to play.

$1-y$ $b+5$

$3n-9$ $3z$

$a-2$ $11-3t$

$\dfrac{3x}{x}$ $2(a+1)$

| $5-t$ | $p+3$ | $3(2-x)$ | $(4-x)^2$ | $t+1$ | $2x-7$ | $6-m$ | $\dfrac{2n}{n}$ | $-8+c$ |

CHECK YOURSELF ON SECTIONS 3.2 AND 3.3

1   Using the order of operations with and without a calculator

Work out, without a calculator:

(a) $9+2\times4$ (b) $5\times(6+2)-4$ (c) $30-4^2$

Use a calculator and give the answers below correct to two decimal places.

(d) $6.14+3\div11$ (e) $0.826-0.27\times0.4$ (f) $5.7+\dfrac{13.6}{14}$

2 Using fractions on a calculator

Use a calculator to work out

(a) $\frac{4}{5} - \frac{3}{8}$

(b) $\frac{4}{7} \times \frac{5}{8}$

(c) $3\frac{1}{2} \div 2\frac{1}{2}$

3 Using brackets on a calculator

Use a calculator and give the answers below correct to two decimal places.

(a) $(2.4 + 1.83)^2$

(b) $32 \times (8.32 - 4.7)$

(c) $\frac{(173 - 69)}{113}$

4 Using negative numbers on a calculator

Use a calculator to work out

(a) $9 \times (-14)$

(b) $-16 - (-30)$

(c) $\frac{-8 \times 4}{-2}$

5 Substituting numbers into a range of formulas

(a) $m = \frac{n + 10}{2}$

Find m when $n = 20$

(b) $y = 4(3x - 1)$

Find y when $x = 7$

(c) Mark sells computers. The more computers he sells, the more money he is paid.

If he sells n computers in any month, his pay P (in pounds) for that month is given by the formula

$P = 800 + 50n$

The table below shows how many computers he sold in February. How much was his pay for February?

week	number of computers sold
1	3
2	5
3	2
4	4

6 Working out values of expressions

Find the value of each expression

(a) $7 - 3y$ if $y = 2$

(b) $3(x + 6)$ if $x = 3$

(c) $4p - 1$ if $p = -2$

(d) $5m - n$ if $m = 6$ and $n = -3$

3.4 Drawing graphs

In section 3.4 you will:

- use lines which are parallel to the axes
- draw graphs
- use graphs
- find the equation of a line

Lines parallel to the axes

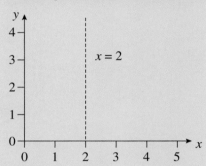

A line parallel to the
y-axis has an equation
x = 'a number'

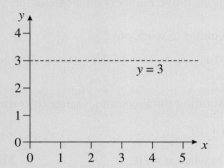

A line parallel to the
x-axis has an equation
y = 'a number'

Exercise 1M

1 Copy the graph and then write down
   the coordinates for each point.

   A (2, 1) H (,)
   B (,) I (,)
   C (,) J (,)
   D (,) K (,)
   E (,) L (,)
   F (,) M (,)
   G (,) N (,)

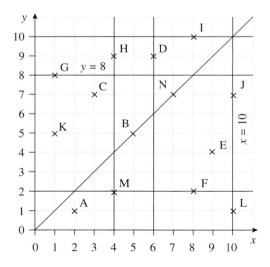

2 L lies on the line x = 10.
   Which other letter lies on x = 10?

3 Which letter lies on x = 6?

4 Which letters lie on x = 4?

5   G lies on the line $y = 8$.
     Which letter lies on $y = 10$?

6   Which letters lie on $y = 2$?

7   Which letters lie on $y = 5$?

8   Which letters lie on $y = 7$?

9   Which letter lies on $x = 9$?

10   The x coordinate of B is the same as the y coordinate. We say that B lies on the line
     $y = x$ (or $x = y$). Which other letter lies on $y = x$?

11   Letter M lies on $x = 4$ *and* $y = 2$. What letter lies on $x = 8$ and $y = 2$?

12   What letter lies on $x = 2$ and $y = 1$?

13   What letter lies on $x = 10$ and $y = 7$?

Exercise 1E

1   Write down the coordinates
     for each point.

     A (2, 4)

     B (5, 2)

     C (−2, 5)

     ⋮

     N (5, −3)

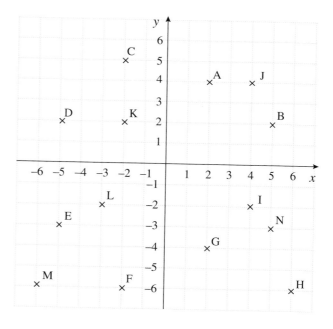

2   Point A lies on the line $x = 2$.
     What other letter lies on $x = 2$?

3   Point N lies on the line $y = -3$.
     Which other letter lies on $y = -3$?

4   Which letters lie on the line $x = -5$?

5   Which letter lies on the line $y = 5$?

6   Which letters lie on the line $y = x$?

7   Which line passes through B and N?

8   Which line passes through A and J?

9   Which line passes through L and I?

10   Which line passes through C, F and K?

In questions (11) and (12) there is a line of dots A, a line of crosses B and a line of circles C.

Write down the equations of the lines in each question.

(11)

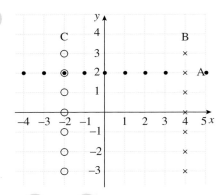

(12)

13   On squared paper, draw axes like those in questions (11) and (12).
   (a) Draw the lines $y = 2$ and $x = 3$.
       Write down the co-ordinates of the point where the two lines meet.
   (b) Draw the lines $y = -2$ and $x = 1$.
       Write down the co-ordinates of the point where the two lines meet.

14   Name two lines which pass through each of the following points.

   (a) (4, 3)   (b) (6, 2)   (c) (7, −3)   (d) (−2, −8)

Drawing graphs

Draw the graph of $y = 3x + 2$
for x-values from 0 to 5
by first completing the table below.

$3x + 2$ means $\boxed{x} \rightarrow \boxed{\times 3} \rightarrow \boxed{+2}$

For each x-value from 0 to 5,
use the equation to find the y-value.

x	0	1	2	3	4	5
y	2	5	8	11	14	17
coordinates	(0, 2)	(1, 5)	(2, 8)	(3, 11)	(4, 14)	(5, 17)

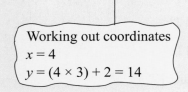

Working out coordinates
$x = 4$
$y = (4 \times 3) + 2 = 14$

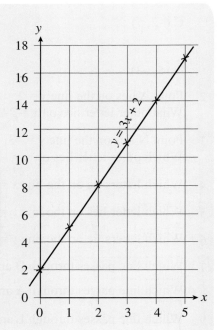

Note:

(a) Start both axes at 0 and take care with scales around 0

(b) Label the axes 'x' and 'y'

(c) Label the graph with its equation

Exercise 2M

For each question, copy and complete the table then draw the graph using the scales given.

1 $y = 2x + 4$ for x-values from 0 to 5

$2x + 4$ means $\boxed{x} \rightarrow \boxed{\times 2} \rightarrow \boxed{+4}$

x	0	1	2	3	4	5
y				10		
coordinates				(3, 10)		

(x-axis: use 1 cm for 1 unit
y-axis: use 1 cm for 2 units)

2 $y = 3x$ for x-values from 0 to 5

$3x$ means $\boxed{x} \rightarrow \boxed{\times 3}$

x	0	1	2	3	4	5
y		3				
coordinates		(1, 3)				

(x-axis: use 1 cm for 1 unit
y-axis: use 1 cm for 2 units)

3 $y = 2x + 1$ for x-values from 0 to 6

$2x + 1$ means $\boxed{x} \rightarrow \boxed{\times 2} \rightarrow \boxed{+1}$

x	0	1	2	3	4	5	6
y					9		
coordinates					(4, 9)		

(x-axis: use 1 cm for 1 unit
y-axis: use 1 cm for 1 unit)

4 $y = \frac{x}{2}$ for x-values from 0 to 7

$\frac{x}{2}$ means $\boxed{x} \rightarrow \boxed{\div 2}$

x	0	1	2	3	4	5	6	7
y						$2\frac{1}{2}$		
coordinates						$(5, 2\frac{1}{2})$		

(x-axis: 1 cm
for 1 unit
y-axis: 2 cm for
1 unit)

5    $y = 6 - x$ for x-values from 0 to 6

6 − x means $\boxed{6} \longrightarrow \boxed{-x}$

x	0	1	2	3	4	5	6
y		5					
coordinates		(1, 5)					

(x-axis: 1 cm for 1 unit
y-axis: 1 cm for 1 unit)

6    $y = 3(x + 1)$ for x-values from 0 to 5

3(x + 1) means $\boxed{x} \longrightarrow \boxed{+1} \longrightarrow \boxed{\times 3}$

(x-axis: 1 cm for 1 unit, y-axis: 1 cm for 2 units)

7    $y = 3(6 - x)$ for x-values from 0 to 6

3(6 − x) means $\boxed{6} \longrightarrow \boxed{-x} \longrightarrow \boxed{\times 3}$

(x-axis: 1 cm for 1 unit, y-axis: 1 cm for 2 units)

8    $y = \frac{1}{2}x + 3$

for x-values from 0 to 8

(x-axis: 1 cm for 1 unit
y-axis: 2 cm for 1 unit)

9    $y = 12 - 2x$

for x-values from 0 to 6

(x-axis: 1 cm for 1 unit,
y-axis: 1 cm for 1 unit)

10    $y = 4x + 1$

for x-values from 0 to 6

(x-axis: 1 cm for 1 unit,
y-axis: 1 cm for 2 units)

11    $y = 20 - 3x$

for x-values from 0 to 6

(x-axis: 1 cm for 1 unit,
y-axis: 1 cm for 2 units)

Exercise 2E

If possible, use a graphical calculator or a computer.

1   Draw the graphs of $y = 2x + 6$,

$y = 2x + 1$, $y = 2x - 2$ and $y = 2x - 5$.

Write down what you notice about each line
and its equation.
(Clue: look at the points where the lines cut the y-axis)

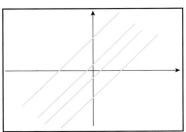

2   Draw the graphs of $y = x + 2$, $y = x + 5$, $y = x - 1$ and $y = x - 3$.
Write down what you notice about each line and its equation.

3   Draw the graphs of $y = 3x$, $y = 3x + 2$, $y = 3x - 4$ and $y = 3x - 2$.
Write down what you notice about each line and its equation.

4   (a) Where do you expect the line $y = 2x + 5$ to cut the y-axis?

    (b) Where do you expect the line $y = 4x - 3$ to cut the y-axis ?

5   Write down which of the two lines below are parallel?

| $y = 6x - 3$ | $y = 2x - 3$ | $y = 6x + 1$ |

6   Write down the equation of any line parallel to $y = 5x + 3$.

7   Draw the graphs of:

    $y = x^2$ $y = 4 \div x$ $y = x^2 + 3$ $y = x^2 - 4$

8   Do you think the graph of $y = x^2 + 1$ would be a straight line?

Using graphs

Exercise 3M

1   In June 2008, the pound (£) was worth 1.6 U.S. Dollars ($).

    This graph converts pounds into dollars.

    (a) What does one little square on the 'Pounds' axis show you?

    (b) What does one little square on the 'Dollars' axis show you?

    Use your graph to find out how
    many dollars are the same as

    (c) £50   (d) £25

    (e) £35   (f) £60

    Use your graph to find out how
    many pounds are the same as

    (g) $48   (h) $70

    (i) $16   (j) $136

    (k) On holiday in the USA, Chad
        bought a meal for $40. How
        many pounds did the meal cost?

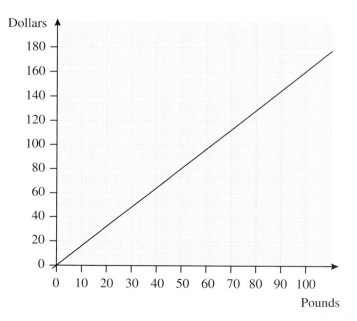

2 A car hire firm charges an initial fee plus
   a charge depending on the number of miles
   driven, as shown.

   (a) Find the total cost for driving 140 miles.

   (b) Find the total cost for driving 600 miles.

   (c) Find how many miles I can drive for a
       cost of £45.

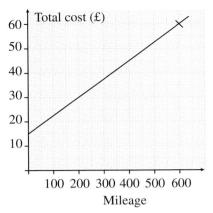

3 A teacher has marked a test out of 80 and wishes to convert
   the marks into percentages. Draw axes as shown and draw a
   straight line through the points (0, 0) and (80, 100).

   (a) Use your graph to convert
       (i) 63 marks into a percentage
       (ii) 24 marks into a percentage

   (b) The pass mark was 60%. How many
       marks out of 80 were needed for a pass?

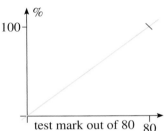

4 The graph converts kilometres (km)
   into miles.

   Use this graph to convert:

   (a) 40 km into miles

   (b) 15 miles into km

   (c) 45 miles into km

   (d) 64 km into miles

   (e) Which is further – 30 km or 20 miles?

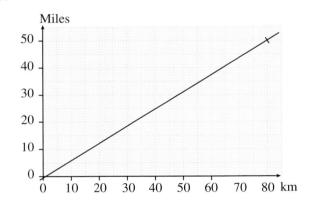

5 Temperature is usually measured in °C (Celsius)
   but can be measured in °F (Fahrenheit).

   (a) Draw axes, as shown, with a scale of 1 cm to 10°.
       Draw a '×' where °F = 32 and °C = 0.
       Draw another '×' where °F = 86 and °C = 30.

   (b) Draw a long straight line through the two points
       above and use your graph to convert:

       (i) 20°C into °F   (ii) −10°C into °F
       (iii) 50°F into °C

   (c) The normal body temperature of a healthy person is 98°F. Sue's temperature is 39°C.
       Should she stay at home today or go to school as usual?

6 Selmin and Katie make different charges for people wanting pages typed professionally.

(a) How much would Selmin charge to type 30 pages?
(b) How much would Katie charge to type 10 pages?
(c) Draw axes for the number of pages typed and the total cost, using the scales given.
(d) On the same diagram, draw a graph for each typist to show their charges for up to 60 pages.
(e) Use your graphs to decide for what number of pages Selmin is the cheaper typist to choose.

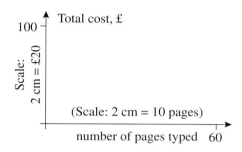

Finding the equation of a line

● This line passes through:

(0, 2), (1, 3), (2, 4), (3, 5), (4, 6).

For each point the y coordinate is two more than the x coordinate. The equation of the line is $y = x + 2$.

We could also say that the x coordinate is always two less than the y coordinate. The equation of the line could then be written as $x = y - 2$.

[Most mathematicians use the equation beginning 'y = '].

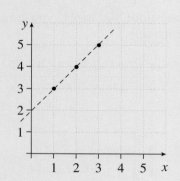

● This line slopes the other way and passes through:
(0, 4), (1, 3), (2, 2), (3, 1), (4, 0).

The sum of the x coordinate and the y coordinate is always 4. The equation of the line is $x + y = 4$.

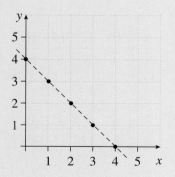

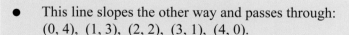

Exercise 3E

1   For each part write down the coordinates of the points marked.
    For each part write down the equation of the line through the points.

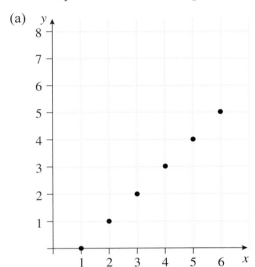

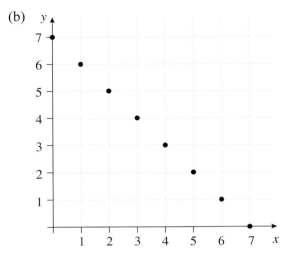

In questions ② to ⑪ you are given the coordinates of several points on a line. Find the equation of each line.

2 | x | 1 | 2 | 3 | 4 | 5 | 6 |
    |---|---|---|---|---|---|---|
    | y | 4 | 5 | 6 | 7 | 8 | 9 |

3 | x | 1 | 2 | 3 | 4 | 5 | 6 |
    |---|---|---|---|---|---|---|
    | y | 6 | 7 | 8 | 9 | 10 | 11 |

4 | x | 1 | 3 | 5 | 7 |
    |---|---|---|---|---|
    | y | 8 | 10 | 12 | 14 |

5 | x | 2 | 4 | 6 | 8 |
    |---|---|---|---|---|
    | y | 0 | 2 | 4 | 6 |

6 | x | 10 | 12 | 14 | 16 |
    |---|---|---|---|---|
    | y | 4 | 6 | 8 | 10 |

7 | x | 1 | 2 | 3 | 4 | 5 |
    |---|---|---|---|---|---|
    | y | 2 | 4 | 6 | 8 | 10 |

8 | x | 2 | 4 | 5 | 6 |
    |---|---|---|---|---|
    | y | 6 | 12 | 15 | 18 |

9 | x | 8 | 7 | 6 | 5 | 4 | 3 |
    |---|---|---|---|---|---|---|
    | y | 0 | 1 | 2 | 3 | 4 | 5 |

10 | x | 5 | 4 | 3 | 2 | 1 | 0 |
    |---|---|---|---|---|---|---|
    | y | 0 | 1 | 2 | 3 | 4 | 5 |

11 | x | 1 | 2 | 3 | 4 | 5 |
    |---|---|---|---|---|---|
    | y | 3 | 5 | 7 | 9 | 11 |

12 Find the equation of the line
through (a) A and B
(b) B and C
(c) C and A

13 Find the equation of the line
through (a) D and E
(b) E and F
(c) D and F

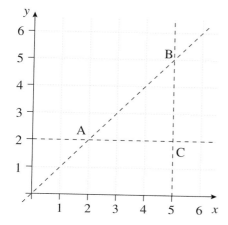

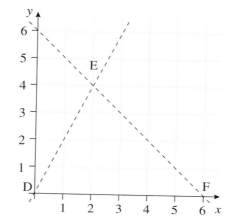

3.5 Reflection

In section 3.5 you will:

- draw reflections on squared paper
- draw reflection using coordinates

Reflections are quite common in everyday life.
Think of examples of reflections:

- in the classroom

- at home

- anywhere

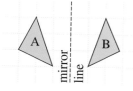

- Triangle B is the image of triangle
  A under reflection in the mirror line. Similarly
  triangle A is the image of triangle B under reflection in the
  same line.

- Extra care is required when the mirror line lies along a diagonal.
- Notice that the line PP' is perpendicular to the mirror line.

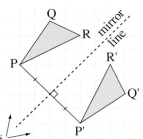

equal distances

- The mirror line can pass through the shape which is being reflected, as shown here.

Exercise 1M

Copy each shape on squared paper and draw the image after reflection in the broken line.

13 Write your own name in capital letters and then reflect the letters in a horizontal line.

14 Draw any shape of your own design (not too complicated!) and then reflect it in either a horizontal, vertical or diagonal line.

Exercise 1E

In questions 1 to 3 first reflect the shape in line 1 and then reflect the image in line 2.

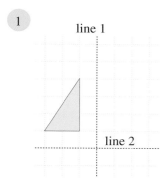
1 line 1 / line 2

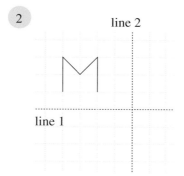
2 line 2 / line 1

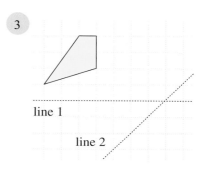
3 line 1 / line 2

Questions 4 to 6 are more difficult reflections. Copy each shape and draw the image after reflection in the broken line.

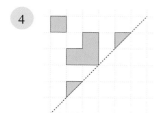
4

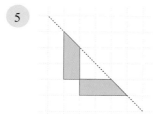
5

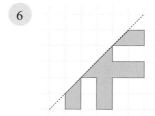
6

7 The photo shows the captain of a ship holding a clock as his ship is slowly sinking.

A clock face has just twelve marks to show the hours. Draw the clockface, showing the hands as they would appear when looked at in a mirror, when the time was

(a) 2.30
(b) 5.45.

8   Part of the sign for a taxi firm has snapped off. The missing part of the first
    letter is a reflection in a line drawn from P to Q.

    On squared paper draw an accurate picture of all the taxi sign before the
    corner part snapped off.

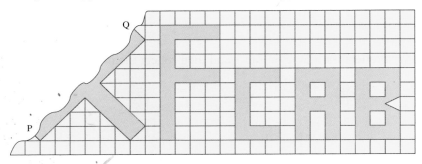

Using coordinates

(a) Triangle 2 is the image of triangle 1 under
     reflection in the *x axis*.
     We will use the shorthand 'Δ' for 'triangle'.

(b) Δ3 is the image of Δ2 under reflection
     in the line $x = -1$.

(c) Δ4 is the image of Δ1 under reflection in
     the line $y = x$.

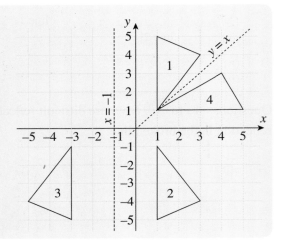

Exercise 2M

1

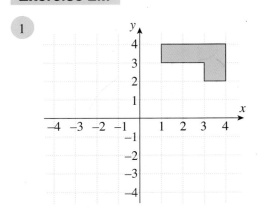

Copy the diagram.

(a) Reflect the shape in the *x* axis.
    Label the image A.

(b) Reflect the shape in the *y* axis.
    Label the image B.

2   Copy the diagram onto squared paper.
    (a) Reflect the shaded triangle in
       $y = 2$. Label the image A.
    (b) Reflect the shaded triangle in
       $x = 1$. Label the image B.
    (c) Reflect the shaded triangle in the
       x axis. Label the image C.

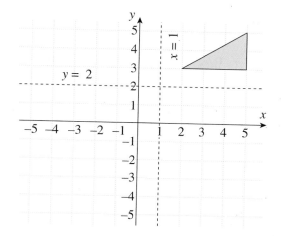

3   Copy the diagram onto squared paper.

  Draw the image of the shaded triangle
  under reflection in:

  (a) $y = 1$, label it ΔA
  (b) $x = -1$, label it ΔB
  (c) $y = x$, label it ΔC

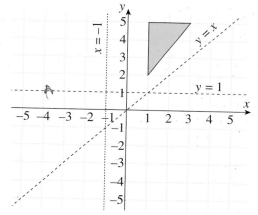

4   (a) Draw x and y axes with values from -6 to $+6$ and draw shape A which has
      vertices at $(3, 1)$, $(5, 3)$, $(5, 1)$, $(4, 0)$
  (b) Reflect shape A in the x axis onto shape B.
  (c) Reflect shape A in the y axis onto shape C.
  (d) Reflect shape A in the line $y = x$ onto shape D.

5   (a) Draw x and y axes with values from -6 to $+6$ and draw shape A
      which has vertices at $(1, -2)$, $(3, -3)$, $(3, -4)$, $(1, -6)$
  (b) Reflect shape A in the y axis onto shape B.
  (c) Reflect shape B (not shape A!) in the line $y = x$ onto shape C.
  (d) Reflect shape C in the line $y = 1\frac{1}{2}$ onto shape D.
  (e) Write down the coordinates of the vertices of shape D.

6   (a) Draw x and y axes with values from -6 to $+6$ and draw shape
      P which has vertices at $(-4, 2)$, $(-4, 3)$, $(-3, 5)$, $(-3, 2)$.
  (b) Reflect shape P in the line $y = 2$ onto shape Q.
  (c) Reflect shape Q in the y axis onto shape R.
  (d) Reflect shape R in the line $y = x$ onto shape S.
  (e) Write down the coordinates of the vertices of shape S.

134

Exercise 2E

1 Write down the equation of
the mirror line for the following reflections:
(a) ΔA → ΔC
(b) ΔA → ΔB
(c) ΔD → ΔG
(d) ΔF → ΔE
(e) ΔF → ΔD

Remember:

The x axis is also the line $y = 0$
The y axis is also the line $x = 0$

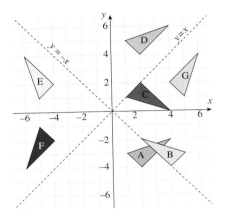

2 (a) Draw x and y axes with values from −6 to +6 and draw Δ1
with vertices at (3, 1), (6, 1), (6, 3).
(b) Reflect Δ1 in the line $y = x$ onto Δ2.
(c) Reflect Δ1 in the y axis onto Δ3.
(d) Reflect Δ2 in the y axis onto Δ4.
(e) Find the equation for the reflection Δ3 onto Δ4.

3 The yellow shape is reflected so that the image of A is A'.

(a) Copy the diagram and draw the mirror line for this reflection.
(b) Draw the image of the yellow shape after reflection in the mirror line.
(c) Draw a new mirror line which passes through point B and is at right angles to the first mirror line.
Draw the image of the yellow shape in this new mirror line.

4 (a) Draw Δ1 with vertices at (−4, 4), (−4, 6), (−1, 6).
(b) Reflect Δ1 in the line $x = -\frac{1}{2}$ onto Δ2.
(c) Reflect Δ2 in the line $y = x$ onto Δ3.
(d) Reflect Δ1 in the line $y = x$ onto Δ4.
(e) Find the equation for the reflection Δ3 onto Δ4.

5 The word 'AMBULANCE' is to be printed on the front of an ambulance so that a person in front of the ambulance will see the word written the right way round, when viewed in the driver's mirror. How should the word be printed on the front of the ambulance?

6 (a) In what country did Napoleon live?
Write your answer in "mirror writing".

(b) Whose statue is on top of a column in Trafalgar Square?

(c) Which famous mathematician made a discovery after an apple fell on his head?

CHECK YOURSELF ON SECTIONS 3.4 AND 3.5

1   Using lines which are parallel to the axes

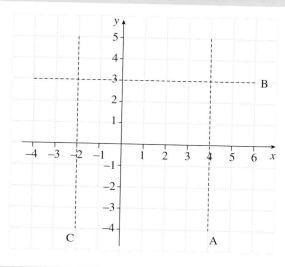

Write down the equation of :
(a) line A
(b) line B
(c) line C
(d) On which line is the point $(4, -2)$?

2   Drawing graphs

Copy and complete the table for $y = 4 - x$ then draw the graph using 1 cm for 1 unit on each axis.

x	0	1	2	3	4
y					
coordinates					

3   Using graphs

In the U.K., petrol consumption for cars is usually quoted in 'miles per gallon'. In other countries the metric equivalent is 'km per litre'.
(a) Convert 20 m.p.g. into km per litre.
(b) Convert 5 km per litre into m.p.g.
(c) A car travels 9 km on one litre of petrol. Convert this consumption into miles per gallon. Work out how many gallons of petrol the car will use, if it is driven a distance of 100 miles.

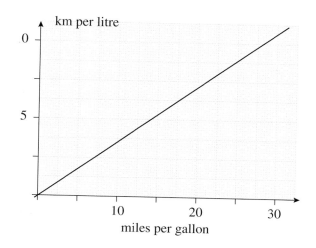

4 Finding the equation of a line

(a) The co-ordinates of several points on a line are given opposite. Write down the equation of the line.

x	1	2	3	4	5	6
y	7	8	9	10	11	12

(b)

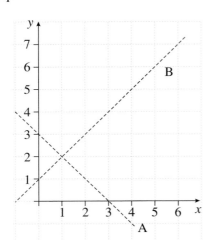

Write down the equation of line A and the equation of line B.

(Look at the co-ordinates of points on each line carefully)

5 Drawing reflections on squared paper

Copy each shape on squared paper and draw the image after reflection in the broken line.

(a)

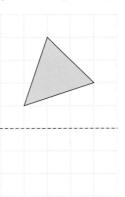

(b)

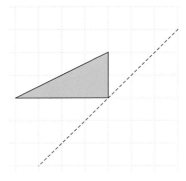

6. Drawing reflections using coordinates

(a) Copy the diagram.

(b) Draw the image of triangle 1 after reflection in the *y*-axis.

(c) Draw the image of triangle 2 after reflection in the line $x = 3$.

(d) Write down the equation of the mirror line for the reflection of triangle 2 onto triangle 3.

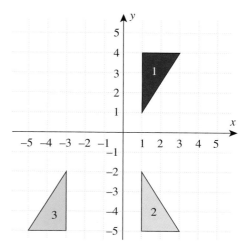

UNIT 3 MIXED REVIEW

Part one

1 Find the value of these expressions when $n = 3$

    (a) $6n$ (b) $7 - n$ (c) n^2

    (d) $\dfrac{n + 9}{n}$ (e) $n^2 - n$ (f) $\dfrac{4n}{n + 3}$

2 Work out the following (remember 'BIDMAS')

    (a) $30 - 6 \times 4$ (b) $17 + 5^2$ (c) $20 - 16 \div 4$
    (d) $(8 - 2)^2$ (e) $13 + 2 \times 3$ (f) $(13 + 2) \times 3$

3 Work out, without a calculator

    (a) 4×0.1 (b) 1.7×10 (c) 12.738×100
    (d) $428.6 \div 100$ (e) 428.6×0.01 (f) $8 \div 0.1$

4 (a) Copy the diagram.
    (b) Reflect the L shape in the *x* axis.
    (c) Reflect the L shape in the line $y = x$.

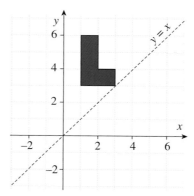

5 A man gives a total of £7 to his two children so that his daughter receives 60p more than his son. How much does his daughter receive?

6 Write down *two* possible answers for the missing digits. Ask a friend to check your solutions.

3 □ 0 □ × □ □ ÷ □ = 60

7 Use a calculator to find the square roots, correct to 1 decimal place.

(a) $\sqrt{19}$ (b) $\sqrt{8}$ (c) $\sqrt{145}$ (d) $\sqrt{7.46}$

8

The velocity, v, of a snowmobile is given by the formula

$v = u + at$

Find v when $u = 0$, $a = 27$ and $t = 3$.

9 Use a calculator to work out the following. Give your answers correct to 1 decimal place or as a fraction.

(a) $16.9 - (2.48 \times 2.37)$ (b) $\dfrac{6.19}{(8.6 - 6.18)}$ (c) $4\frac{1}{3} - \frac{2}{5}$

(d) $\left(\dfrac{7.9}{1.46}\right)^2$ (e) $\left(\dfrac{9.25}{3.5}\right) - 1.43$ (f) $3\frac{1}{2} \div \frac{3}{8}$

10 It costs 35p per minute to hire a powerful computer. How much will it cost to hire the computer from 07:40 to 08:15?

11 Draw the graph of $y = 2x + 3$ for values of x from 0 to 4.

x	0	1	2	3	4
y					

12 (a) Find two consecutive numbers with a product of 552.
(b) Find any two numbers with a product of 837.
(c) Find a pair of numbers with a sum of 19 and a product of 48.

13 Copy this diagram onto squared paper and then draw its reflection in the broken line.

14 Jim and Marie want to carpet their living room.
The dimensions of the room are shown opposite.
They can buy a piece of 'Munster Gold' carpet
for £75 or 'Durban Twist' carpet. The 'Durban Twist'
carpet is 4m wide and costs £16.83 per metre length.

(a) How much will the 'Durban Twist' carpet
cost for the living room?
(b) What area of 'Durban Twist' carpet would be wasted?
(c) Which is the cheaper to buy – Munster Gold or
Durban Twist? Write down the difference in the cost?

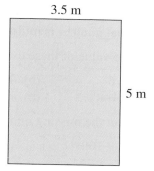

3.5 m

5 m

15 The cost C of Carol's shopping is given by the formula

$$C = n^2 + 8n$$

Where n is the number of hours she spends shopping.
Find C when Carol spends 5 hours shopping.

Part two

1 Work out, without a calculator
(a) $7.46 + 5$ (b) 25×0.3 (c) $678.4 \div 100$
(d) 0.8×0.04 (e) 1.2×0.6 (f) $9 \div 5$

2 Draw axes with x and y from 0 to 6.

Plot   A(1, 4)   B(1, 1)   C(3, 1)
Plot   D(5, 4)   E(5, 1)   F(3, 1)

Write down the equation of the mirror line which reflects triangle ABC onto triangle DEF.

3 Write brackets to make the calculations correct.
(a) $7 + 3 \times 6 = 60$ (b) $20 - 4 \div 2 = 18$
(c) $8 \times 2 + 3 - 2 = 38$ (d) $19 \times 5 - 2 = 3 \times 14 + 17$

4 Draw the graph of $y = 6 - x$ for values of x from 0 to 6.

x	0	1	2	3	4	5	6
y							

5 The maximum velocity v of a supermarket
trolley depends on the mass m of the person
flying behind the trolley and the saving s on
a special offer.

$$v = \frac{s^2}{m - 10}$$

Find v when $s = 20$ and $m = 60$.

6   (a) Write in order, smallest first: £1.25, 65p, £0.8
     (b) What number is mid-way between 3.4 and 3.5?

7 Find the value of these expressions when $n = -2$

    (a) $n + 6$ (b) $4n$ (c) $n - 4$
    (d) $2n + 4$ (e) n^2 (f) $5n - 1$

8 Work out the missing numbers

    (a) $0.1 \times 100 = \boxed{}$ (b) $\left(\boxed{}\right)^2 = 225$ (c) $\boxed{} \times 3 = 192$

    (d) $35 \div 100 = \boxed{}$ (e) $0.3 \times 0.9 = \boxed{}$ (f) $4 \times \boxed{} = 2.8$

9 I am a 3 digit number. The product of my digits is 4. I am an odd number less than 200. What am I?

10 Peter Gibson's paintings became very fashionable in 2009. His master piece titled 'Now' was sold for €65 000. The painting was bought by its previous owner in 1998 for £400. Calculate the price increase in euros. [£1 = €1.25]

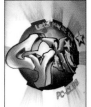

11 Work out the following with a calculator, giving each answer correct to 2 decimal places.

    (a) $(4.17 + 2.6) \div 1.89$ (b) $\dfrac{(-7)^2}{2.43}$ (c) $\dfrac{7.4}{(2.63 + 1.76)}$

12

    | Plan A |
    | £12.99 fixed charge |
    | 3.3p per unit used |

Lisa uses 2140 units of electricity one month and is charged using Plan A opposite.

    | Plan B |
    | No fixed charge |
    | 4.6p per unit used |

Her mother uses 1870 units of electricity and is charged using Plan B opposite.
Who pays more money and by how much?

13 Find the value of c, using each formula and the values given.

    (a) $c = mx + 3$ when $m = 4$ and $x = 9$
    (b) $c = p - pq$ when $p = 10$ and $q = 0.5$
    (c) $c = (a + b)^2$ when $a = 2$ and $b = -6$

14 This graph shows the amount of oil used by a central-heating boiler for the month of November (30 days)

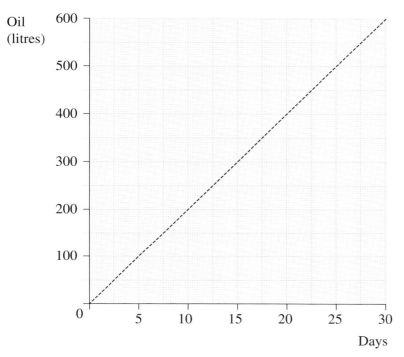

(a) What do 2 small squares on the horizontal axis show?
(b) How much oil was used in (i) 25 days (ii) 17 days?
(c) How long was the boiler running if it used
    (i) 180 litres   (ii) 420 litres   (iii) 240 litres
(d) Barney has 300 litres of oil. Is this enough to use the boiler for a fortnight?

15 The photo shows objects reflected in a mirror with colours changed also .
    (a) Draw a diagram of your own design with black sections and white sections.
    (b) Draw a reflection of your design in a similar way to that shown in the photo.

Puzzles and Problems 3

Coordinate puzzles

1 Draw a pair of axes with the values shown.

Plot the points below and join them up with a ruler in the order given.

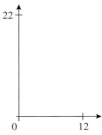

| $(11, 4\frac{1}{2})$ | $(11, 17)$ | $(10, 21)$ | $(4, 21)$ | $(2, 17)$ |
| $(2, 14)$ | $(1\frac{1}{2}, 13)$ | $(1\frac{1}{2}, 11\frac{1}{2})$, | $(2, 11)$ | |

On the same picture, plot the points below and join them up with a ruler in the order given. Do not join the last point in the box above with the first point in the new box.

$(5, 21)$ $(6, 22)$ $(8, 21)$ $(8, 20)$

On the same picture, plot the points below and join them up with a ruler in the order given.

$(6, 21)$ $(7, 22)$ $(8, 22)$ $(9, 21)$ $(9, 20)$

On the same picture, plot the points below and join them up with a ruler in the order given.

| $(2\frac{1}{2}, 3)$ | $(5, 3)$ | $(6\frac{1}{2}, 5)$ | $(6\frac{1}{2}, 9)$ | $(4, 10)$ | $(2, 10)$ | $(1, 8)$ |
| $(4, 8)$ | $(5, 7)$ | $(5\frac{1}{2}, 6)$ | $(5\frac{1}{2}, 5)$ | $(5, 4)$ | $(3, 4)$ | $(3, 3)$ |

On the same picture, plot the points below and join them up with a ruler in the order given.

$(3, 1\frac{1}{2})$ $(1\frac{1}{2}, \frac{1}{2})$ $(2\frac{1}{2}, 3)$ $(4, \frac{1}{2})$ $(5, 2\frac{1}{2})$ $(7, \frac{1}{2})$ $(11\frac{1}{2}, 2\frac{1}{2})$ $(11\frac{1}{2}, 4\frac{1}{2})$ $(5, 2\frac{1}{2})$

On the same picture, plot the points below and join them up with a ruler in the order given.

| $(2, 14)$ | $(3, 14)$ | $(4, 13)$ | $(4, 12)$ | $(4, 13)$ | $(5, 14)$ | $(7, 14)$ | $(8, 13)$ |
| $(8, 11)$ | $(7, 10)$ | $(5, 10)$ | $(4, 11)$ | $(4, 12)$ | $(1\frac{1}{2}, 10\frac{1}{2})$ | $(1\frac{1}{2}, 10)$ | $(2, 10)$ |

On the same picture, plot the points below and join them up with a ruler in the order given.

$(10, 11)$ $(11\frac{1}{2}, 11)$ $(11\frac{1}{2}, 12)$ $(10, 12)$ $(10, 14)$ $(11, 12)$ $(11\frac{1}{2}, 14)$ $(12, 12)$

On the same picture, plot the points below and join them up with a ruler in the order given.

$(2, 8)$ $(3\frac{1}{2}, 5)$ $(3\frac{1}{2}, 4)$ $(5, 5)$ $(5\frac{1}{2}, 5)$ $(5, 5)$ $(4\frac{1}{2}, 4)$

Draw a ● at $(2, 12)$ and a ● at $(6, 12)$

Colour me in.

2 Draw a pair of axes with the values shown.

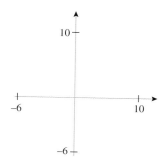

Plot the points below and join them up with a ruler in the order given.

$(2, 0)$ $(2\frac{1}{2}, 1)$ $(5\frac{1}{2}, 1)$ $(6, 0)$ $(6, -2)$ $(5\frac{1}{2}, -3)$ $(2\frac{1}{2}, -3)$ $(2, -2)$ $(2, 0)$

On the same picture plot the points below and join them up with a ruler in the order given.
Do not join the last point in the box above with the first point in the new box.

$(3, 1)$ $(3, 2)$ $(1, 2)$ $(0, 3)$ $(0, 4)$ $(1, 5)$ $(3, 5)$ $(4, 4)$ $(5, 5)$ $(6, 5)$
$(7, 4)$ $(7, 3)$ $(6, 2)$ $(5, 2)$ $(5, 1)$ $(5, 2)$ $(4, 3)$ $(4, 4)$ $(4, 3)$ $(3, 2)$

On the same picture, plot the points below and join them up with a ruler in the order given.

$(3, 7)$ $(3, 8)$ $(4, 8)$ $(5\frac{1}{2}, 8\frac{1}{2})$ $(5\frac{1}{2}, 6\frac{1}{2})$ $(4, 7)$ $(4, 8)$

On the same picture, plot the points below and join them up with a ruler in the order given.

$(5\frac{1}{2}, 0)$ $(5\frac{1}{2}, -2)$ $(3\frac{1}{2}, -2)$ $(3\frac{1}{2}, -1\frac{1}{2})$ $(5, -1\frac{1}{2})$ $(5, -\frac{1}{2})$ $(3\frac{1}{2}, -\frac{1}{2})$ $(3\frac{1}{2}, 0)$ $(5\frac{1}{2}, 0)$

On the same picture, plot the points below and join them up with a ruler in the order given.

$(4, 7)$ $(3, 7)$ $(1\frac{1}{2}, 6\frac{1}{2})$ $(1\frac{1}{2}, 8\frac{1}{2})$ $(3, 8)$

On the same picture, plot the points below and join them up with a ruler in the order given.

(6, −1)	(8, −1)	(7, 2)	(10, 5)	(7, 6)	(6, 10)	(3, 8)
(1, 10)	(−1, 7)	(−4, 7)	(−3, 4)	(−5, 2)	(−3, 1)	(−3, −2)
(−1, −1)	(0, −4)	$(4\frac{1}{2}, -4)$	(5, −3)			

On the same picture, plot the points below and join them up with a ruler in the order given.

(−2, 2)   (−3, 2)   (−3, 3)   (−2, 3)

On the same picture, plot the points below and join them up with a ruler in the order given.

$(-2, 2\frac{1}{2})$ $(-2\frac{1}{2}, 2\frac{1}{2})$

Draw a ● at (1, 3) and a ● at (6, 3)

Colour me in.

Mental Arithmetic Practice

Ideally a teacher will read out each question twice, with pupils' books closed.

Test 1

1. By how much is three kilos more than 800 grams?

2. How many 20p coins do I need to make £400?

3. How many square centimetres are there in one square metre?

4. How much more than £108 is £300?

5. Two angles of a triangle are 44° and 54°. What is the third angle?

6. Work out 10% of £5000.

7. My watch reads ten past eight. It is 15 minutes fast. What is the correct time?

8. A 50p coin is 2 mm thick. What is the value of a pile of 50p coins 2 cm high?

9. Add together £2.35 and £4.15.

10. A ship was due at noon on Friday but arrived at 8.00 a.m. on Saturday. How many hours late was the ship?

11. By how much is half a metre longer than 1 millimetre? (answer in mm).

12. What number is thirty-five more than eighty?

13. How many minutes are there in two and a half hours?

14. From nine times seven take away five.

15. A T.V. show lasting 45 minutes starts at 10 minutes to eight. When does it finish?

16. A train travels at an average speed of 48 mph. How far does it travel in 2 hours?

17 What is the perimeter of a square of side 14 cm?

18 A string of length 390 cm is cut in half. How long is each piece?

19 A half is a quarter of a certain number. What is the number?

20 A man died in 1993 aged 58. In what year was he born?

21 *Roughly* how many millimetres are there in one foot?

22 Write down ten thousand pence in pounds.

23 What is a quarter of two hundred and ten?

24 Find two ways of making 66p using five coins.

25 John weighs 8 stones and Jim weighs 80 kg. Who is heavier?

Test 2

1 What number is 10 less than nine thousand?

2 I want to buy 4 records, each costing £4.49. To the nearest pound, how much will my bill be?

3 How many magazines costing 95p can I buy with £10?

4 What is the total of 57 and 963?

5 What is a half of a half of 10?

6 True or false: 3 feet are slightly longer than 1 metre.

7 A triangle has a base 4 cm and a height of 10 cm. What is its area?

8 What number is exactly mid-way between 3.7 and 3.8?

9 Work out two squared plus three squared.

10 The pupils in Darren's class are given lockers numbered from 32 to 54. How many pupils are there in Darren's class?

11 Write 7 divided by 100 as a decimal.

12 Jane is 35 cm taller than William, who is 1.34 metres tall. How tall is Jane?

13 A toy train travels 6 metres in one second. How far will it go in one minute?

14 Which is larger: 2 cubed or 3 squared?

15 What number is next in the series 1, 2, 4, 8,…?

16 Write the number '$2\frac{1}{2}$ million' in figures.

17 Joe borrowed £4.68 from his father. He paid him back with a £10 note. How much change did he receive?

18 What is a tenth of 2.4?

19 I think of a number and subtract 6. The result is equal to 7 times 3. What is the number?

20 Write down the next prime number after 32.

21 How much longer is 7.5 metres than 725 centimetres?

22 How many lines of symmetry does a square have?

23 What is a quarter of a half?

24 Work out 200 times 300.

25 How many edges does a cube have?

A long time ago!   3

The Fibonacci sequence

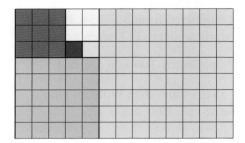

This rectangle is made from six squares drawn on centimetre squared paper. Write down the length of one side in each of the squares.

Can you arrange the numbers to make a pattern?

What would be the next number in your pattern?

Write down a rule for your pattern.

Fibonacci was born in Pisa, Italy. He lived in the 13th century.
He worked on the pattern 1, 1, 2, 3, 5, 8, ...
Each number is found by adding the two terms immediately before it.
The next number is 13 from 5 + 8.
Fibonacci found that these numbers helped to explain things to do with spirals in flowers, shells, the breeding of rabbits, pine cones, the family tree of honeybees and many other cases.

Exercise

1 Write down the first twenty-two numbers in the Fibonacci sequence 1, 1, 2, 3, 5, 8, ...

2 **Assembly Rules**

In Hatford High School, two boys are *not* allowed to sit next to each other in any single row of chairs in Assembly.

- If a row has 1 chair only, either a boy or a girl sits on the chair so there are 2 ways of filling the chair – B or G (B for Boy, G for Girl)
- If a row has 2 chairs only, there are 3 ways of filling the chairs – BG or GB or GG
- If a row has 3 chairs only, there are 5 ways of filling the chairs – BGG or BGB or GBG or GGB or GGG (remember: BB *not* allowed next to each other)

(a) Show all the different ways of filling the chairs if a row has 4 chairs only.

(b) How many different ways are there of filling the chairs if a row has 10 chairs only?

(c) How many different ways are there of filling the chairs if a row has 20 chairs only?

3 **RESEARCH:**

(a) Find out more about Fibonacci's life.

(b) List as many things as you can which are connected to Fibonacci numbers.

(c) Find a picture which shows how rabbits breeding give Fibonacci numbers.

UNIT 4

4.1 Describing data

In section 4.1 you will:

- use the mean, median, mode and range of a set of data
- compare sets of data
- find averages from frequency tables
- draw and use stem and leaf diagrams

The mean

All the data is added and the total is divided by the number of items. In everyday language the word 'average' usually stands for the mean.

The median

When the data is arranged in order of size, the median is the one in the middle. If there are two 'middle' numbers, the median is in the middle of these two numbers.

> The word 'average' is used to describe a *typical* member of a set of data.

The mode

The mode is the number or quality (like a colour) which occurs most often. Sometimes a set of data will have no mode, two modes or even more and this is a problem which we cannot avoid.

Range

The range is not an average but is the difference between the largest value and the smallest value in a set of data. It is useful in comparing sets of data when the *spread* of the data is important.

The marks in a spelling test were: 7, 8, 6, 6, 5, 3, 9, 8

(a) mean mark $= \dfrac{7 + 8 + 6 + 6 + 5 + 3 + 9 + 8}{8} = \dfrac{52}{8} = 6.5$

(b) arrange marks in order: 3 5 6 6 7 8 8 9

the median is the half way number $= \dfrac{6 + 7}{2} = 6.5$

(c) there are two modes 6 and 8.

(d) range $= 9 - 3 = 6$

Exercise 1M

1. (a) Find the mean of   2, 4, 5, 9, 10.
   (b) Find the median of   1, 3, 3, 4, 5, 7, 8, 11, 14, 14, 16.
   (c) Find the mode of   3, 3, 3, 3, 4, 4, 5, 6, 6, 6, 7, 7.
   (d) Find the range of   7, 8, 11, 14, 26, 30.

2. (a) Find the mean of the numbers 4, 13, 5, 7, 9, 6, 5.
   (b) Find the median of the numbers 6, 20, 1, 16, 2, 12, 6, 3, 8, 6, 8.
   (c) Find the mode of the numbers 13, 2, 11, 2, 10, 4, 5, 10, 8, 10

3. These digits are made using 5p coins.
   (a) Count the number of coins in each of the digits from 1 to 9.
   (b) What is the median number of coins used in a digit?
   (c) Work out the mean value of the coins used in a digit when the number 654 is formed.

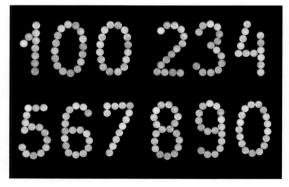

4. In several different shops the price of a certain DVD was £5.95, £3.99, £2.99, £4.75, £3.50, £2.95, £6.50. What is the median price of the DVD?

5. Six girls have heights of 1.48 m, 1.51 m, 1.47 m, 1.55 m, 1.40 m and 1.59 m.
   (a) Find the mean height of the six girls.
   (b) Find the mean height of the remaining five girls when the tallest girl leaves.

6. The temperatures at midnight in nine towns were, in °C,

   1°,   0°,   −3°,   − 4°,   3°,   −6°,   2°,   −2°,   −1°.

   What was the median temperature?

7 Find the range of the following sets of numbers:
   (a) 4, 11, 3, 8, 22, 5, 7, 30, 18
   (b) 9, 18, 100, 64, 11, 26
   (c) 4, – 2, 6, 4, 5, 10, 3.

8 Becky throws a dice eight times and wins 50p if the mean score is more than 3. The dice shows 6, 1, 2, 5, 6, 4, 5, 3. Find the mean score. Does Becky win 50p?

9 The heights of the people shown are, in m,
   1.82   1.71   1.74   1.69   1.73
      1.64   1.8   1.77   1.84
   (a) Find the median height of these people.
   (b) Two more people of heights 1.61 m and 1.7 m join this group. What is the median height of this new group of eleven people?

Exercise 1E

1 The range for nine numbers on a card is 60. One number is covered by a piece of Blu-Tack. What could that number be?
   [There are two possible answers.]

55	22	13
38	61	10
24	44	

2 The mean of the numbers 2, 6, 8, 5, and n is 6. Find the value of n.

3 Lauren has five cards. The five cards have a mean of 7 and a range of 4. What are the missing numbers?

   7   7   7   ☐   ☐

4 There were ten children on a coach journey. The mean age of the children was 11 and the range of their ages was 4. Write each statement below and then write next to it whether it is *True, Possible* or *False*.
   (a) The youngest child was 9 years old.
   (b) Every child was 11 years old.
   (c) All the children were at least 10 years old.

5 Twelve skydivers take part in a jump. They were born in the following years:
   1987   1983   1965   1971   1970   1980
   1956   1967   1984   1985   1962   1978
   Work out the mean age of the skydivers   (a) in 2009
                                            (b) in 2025

6   In a history test, Andrew got 62%. For the whole class, the mean mark was 64% and the median mark was 59%. Which 'average' tells him whether he is in the 'top' half or the 'bottom' half of the class?

7   For the set of numbers below, find the mean and the median.

$$1, 3, 3, 3, 4, 6, 99.$$

Which average best describes the set of numbers?

8   The median of the numbers 5, 7, 2, 12, 11 and x is 8. Find the value of x.

9   Write down five numbers so that:
the mean is 7
the median is 6
the mode is 4.

Comparing sets of data

To compare 2 sets of data, always write at least 2 things:

1 Compare an average (i.e. mean, median or mode).

2 Compare the range of each set of data (this shows how spread out the data is).

Exercise 2M

1   The Comets and the Typhoons are 2 athletics teams. They each have runners in the 100 m races.

Their best times (in seconds) are listed below:

The Comets: 10.7   10.5   11   10.8   11.2   11.1   10.9
The Typhoons: 10.9   10.4   11.1   10.7   10.6

Use the median and range to write a sentence to compare the times taken by the runners for the Comets and the Typhoons in the 100 m race.

2   The weights of the tigers in a safari park in Spain are as follows:

65 kg, 71 kg, 72 kg, 85 kg, 91 kg, 92 kg, 94 kg, 101 kg

(a) Find the mean weight of these tigers and the range of their weights.

(b) At another park in Portugal the mean weight of the tigers was 96 kg and the range of their weights was 120 kg. Write one or two sentences to compare the weights of the tigers at these two parks.

3 The heights in metres of the children in year 8 classes in two schools were recorded.

School A	1.60	1.59	1.63	1.57	1.64	1.58	1.57	1.62	1.57	1.64
School B	1.55	1.42	1.65	1.48	1.50	1.64	1.44	1.69	1.41	1.40

(a) Work out the mean height and the range for school A.

(b) Work out the mean height and the range for school B.

(c) Write a sentence to compare the heights of the children in the two schools.

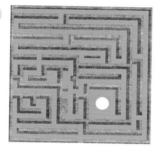

In an experiment firstly red ants and then black ants were released at the dot in a maze. The time they took to escape was recorded. Here are the results. The times are in seconds.

Red ants: 7   9   10   13   13   22   23   26   30

Black ants: 8   8   11   12   13   13   14   15   17

Write a sentence to compare the times taken to escape for the red and black ants.

Averages from frequency tables

Twenty children were asked how many computer games they had bought during one year. The results are below.

5   4   4   0   1   2   2   6   1   2

3   5   2   5   1   0   3   3   5   2

This data can be recorded in a frequency table.

number of computer games	0	1	2	3	4	5	6
frequency (number of children)	2	3	5	3	2	4	1

Use the table to work out the mean number of computer games.

$$\text{mean} = \frac{(2 \times 0) + (3 \times 1) + (5 \times 2) + (3 \times 3) + (2 \times 4) + (4 \times 5) + (1 \times 6)}{20}$$

↑ total number of children

$$\text{mean} = \frac{56}{20} = 2.8$$

Exercise 2E

1 The table below shows the number of children in each of 100 families.

number of children	0	1	2	3	4	5	6	7
frequency	4	24	22	19	15	7	7	2

Copy and complete: mean number of children $= \dfrac{(4 \times 0) + (24 \times 1) + (\dots)}{100} = \dfrac{\square}{100} = \square$

2 The table below shows the number of cars for each house on Carter Road in Romford.

number of cars	0	1	2	3
frequency	7	12	11	10

Copy and complete: mean number of cars $= \dfrac{(7 \times 0) + (12 \times 1) + (\dots) + (\dots)}{40}$

$$= \dfrac{\square}{40} = \square$$

3 The frequency table shows the weights of 30 eggs laid by the hens on a free range farm.

weight	44 g	48 g	52 g	56 g	60 g
frequency	5	6	7	9	3

Find the mean weight of the eggs, giving your answer to one decimal place.

4 The frequency table shows the weights of the 40 pears sold in a shop.

weight	70 g	80 g	90 g	100 g	110 g	120 g
frequency	2	7	9	11	8	3

Calculate the mean weight of the pears.

5 The marks, out of 10, achieved by 25 teachers in a spelling test were as follows:

mark	5	6	7	8	9	10
frequency	8	7	4	2	3	1

Find (a) the mean mark

      (b) the modal mark (this means the 'mode',
          ie. which test mark did more teachers get than any other)

6 The number of daily portions of fruit and vegetables eaten by 30 people is shown in the table below:

number of portions	0	1	2	3	4	5	6
frequency	2	3	3	7	3	9	3

(a) Find the mean number of portions eaten each day.

(b) Find the modal number of portions eaten each day (ie. the 'mode', the number of portions eaten by more people than any other)

7 Max and his dad go fishing twice every month. The tables below show how many fish each of them caught every time they went fishing one year.

(a) Find the mean number of fish caught by each of them.

(b) On an 'average' fishing trip, who caught more fish?

Max

number of fish	0	1	2	3	4	5	6	7
frequency	3	4	2	1	5	2	6	1

Dad

number of fish	0	1	2	3	4	5	6	7
frequency	2	5	3	4	5	3	0	2

Stem and leaf diagrams

Here are the marks of 20 girls in a science test.

47	53	71	55	28	40	45	62	57	64
33	48	59	61	73	37	75	26	68	39

We will put the marks into groups 20–29, 30–39.:... 70–79.

We will choose the tens digit as the 'stem' and the units as the 'leaf'.

The first four marks are shown [47, 53, 71, 55]

Stem (tens)	Leaf (units)
2	
3	
4	7
5	3 5
6	
7	1

The complete diagram is below ...... and then with the leaves in numerical order:

Stem	Leaf
2	8 6
3	3 7 9
4	7 0 5 8
5	3 5 7 9
6	2 4 1 8
7	1 3 5

Stem	Leaf
2	6 8
3	3 7 9
4	0 5 7 8
5	3 5 7 9
6	1 2 4 8
7	1 3 5

A key is included to show what the numbers mean.

Key

4|7 means 47

The diagram shows the shape of the distribution. It is also easy to find the mode, the median and the range.

Exercise 3M

1   The marks of 24 children in a test are shown

41	23	35	15	40	39	47	29
52	54	45	27	28	36	48	51
59	65	42	32	46	53	66	38

Stem	Leaf
1	
2	3
3	5
4	1
5	
6	

Draw a stem and leaf diagram. The first three entries are shown.

2   Draw a stem and leaf diagram for each set of data below

(a)
24	52	31	55	40	37	58	61	25	46
44	67	68	75	73	28	20	59	65	39

Stem	Leaf
2	
3	
4	
5	
6	
7	

(b)
30	41	53	22	72	54	35	47
44	67	46	38	59	29	47	28

3   The numbers shown below give the midday temperatures for Wells in June 2009. Draw an ordered stem and leaf diagram to show this data.

18	23	24	22	19	17	16	21	23	25
21	19	17	18	22	21	24	20	23	21
25	28	27	30	27	23	19	18	23	25

Exercise 3E

1 Here is the stem and leaf diagram
   showing the masses, in kg,
   of some people on a ferris wheel.

   (a) Write down the range of
       the masses.
   (b) How many people were on
       the wheel?
   (c) What is the median mass?

Stem	Leaf
3	3 7
4	1 2 7 7 8
5	1 6 8 9
6	0 3 7
7	4 5
8	2

Key

5|9 means 59

2 The stem and leaf diagrams below show the ages of patients in two hospital wards, the Carlton
   Ward and the Holbrook Ward.

The Carlton Ward

Stem	Leaf
2	1 4
3	0 3 6
4	4 4 7 9
5	3 6

Key

3|6 means 36

The Holbrook Ward

Stem	Leaf
5	1 4
6	3 5 8
7	0 1 6 8
8	2 4 7
9	5

Key

7|8 means 78

   (a) Find the range and the median age of the patients for each ward.

   (b) Write two sentences to compare the ages of the patients in the different wards
       (One sentence should involve how spread out the ages are (range) and the second
       sentence should involve an average (median)).

3 In this question the stem shows the units digit and the leaf shows the first digit after the
   decimal point.

   Draw the stem and leaf diagram using the following data:

2.4	3.1	5.2	4.7	1.4	6.2	4.5	3.3
4.0	6.3	3.7	6.7	4.6	4.9	5.1	5.5
1.8	3.8	4.5	2.4	5.8	3.3	4.6	2.8

Stem	Leaf
1	
2	
3	
4	
5	
6	

   (a) What is the median?
   (b) Write down the range.

Key

3|7 means 3.7

4.2 Rotation and combined transformations

In section 4.2 you will:

- rotate shapes
- find the centre of a rotation
- combine transformations

Rotation

Rotate the triangle through 90° anticlockwise about the point O.

The diagram on the right shows how tracing paper may be used.

Notice that we need three things to describe fully a rotation:

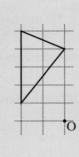
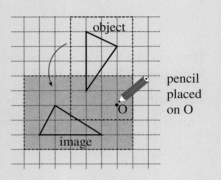

(a) the angle,
(b) the direction, (clockwise or anticlockwise)
(c) the centre of rotation.

Exercise 1M

In questions 1 to 6 draw the shape and then draw and shade its new position (the image).

Take O as the centre of rotation in each case.

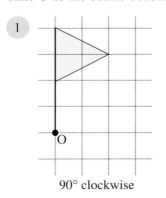

1

90° clockwise

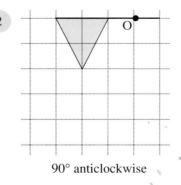

2

90° anticlockwise

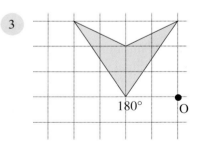

3

180°

4

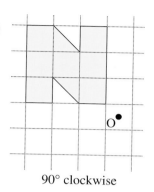

90° clockwise

5

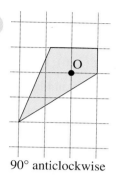

90° anticlockwise

6

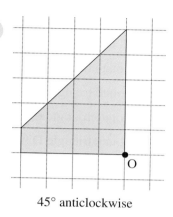

45° anticlockwise

7

Describe the rotation which

(a) moves the red piece onto the yellow piece,

(b) moves the green piece onto the yellow piece.

Exercise 1E

1   Copy the diagram shown, using axes from −6 to 6.

(a) Rotate triangle A 90° clockwise about (0, 0).
Label the new triangle P.

(b) Rotate triangle B 180° about (0, 0).
Label the new triangle Q.

(c) Rotate shape C 90° anticlockwise about (2, 2).
Label the new shape R.

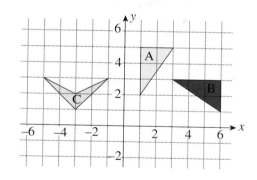

2   Copy the diagram shown.

(a) Rotate shape A 90° anticlockwise about
(−3, −4). Label the new shape P.

(b) Rotate triangle B 90° clockwise about
(1, 0). Label the new shape Q.

(c) Rotate shape C 90° clockwise about
(2, 1). Label the new shape R.

(d) Rotate shape C 180° about (−2, 3).
Label the new shape S.

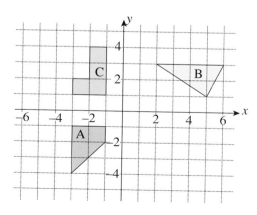

3 (a) Draw axes with values from –6 to 6 and draw triangle A with vertices at (2, 6), (6, 6), (6, 4).

   (b) Rotate triangle A 90° clockwise about (2, 6). Draw and label the new triangle B.

   (c) Rotate triangle B 180° about (2, 0). Draw and label the new triangle C.

   (d) Rotate triangle C 90° clockwise about (1, 0). Draw and label the new triangle D.

   (e) Rotate triangle D 90° anticlockwise about (–1, 4). Draw and label the new triangle E.

   (f) If triangle E is in the correct position you can now easily rotate triangle E onto triangle A. Write down the angle, direction and centre for this rotation.

Finding the centre of a rotation

Exercise 2M

In questions 1 to 4 copy each diagram. Draw the coloured shape on tracing paper. Place the tip of a pencil on different points until the shape can be rotated onto the shaded shape. Mark the centre of rotation with a dot.

1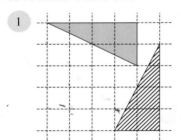

2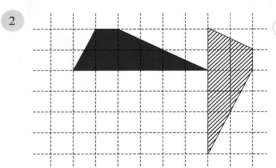

3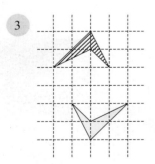

4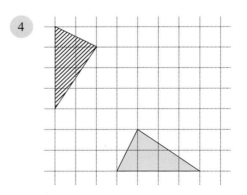

5 Find the coordinates of the centres of the following rotations:

(a) Δ1 → Δ2
(b) Δ1 → Δ3
(c) Δ1 → Δ4
(d) Δ3 → Δ5

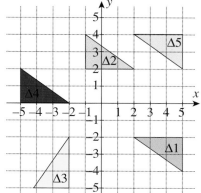

6 Copy the two squares carefully. It is possible to rotate the blue square onto the shaded square using three different centres of rotation. Find and mark these three points.

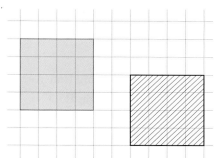

Combinations of two transformations

Reflection, rotation and translation are all transformations. Sometimes we need a combination of transformations to move a shape where we want to.

Exercise 2E

1

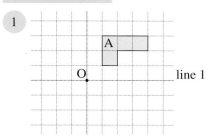

Copy this diagram.
(a) Reflect shape A in line 1 onto shape B.
(b) Reflect shape B in line 2 onto shape C.
(c) What single transformation will move shape A onto shape C?

2 Copy this diagram.
(a) Rotate triangle D 90° clockwise about (0, 0). Label the new triangle E.
(b) Rotate triangle E 90° clockwise about (0, 0). Label the new triangle F.
(c) What single transformation will move triangle D onto triangle F?

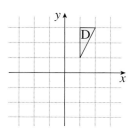

3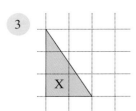

(a) Draw triangle X.

(b) Translate triangle X 4 units right onto triangle Y.

(c) Translate triangle Y 1 unit right and 2 units up onto triangle Z.

(d) What single translation will move triangle X onto triangle Z?

4 Copy the diagram opposite. Describe the transformations below. Mark any points and lines necessary to find the answers.

(a) Triangle A onto triangle B in one move.

(b) Triangle B onto triangle C in one move.

(c) Triangle D onto triangle C in one move.

(d) Triangle A onto triangle C in two moves.

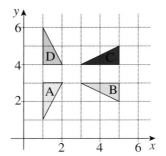

5 Describe fully the following transformations.

(a) Triangle A onto triangle B.

(b) Triangle B onto triangle C.

(c) Triangle A onto triangle D.

(d) Triangle C onto triangle E.

(e) Triangle A onto triangle C.
   (in two transformations)

(f) Triangle A onto triangle E.
   (in two or three transformations)

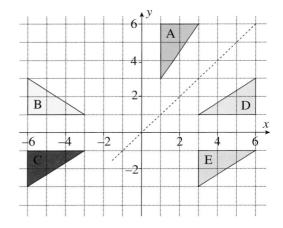

Making rotation patterns – a design activity

1 ● On *tracing paper* draw this pattern. The angle between the lines must be 120°. Each line is marked every $\frac{1}{2}$ cm as shown. We will call this pattern a *spoke* pattern.

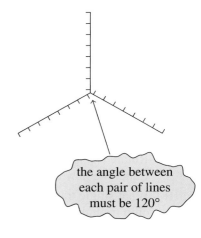

the angle between each pair of lines must be 120°

- In your book or on squared paper copy this design. We will call this a *spoke*.

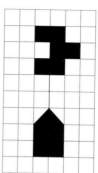

- Trace this spoke onto your *tracing paper* as shown opposite.

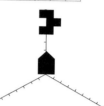

- Turn the tracing paper and trace the spokes as shown on the tracing paper.

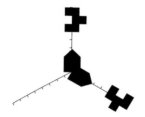 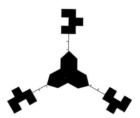

2 Using the method above, or a method of your own, draw these rotation patterns.

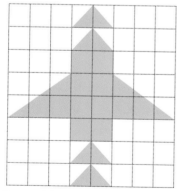

Draw this shape in your book.

Draw this on the tracing paper.

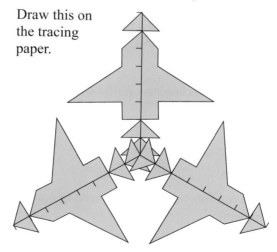

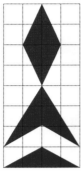

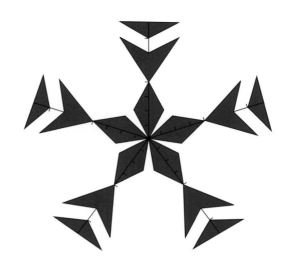

The angles between the lines on the spoke pattern will be $360° \div 5 = 72°$

3 Experiment with patterns of your own. Here are some you could try.

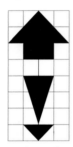

use 9 spokes

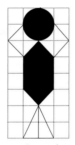

use 8 spokes

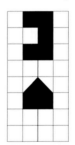

use 12 spokes

CHECK YOURSELF ON SECTIONS 4.1 AND 4.2

1   Using the mean, median, mode and range of a set of data

6   3   9   2   9   8   2   9

For the numbers above, find

(a) the mode   (b) the mean   (c) the range   (d) the median

(e) The five cards below have a mean of 6 and a median of 6. What are the two missing numbers?

4   7   11

2   Comparing sets of data

Children in class 8B and 8C have a maths test. The marks for 10 children from each class are shown below:

Class 8B: 8 7 6 6 9 6 4 7 2 5   Class 8C: 4 7 3 9 9 8 6 9 8 7

Use the means and ranges to write two sentences to compare the marks for each class.

3   Finding averages from frequency tables

A golfer played the same hole 30 times with the following results.

score	3	4	5	6	7	8
frequency	3	13	5	3	2	4

(a) Find her mean score.

(b) Find her modal score (mode).

4   Drawing and using stem and leaf diagrams

(a) The scores in a French test are
shown opposite.
Draw an ordered stem and leaf diagram
to show these scores.

37	49	27	67	37	19	77	45	62
39	34	47	43	48	64	29	41	38
52	56	48	61	68	43	51		

(b)

Stem	Leaf
3	5
4	2 3 4
5	1 5 7
6	8 8 9
7	5

This stem and leaf diagram shows the ages of some people at a birthday party. Find the range of the ages and the median for the ages.

Key

5|7 means 57

5   Rotating shapes

Copy the diagram shown. Use tracing paper to:

(a) rotate triangle A 180° about (0, 0).
    Draw and label the new triangle B.

(b) rotate triangle A 90° clockwise about (4, −1).
    Draw and label the new triangle C.

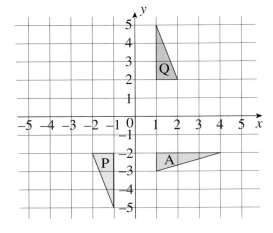

6   Finding the centre of a rotation

(a) On the diagram above triangle A is rotated 90° clockwise onto triangle P.
    Use tracing paper to find the centre of rotation.

(b) Triangle A is rotated 90° anticlockwise onto triangle Q. Use tracing paper to
    find the centre of rotation.

7   Combining transformations

Copy the diagram.

(a) Describe the transformation which moves
    triangle P onto triangle Q.

(b) Describe how triangle P is moved onto
    triangle R using two transformations.

(c) Reflect triangle A in the y-axis.
    Label this new triangle B.

(d) Reflect triangle B in the x-axis.
    Label this new triangle C.

(e) What single transformation will move
    triangle A onto triangle C?

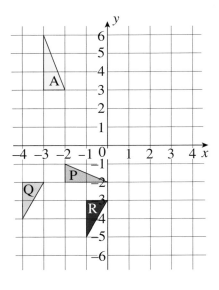

4.3 Interpreting and sketching real-life graphs

In section 4.3 you will:

● interpret and sketch real-life graphs

Exercise 1M

1   A scientist records the height of a growing plant every day for 20 days. The results are shown below.

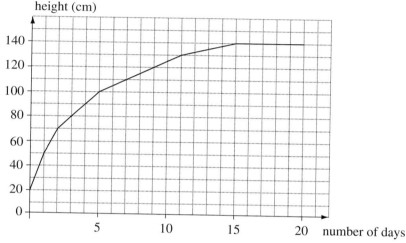

(a) What was the height of the plant after 5 days?
(b) After how many days was the height
   (i) 70 cm   (ii) 105 cm?
(c) What was the greatest increase in height in one day?
(d) What was the full-grown height of the plant?

2   Which of the graphs **A** to **D** best fits each of the following statements?
(a) 'The price of petrol was steady for several years but has fallen recently.'
(b) 'The cost of air flights was falling slowly until 2008, but is now rising.'
(c) 'The birthrate in Italy has fallen steadily over the the last decade.'
(d) 'The weight of the bird increased steadily after hatching.'

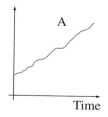
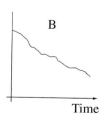
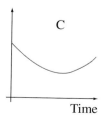
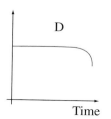

3   The number of children inside a school is counted every ten minutes from 7.30 a.m. until 9.00 a.m., when the bell rings; the results are shown below.

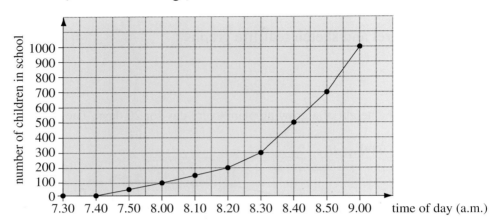

(a) How many children were inside the school at
    (i) 8.00 a.m.?   (ii) 8.35 a.m.?   (iii) 8.55 a.m.?

(b) How many children arrived between 7.30 a.m. and 8.30 a.m.?

(c) Estimate when the first children arrived.

(d) How many children arrived during the last 10 minutes before the bell rang at 9.00 a.m.?

(e) At what time were there 250 children in school?

4   The graph shows the mass of crisps in a packet during the time after opening the packet.

(a) Where all the crisps eaten?

(b) What is the mass of a full packet of crisps?

(c) Explain the shape of the graph. Why are some vertical lines on the graph longer than others?

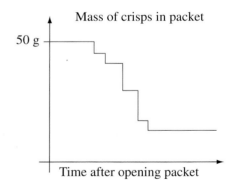

5
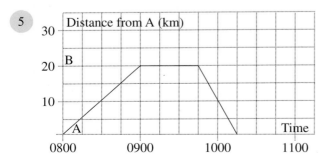

The graph shows a car journey from A to B and back to A.

(a) How far is it from A to B?

(b) For how long does the car stop at B?

(c) At what two times is the car half between A and B?

6 A packet of frozen fish is taken out of a freezer and left on a kitchen table for 4 hours. The fish is then heated in a frying pan. Sketch a graph to show the temperature of the fish after it is taken from the freezer.

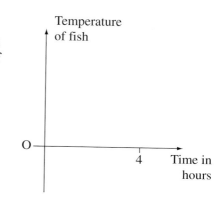

7

The graph above shows Sue's journey between home and the airport.
(a) When did she arrive at the airport?
(b) When did she arrive home?
(c) What happened between 0700 and 0730?
(d) At what speed did she travel
    (i) from home to the airport   (ii) from the airport back to her home?

8 The graph shows a return journey from A.
(a) When is the car halfway between A and C on the outward journey?
(b) Between what times does the car stop at B?
(c) When is the car halfway between C and B on the return journey?
(d) Find the speed of the car
    (i)   From A to C
    (ii)   From C back to B
    (iii) From B back to A.

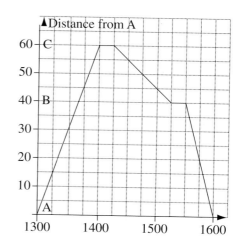

Exercise 1E

1 This diagram shows the temperature and rainfall readings in one week.
The rainfall is shown as the
bar chart. The temperature
is shown as the line graph.

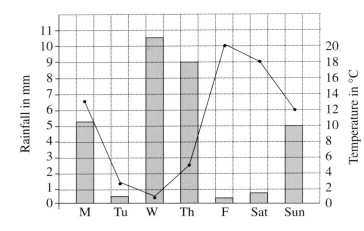

(a) Use *both* graphs to describe the weather on Wednesday.

(b) On which two days was the weather fairly wet and warm?

(c) Compare the weather on Tuesday and Saturday.

2 Water is poured at a constant rate into
each of the containers A, B and C.
The graphs X, Y and Z shows how the
water level rises.
Decide which graph fits each container.
State your reasons.

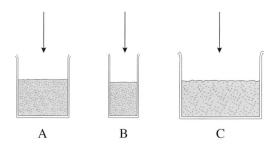

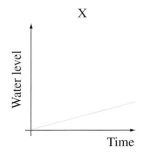

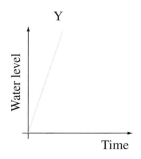

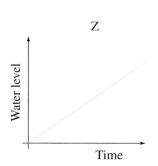

3 This graph shows a car journey from London to Stevenage and back.

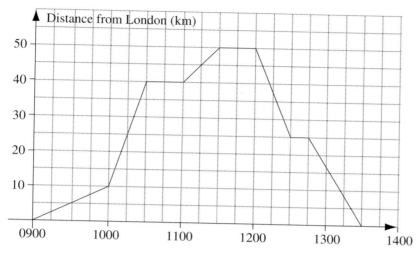

(a) For how long in the whole journey was the car at rest?

(b) At what time was the car half way to Stevenage on the outward journey?

(c) Between which two times was the car travelling at its highest speed?

4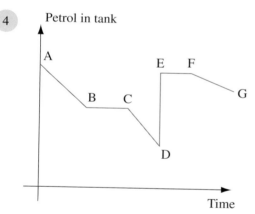

The graph shows the amount of petrol in the tank of a car.

Explain briefly what you think is happening in each section of the graph:
AB, BC, CD, DE, EF, FG.

5

A graph is drawn to show the value of a car over a period of 4 years. The car was bought for £9000. At the end of the fourth year the car was in an accident. Sketch a graph to show how you think the value of the car might change over the years.

6 (a) Draw axes like those in question 3 but go up to 70 km on the vertical axis and up to 4 hours on the horizontal axis.

   (b) Draw the graph for the following journey:

   Part 1. Car leaves home at 13:00 and travels at 40 km/h for 30 minutes.

   Part 2. Car stops for 45 minutes.

   Part 3. Car travels away from home at 50 km/h for one hour.

   Part 4. Car stops for 30 minutes.

   Part 5. Car returns home at 70 km/h.

   (c) Answer the following questions:

   (i) How far from home is the car at 14:45?

   (ii) At what time does the car return home?

7 The petrol consumption of a car depends on the speed, as shown below.

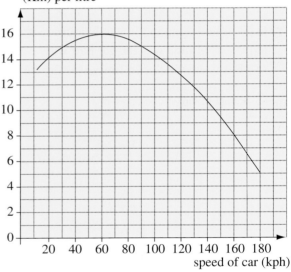

petrol consumption (Km) per litre

speed of car (kph)

   (a) What is the petrol consumption at a speed of

   (i)   30 km per hour

   (ii)   100 km per hour

   (iii) 180 km per hour?

   (b) At what speed is the petrol consumption

   (i)   8 km per litre

   (ii)   12 km per litre

   (iii) 9 km per litre?

   (c) At what speed should the car be driven in order to use the least amount of petrol?

   (d) A car is driven at 160 km per hour. How far can it travel on 20 litres of petrol?

8 Draw a vertical axis which goes up to 50 km and a horizontal axis which goes up to 4 hours.

   At 17 00 Lisa leaves her home and cycles at 20 km/h for 1 hour. She stops for $\frac{1}{4}$ hour and then continues her journey at a speed of 40 km/h for the next $\frac{1}{2}$ hour. She then stops for $\frac{3}{4}$ hour. Finally she returns home at a speed of 40 km/h.

   Draw a travel graph to show Lisa's journey. When did she arrive home?

4.4 Brackets and equations

In section 4.4 you will:

- multiply out single brackets
- solve linear equations
- solve linear equations involving brackets
- solve problems by trial and improvement
- form equations to solve problems

Multiplying out single brackets

A number or symbol outside the brackets multiplies each number or symbol inside the brackets.

$5(x + 2) = 5x + 10$

$2(1 + 3x) = 2 + 6x$

$3(x - 2) = 3x - 6$

$a(x + b) = ax + ab$

Find expressions for the area and the perimeter of the photo

Area $= 7(x + 5)$

$\quad = 7x + 35$

Perimeter $= x + 5 + x + 5 + 7 + 7$

$\quad = 2x + 24$

7

$x + 5$

Exercise 1M

Multiply out

1 $5(x + 3)$

2 $2(x + 6)$

3 $3(x + 4)$

4 $7(x - 2)$

5 $3(x - 5)$

6 $4(x + 6)$

7 $2(x - 1)$

8 $3(2x + 3)$

9 $5(2x - 5)$

10 $4(2x + 1)$

11 $6(3x - 4)$

12 $3(2x + 4)$

13 $5(3x - 6)$

14 $8(3x - 2)$

15 $7(4x + 3)$

16 $6(2 + 5x)$

17 $3(5 + 3x)$

18 $2(6x - 4)$

172

19 (a) Write an expression for the area of
        the picture.
    (b) Write an expression for the perimeter
        of the picture.

7

$x + 3$

Expand (multiply out) the following expressions:

20 $a(x + y)$

21 $a(b + c)$

22 $b(m - n)$

23 $m(p - q)$

24 $y(x + m)$

25 $n(p + 4)$

26 $x(y + 3)$

27 $p(q - 7)$

28 $m(3 + n)$

29 $n(n + 2)$

30 $4(m + 6)$

31 $p(p - 9)$

32 $2(x + y)$

33 $x(x - 3)$

34 $a(5 + a)$

35 $y(4x + 2)$

36 $3(5a - 2)$

37 $6(10 - 3n)$

38 Copy and complete

(a) $3(2x + \boxed{}) = 6x + 21$

(b) $4(\boxed{} + \boxed{}) = 12x + 20$

(c) $\boxed{}(6 - 3x) = 36 - 18x$

(d) $\boxed{}(9 - \boxed{}) = 27 - 24x$

Using negative numbers

Remember: $-4 \times (-4) = 16$ $-4 \times (+4) = -16$

$-3(a - 2) = -3a + 6$ because $-3 \times (-2) = +6$

$-3(a + 2) = -3a - 6$ because $-3 \times (+2) = -6$

Exercise 1E

1   Copy and complete

(a) $-2(m + 4) = -2m - \boxed{}$

(b) $-4(n - 3) = -4n + \boxed{}$

(c) $-2(x - 3) = -2x \boxed{} 6$

(d) $-5(y + 3) = -5y \boxed{} 15$

Expand (multiply out) the following expressions:

2    $-4(a - 2)$

3    $-6(m - 3)$

4    $-3(n + 4)$

5    $-2(y + 8)$

6    $-4(3 + w)$

7    $7(6 - 2x)$

8    $-8(n - 4)$

9    $3(3y + 7)$

10    $-5(4 - 2m)$

11    $-6(4w - 2)$

12    $-7(4 + 2n)$

13    $3(2 + 7a)$

14    $-9(3 + 2m)$

15    $-4(5 - 3p)$

16    $8(3m - 6)$

17    $-3(4q - 7)$

18    $5(6 - 7a)$

19    $-6(3 + 9m)$

20    $-10(4 + 5n)$

21    $-4(6a - 6)$

22    $-4(3 - 2x)$

Remove the brackets and simplify.

(a) $3(x + 2) + 2(x + 1)$

     $= 3x + 6 + 2x + 2$

     $= 5x + 8$

(b) $4(x + 1) + 2(2x + 3)$

     $= 4x + 4 + 4x + 6$

     $= 8x + 10$

Remember: First remove the brackets then collect the like terms.

Exercise 2M

Remove the brackets and simplify.

1    $2(x + 1) + 3(x + 3)$

2    $3(x + 4) + 2(x + 1)$

3    $4(x + 2) + 2(x + 2)$

4    $5(x + 1) + 3(x + 2)$

5    $5(x + 1) + 4(x + 3)$

6    $6(x + 3) + 4(x + 3)$

7    $2(4x + 3) + 4(3x + 4)$

8    $3(4x + 5) + 2(x + 5)$

9    $6(2x + 1) + 3(1 + 2x)$

10    $2(3x + 2) + 6(2x + 3)$

11

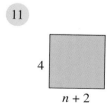 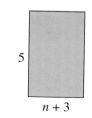

Find an expression for the total area of the three rectangles. Simplify your answer.

174

In questions 12 to 21 remove the brackets and simplify.

12 $3(2x + 4) + 2(x + 1)$

13 $5(3 + 2x) + 10x$

14 $6x + 3(2x + 3)$

15 $9 + 3(3x + 1)$

16 $5 + 4(2 + 3x)$

17 $5(3x + 2) + 3(x + 1) + 4x$

18 $x + 6(3x + 2)$

19 $4(x + 1) + 2x + 4(2x + 4)$

20 $6(2x + 3) + 3(3x + 4)$

21 $5x + 2(3x + 7) + 9$

Remove the brackets and simplify.

(a) $3(n + 3) - 2(n + 1)$

$= 3n + 9 - 2n - 2$

$= n + 7$

(b) $3(a + b) - 2(a - 2b)$

$= 3a + 3b - 2a + 4b$

$= a + 7b$

Exercise 2E

Remove the brackets and simplify.

1 $5(x + 2) + 3(x - 2)$

2 $4(3x + 1) + 2(2x - 1)$

3 $5(3x - 1) + 6(2x + 1)$

4 $4(n + 3) - 2(n + 1)$

5 $8(a + 1) - 3(a + 2)$

6 $7(m + 3) - 2(m - 1)$

7 $3(a + b) + 5(2a + b)$

8 $3(3a + b) - 2(a + b)$

9 $4(2a + b) - 2(a - b)$

10 $5(a - b) - 3(a - 2b)$

11 Jack has $3(2a + 4)$ coins. He spends $2(3 - a)$ coins. Write down and simplify an expression for the number of coins he now has.

Remove the brackets and simplify.

12 $5(2n + 1) - 3(n + 1)$

13 $7(3n + 2) - 2(4n - 3)$

14 $6(3m + 4) - 4(2 - m)$

15 $8(2y + 6) - 5(3y + 4)$

16 $4(6a + 4) - 2(7 - 3a)$

17 $6(4x + 9) - 2(5x + 4)$

Rules for solving equations

The main rule when solving equations is

‘Do the same thing to both sides’

You may *add* the same thing to both sides.
You may *subtract* the same thing from both sides.
You may *multiply* both sides by the same thing.
You may *divide* both sides by the same thing.

Solve the equations. The circles show what is done to both sides of the equation.

(a) $n + 5 = 12$
(-5) (-5)
$n = 7$

(b) $n - 7 = 11$
$(+7)$ $(+7)$
$n = 18$

(c) $2n + 3 = 15$
(-3) (-3)
$2n = 12$
$(\div 2)$ $(\div 2)$
$n = 6$

(d) $3n - 5 = 16$
$(+5)$ $(+5)$
$3n = 21$
$(\div 3)$ $(\div 3)$
$n = 7$

Exercise 3M

Solve the equations.

1   $n + 4 = 15$

2   $n + 6 = 14$

3   $n - 3 = 3$

4   $n - 4 = 21$

5   $8 + n = 50$

6   $20 = n + 3$

7   $7 + n = 27$

8   $0 = n - 4$

9   $5 = n - 41$

10   $27 = 8 + n$

11   $9 + n = 9$

12   $n - 14 = 17$

Solve these

13   $3a = 21$

14   $5m = 35$

15   $2n + 1 = 7$

16   $3x + 2 = 14$

17   $5y + 3 = 33$

18   $3m + 2 = 17$

19   $4p + 7 = 19$

20   $4n + 6 = 30$

21   $6y + 5 = 41$

22   $6n + 4 = 22$

23   $3m + 9 = 24$

24   $5a + 16 = 36$

Finally solve these equations

25 $6n - 7 = 17$

26 $5x - 3 = 7$

27 $4p - 9 = 23$

28 $3m - 4 = 11$

29 $2m - 11 = 9$

30 $3a - 5 = 10$

31 $31 = 7y + 3$

32 $14 = 3a - 1$

33 $5 + 3n = 11$

34 $21 = 9a - 6$

35 $8 + 4m = 8$

36 $30 = 6y - 12$

Equations with the unknown on both sides

(a) $2n + 3 = n + 7$

$(-n)\ (-n)$

$n + 3 = 7$

$(-3)\ (-3)$

$n = 4$

(b) $5n - 3 = 2n + 9$

$(-2n)\ (-2n)$

$3n - 3 = 9$

$(+3)\ (+3)$

$3n = 12$

$n = 4$

Exercise 3E

Solve the equations.

1 $6n + 4 = 3n + 19$

2 $4n + 2 = 2n + 8$

3 $7n + 1 = 4n + 13$

4 $10n - 3 = 7n + 21$

5 $8n + 6 = 4n + 30$

6 $6n - 5 = 4n + 15$

7 $5n - 4 = 2n + 2$

8 $9n - 10 = 4n + 10$

9 $4n - 17 = n + 10$

10 $7n + 9 = 5n + 21$

11 Ben has $(3n + 12)$ books and Megan has $(n + 52)$ books.
If they have an equal number of books, find the value of n.
How many books does Ben have?

Now solve these equations.

12 $7x + 1 = 6x + 8$

13 $4x + 3 = x + 9$

14 $6x - 1 = 3x + 8$

15 $3x + 7 = x + 15$

16 $5x - 4 = 2x + 5$

17 $1 + 3x = x + 2$

18 $4x - 11 = 2x + 11$

19 $6x = 3x + 24$

20 $5x - 4 = x$

21 $1 + 5x = 3x + 13$

Equations involving brackets

Remove the brackets first.

(a) $3(2x + 1) = 15$
$6x + 3 = 15$
$(-3) \quad (-3)$
$6x = 12$
$(\div 6) \quad (\div 6)$
$x = 2$

(b) $4(3x - 1) = 8$
$12x - 4 = 8$
$(+4) \quad (+4)$
$12x = 12$
$(\div 12) \quad (\div 12)$
$x = 1$

Exercise 4M

1. Copy and complete:

   (a) $3(n + 2) = 21$
   $3n + \boxed{} = 21$
   $3n = \boxed{}$
   $n = \boxed{}$

   (b) $5(2n - 6) = 30$
   $10n - \boxed{} = 30$
   $10n = \boxed{}$
   $n = \boxed{}$

Solve these equations.

2. $2(n + 1) = 10$
3. $2(n + 3) = 12$
4. $3(n + 4) = 21$
5. $3(n - 2) = 12$
6. $3(2n + 1) = 9$
7. $4(n - 2) = 8$
8. $5(n + 1) = 5$
9. $2(3n - 1) = 10$
10. $2(3n + 2) = 10$
11. $2(n + 3) = 12$
12. $4(n + 1) = 24$
13. $6(n + 2) = 54$

Now solve these.

14. $5(a + 1) = 20$
15. $3(m - 1) = 18$
16. $4(b + 3) = 20$
17. $3(2n + 3) = 39$
18. $14 = 2(3y + 1)$
19. $16 = 4(p - 2)$
20. $18 = 2(2m + 3)$
21. $5(2a + 2) = 10$
22. $3(2w - 7) = 3$

Exercise 4E

1. Copy and complete:

   (a) $4(n + 3) = 2(n + 11)$
   $4n + \boxed{} = 2n + \boxed{}$
   $2n = \boxed{}$
   $n = \boxed{}$

   (b) $3(3x - 2) = 2(2x + 7)$
   $9x - \boxed{} = 4x + \boxed{}$
   $5x = \boxed{}$
   $x = \boxed{}$

Solve these equations.

2 $3(n + 2) = 2(n + 5)$

3 $4(n + 1) = 3(n + 3)$

4 $2(n + 5) = n + 13$

5 $5(2n + 3) = 3(3n + 7)$

6 $6n - 10 = 2(n + 7)$

7 $3(n - 1) = 2(n + 6)$

Now solve these.

8 $5(x - 2) = 3(x + 2)$

9 $2(2x - 3) = 3(x + 7)$

10 $6(2x + 1) = 10x + 22$

11 $7(3x - 5) = 5(2x + 4)$

12 $5(5x + 2) = 2(3x + 5)$

13 $7(2x - 1) = 7$

14 $7(x - 3) = 2(2x + 3)$

15 $4(x + 2) = 3x + 10$

Trial and improvement

Exercise 5M

Use a calculator to find the answers to these questions by trying different numbers until you find the dimensions that give the required area.

1 In the 3 rectangles below, the length is *twice* the width. Find the dimensions of each rectangle.

(a)

area = 98 cm²

(b)

area = 12.5 cm²

(c)
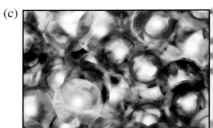
area = 9.68 cm²

2 For each picture below, the length is *three* times the width.
Find the dimensions of each rectangle.

(a)
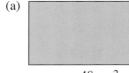
area = 48 cm²

(b)

area = 36.75 cm²

(c)

area = 3.63 cm²

3 In each rectangle below, the length is *1* cm *greater* than the width.
Find the dimensions of each rectangle.

(a)

area = 72 cm²

(b)

area = 210 cm²

(c)

area = 60.59 cm²

Sometimes we cannot find an *exact* answer. We can at least try out different numbers with a calculator until we get closer and closer to the answer.

 x

The area of the rectangle is 59 cm². Find the value of x to one decimal place which gives the area nearest to 59 cm².

$x + 3$

We guess first (the *trial*)

try $x = 7$ $x(x + 3) = 7 \times 10 = 70$ too large

We try a lower number (the *improvement*)

try $x = 6$ $x(x + 3) = 6 \times 9 = 54$ too small

try $x = 6.5$ $x(x + 3) = 6.5 \times 9.5 = 61.75$ too large

try $x = 6.3$ $x(x + 3) = 6.3 \times 9.3 = 58.59$ too small

try $x = 6.4$ $x(x + 3) = 6.4 \times 9.4 = 60.16$ too large

We want an answer of 59 so x must be between 6.3 and 6.4.

$x = 6.3$ gives an answer which is nearer than the answer given by $x = 6.4$.

Answer: $x = 6.3$ cm to 1 decimal place.

Exercise 5E

1    x

The area of this rectangle is 108 cm².

$x + 4$

Copy and complete this table to find x to one decimal place.

trial	calculation $x(x + 4)$	too large or too small?
$x = 8$	$8 \times 12 = \ldots$	too small
$x = 9$	$9 \times 13 = \ldots$	too large
$x = 8.5$	$8.5 \times 12.5 = \ldots$	too ....
$x = 8.6$	$8.6 \times 12.6 = \ldots$	too ....
So $x = \ldots$ cm to 1 decimal place		

180

2 The area of this rectangle is 50 cm².

x + 6

Copy and complete this table to find x to one decimal place.

trial	calculation $x(x+6)$	too large or too small?
$x = 5$	$5 \times 11 = \ldots$	too large
$x = 4$	$4 \times 10 = \ldots$	too small
$x = 4.5$	$4.5 \times 10.5 = \ldots$	too …
$x = 4.8$	$4.8 \times 10.8 = \ldots$	too …
$x = 4.6$	$4.6 \times 10.6 = \ldots$	too …
$x = 4.7$	$4.7 \times 10.7 = \ldots$	too …
So $x = \ldots$ cm to 1 decimal place		

3 Use trial and improvement for each rectangle below to find the value of x to 1 decimal place.

(a)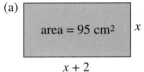

area = 95 cm² x

x + 2

(b)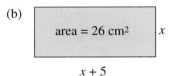

area = 26 cm² x

x + 5

(c)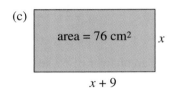

area = 76 cm² x

x + 9

4

The volume of this cube is 300 cm³.

Volume = $x \times x \times x = x^3$

Use trial and improvement to find x to 1 decimal place.

5 Use trial and improvement to solve these equations to 1 decimal place.

(a) $x^2 + x = 22$ (b) $x^2 - x = 47$

Problem solving

The length of a rectangle is three times its width. The perimeter is 40 cm.
Find the width of the rectangle.

Let the width be x.
So the length is $3x$.
From the equation:

$3x + x + 3x + x = 40$

$8x = 40$

$x = 5$

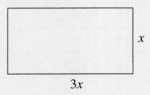

x

$3x$

So the width is 5 cm. [Check $5 + 15 + 5 + 15 = 40$ ✓]

Exercise 6M

In questions ① to ⑦ I am thinking of a number. Use the information to form an equation and then solve it to find the number.

① If we multiply the number by 3 and then add 1, the answer is 25.

② If we multiply the number by 10 and then subtract 3, the answer is 57.

③ If we multiply the number by 5 and then add 8, the answer is 68.

④ If we multiply the number by 4 and then subtract 3, the answer is 13.

⑤ If we double the number and add 7, the answer is 23.

⑥ If we treble the number and subtract 7, the answer is 14.

⑦ If we double the number and subtract 20, the answer is 22.

⑧ In the triangle, BC is twice as long as AB. AC is 9 cm long. If the perimeter is 24 cm, form an equation and solve it to find x.

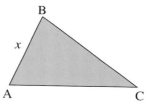

⑨ The sum of three consecutive numbers is 63. Let the first number be n and write down the other two numbers in terms of n. Find the three numbers.

⑩ The length of a photo is twice its width. The perimeter is 30 cm. Find the width.

⑪ The length of a rectangle is three times its width. If the perimeter is 32 cm, find its width. (Hint: let the width be x)

⑫ Form equations to find x.

(a)

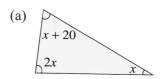

(b)

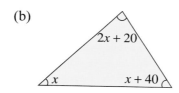

182

Exercise 6E

In questions 1 to 6 form an equation with brackets and then solve it to find the number.

1. If we add 3 to the number and then double the result, the answer is 140.

2. If we subtract 5 from the number and then treble the result, the answer is 15.

3. If we add 7 to the number and then multiply the result by 3, the answer is 36.

4. If we subtract 4 from the number and then multiply the result by 5, the answer is 15.

5. If we double the number, add 3 and then multiply the result by 4, the answer is 44.

6. If we double the number, subtract 5 and then multiply the result by 7, the answer is 7.

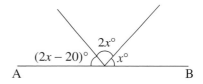

7. If AB is a straight line, form an equation involving x and solve it to find x.

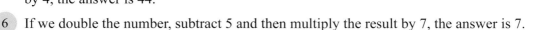

8. The sum of three consecutive numbers is 165. Find the three numbers.

9.
   $2x + 1$

   The rectangle has an area of 27 square units. Form an equation and solve it to find x.

   3

10. The total mass of three stones A, B and C is 60 kg.
    Stone B is twice as heavy as stone A.
    Stone C is 30 kg heavier than stone A.
    Find the mass of stone A. [Call it x kg.]

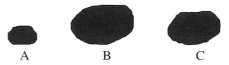

A   B   C

11.
    $x + 1$

    The perimeter of this rectangle is 40 cm. Find x and hence find the area of the rectangle.

    $3x - 1$

12. The angles in a triangle are $x°$, $(2x + 50)°$ and $70°$. Find the angles in the triangle.

13 In an arithmagon, the number in a square is the sum of the numbers in the two circles either side of it.

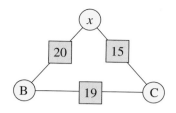

(a) Explain why the number in circle B is $20 - x$.

(b) Explain why the number in circle C is $15 - x$.

(c) Form an equation across the lowest side of the triangle. Solve the equation to find x.

14 Use the method above to find x in these arithmagons.

(a)

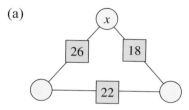

(b)

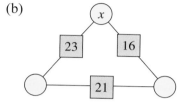

(c)

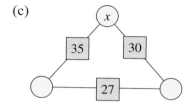

CHECK YOURSELF ON SECTIONS 4.3 AND 4.4

1   Interpreting and sketching real-life graphs

(a) The graph shows the water level when Simon has a bath.

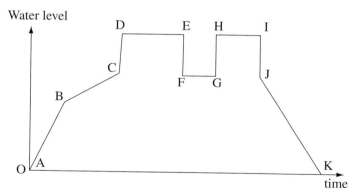

For JK the 'bath is being emptied'. Describe what is happening for each part of the graph. Here are some possibilities:

Simon gets out of bath	One tap is on

Bath is emptied	Simon lies in bath memorising maths formulas

Simon gets into bath	Two taps are on

Simon is out of bath looking for shampoo

(b) Draw a vertical axis which goes from 0 km to 60 km. Draw a horizontal axis which goes from the time 12:00 up to 16:00.

Draw a travel graph to show Helen's journey below.

'At 12:00 Helen leaves home and travels at a speed of 30 km/h. At 13:00 she stops for $\frac{1}{2}$ hour and then continues her journey at a speed of 60 km/h for the next $\frac{1}{2}$ hour. She then stops for $\frac{1}{4}$ hour. Finally she returns home at a speed of 60 km/h.'

(c) At what time did Helen arrive home?

2 Multiplying out single brackets

Expand (multiply out) and simplify when possible:

(a) $5(x - 4)$ (b) $3(4x + 2)$ (c) $n(n - 8)$

(d) $4(x + 3) + 7(x + 2)$ (e) $3(2x + 7) + 2(4x - 1)$

3 Solving linear equations

Solve these equations.

(a) $5n - 3 = 27$ (b) $4x + 3 = 2x + 15$ (c) $7n - 5 = 3n + 15$

4 Solving linear equations involving brackets

Solve these equations.

(a) $4(n + 3) = 36$ (b) $3(2x - 3) = 21$ (c) $6(2x + 3) = 2(5x + 13)$

5 Solving problems by trial and improvement

For each rectangle below, use trial and improvement to find x to one decimal place (use a calculator).

(a)

area = 30 cm^2 x

$x + 3$

(b)

area = 80 cm^2 x

$x + 5$

6 Forming equations to solve problems

(a)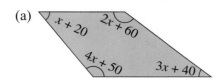

The angles in a quadrilateral add up to 360°.
Form an equation then use it to find the value of x.

(b) If I treble a number, take away 6 and then multiply the result by 2, the answer is 18. Find the number.

(c)

Triangle ABC is isosceles so the sides AB and BC are equal. Form an equation then use it to find the value of x. How long is side BC if all the measurements are in cm?

4.5 Fractions review

In section 4.5 you will:

- add and subtract fractions

- multiply fractions

- convert between fractions, decimals and percentages

Adding and subtracting fractions

Exercise 1M

1

A	C	D	E	F	I	M	N	O	R	S	T	W	Y
$\frac{2}{5}$	$\frac{1}{4}$	$\frac{3}{8}$	$\frac{7}{10}$	$\frac{5}{9}$	$\frac{1}{2}$	$\frac{1}{10}$	$\frac{2}{3}$	$\frac{3}{7}$	$\frac{2}{9}$	$\frac{3}{10}$	$\frac{3}{4}$	$\frac{5}{6}$	$\frac{3}{20}$

Cancel down each fraction below as far as possible. Find the matching letter in the table above. Rearrange the first four letters to make one word and the remaining letters to make another word.

$\boxed{\dfrac{18}{60}}$ $\boxed{\dfrac{6}{15}}$ $\boxed{\dfrac{6}{40}}$ $\boxed{\dfrac{21}{30}}$ $\boxed{\dfrac{27}{36}}$ $\boxed{\dfrac{9}{21}}$ $\boxed{\dfrac{35}{63}}$ $\boxed{\dfrac{13}{26}}$ $\boxed{\dfrac{45}{150}}$ $\boxed{\dfrac{12}{30}}$ $\boxed{\dfrac{9}{36}}$ $\boxed{\dfrac{10}{15}}$ $\boxed{\dfrac{16}{72}}$

2 Copy and fill in each empty box.

(a) $\dfrac{2}{3} = \dfrac{\square}{12}$

(b) $\dfrac{1}{4} = \dfrac{\square}{12}$

(c) $\dfrac{3}{5} = \dfrac{\square}{40}$

(d) $\dfrac{3}{8} = \dfrac{\square}{40}$

3 Answer true or false:

(a) $\dfrac{2}{3} + \dfrac{1}{4} = \dfrac{3}{7}$

(b) $\dfrac{3}{5} - \dfrac{3}{8} = \dfrac{9}{40}$

4   Work out the following, cancelling answers where possible.

(a) $\frac{1}{4} + \frac{2}{7}$ (b) $\frac{3}{8} + \frac{1}{6}$ (c) $\frac{5}{9} - \frac{2}{5}$ (d) $\frac{3}{4} - \frac{2}{9}$

(e) $\frac{7}{10} - \frac{3}{8}$ (f) $\frac{3}{20} + \frac{7}{10}$ (g) $\frac{8}{9} - \frac{3}{7}$ (h) $\frac{1}{8} + \frac{3}{11}$

5   Pete eats $\frac{1}{5}$ of a box of chocolates and his sister eats $\frac{3}{7}$ of the box of chocolates. What fraction of the box of chocolates has *not* been eaten?

6   Which problem below gives the odd answer out?

(a) $\frac{3}{10} + \frac{1}{20}$ (b) $\frac{1}{5} + \frac{1}{4}$ (c) $\frac{3}{4} - \frac{2}{5}$

Exercise 1E

1   Liz eats $\frac{4}{15}$ of a pear then her brother eats $\frac{5}{9}$ of the same pear. What fraction of the pear is left?

2   Josh and Lee each weigh the same amount. In April, Josh puts on $\frac{5}{8}$ of a stone and Lee puts on $\frac{1}{4}$ of a stone. In May, Josh loses $\frac{1}{3}$ of a stone and Lee puts on $\frac{1}{6}$ of a stone. Who weighs more by the end of May and by how much?

3   Work out, leaving each answer as a mixed number.

(a) $2\frac{1}{2} + \frac{3}{4}$ (b) $1\frac{1}{2} + \frac{2}{3}$ (c) $3\frac{1}{2} - 1\frac{3}{4}$

(d) $1\frac{1}{3} + 1\frac{1}{2}$ (e) $2\frac{1}{4} - \frac{3}{5}$ (f) $2\frac{2}{3} - 1\frac{3}{4}$

(g) $1\frac{2}{3} + 2\frac{1}{4}$ (h) $2\frac{1}{2} + 1\frac{5}{6}$ (i) $3\frac{1}{3} - 1\frac{4}{5}$

4   What fraction of this UK flag is white if $\frac{3}{8}$ of the flag is red and $\frac{1}{3}$ is blue?

5   Four of the fractions below have a total of $2\frac{1}{2}$. White down the four fractions.

 $\frac{3}{4}$ $\frac{5}{8}$ $1\frac{1}{3}$ $\frac{5}{6}$ $\frac{1}{12}$ $\frac{1}{3}$ $\frac{2}{5}$

Multiplying fractions

Exercise 2M

1. Which is larger? $\left(\frac{2}{3} \text{ of } 36 \right)$ or $\left(\frac{3}{5} \text{ of } 35 \right)$

2. Which is smaller? $\left(\frac{5}{8} \text{ of } 40 \right)$ or $\left(\frac{5}{6} \text{ of } 30 \right)$

3. There are 360° in a circle. If you turn from North to South-East in a clockwise direction, what angle do you turn?

4. Work out

    (a) $\frac{4}{9}$ of 63 (b) $\frac{2}{5}$ of 45 (c) $\frac{5}{7}$ of 42 (d) $\frac{9}{10}$ of 60

5.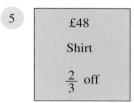

    | £48 Shirt $\frac{2}{3}$ off | £40 trousers $\frac{1}{4}$ off | £49 skirt $\frac{2}{7}$ off |

    Jane buys the cheapest item from those listed above. How much money will she have left over from £50?

6. Work out

    (a) $\frac{3}{20}$ of 1 metre (b) $\frac{7}{10}$ of 4 kg (c) $\frac{3}{5}$ of 1 hour

7. How many days are there in $\frac{4}{7}$ of a fortnight?

8. What angle does the minute hand turn through from 10:15 to 10:35?

Exercise 2E

1. Work out, cancelling when possible.

    (a) $\frac{3}{8} \times \frac{1}{5}$ (b) $\frac{5}{6} \times \frac{5}{7}$ (c) $\frac{4}{9} \times \frac{2}{5}$ (d) $\frac{6}{7} \times \frac{2}{3}$

    (e) $\frac{1}{7} \times \frac{2}{5}$ (f) $\frac{3}{10} \times \frac{5}{6}$ (g) $\frac{2}{3} \times \frac{1}{8}$ (h) $\frac{4}{5} \times \frac{3}{11}$

    (i) $\frac{7}{10} \times \frac{8}{9}$ (j) $\frac{5}{8} \times \frac{4}{5}$ (k) $\frac{1}{4} \times \frac{9}{10}$ (l) $\frac{7}{20} \times \frac{5}{6}$

2 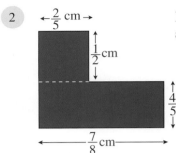 Find the total area of this shape by finding the area of each rectangle and adding them together.

3 Which is larger?

4 Work out, cancelling when possible.

(a) $\frac{3}{8} \times 12$ (b) $\frac{4}{9} \times 15$ (c) $\frac{3}{4} \times 6$ (d) $\frac{7}{10} \times 25$

5 Copy and complete:

(a) $3\frac{1}{2} \times \frac{2}{5}$

$= \frac{\square}{2} \times \frac{2}{5}$

$= \frac{\square}{10}$

$= \frac{\square}{5}$

$= \square\frac{\square}{5}$

(b) $2\frac{2}{3} \times 1\frac{1}{4}$

$= \frac{\square}{3} \times \frac{\square}{4}$

$= \frac{\square}{12}$

$= \frac{\square}{3}$

$= \square\frac{\square}{3}$

6 Marney had $2\frac{1}{2}$ loaves of bread. $\frac{3}{10}$ of this bread went rotten.

How many loaves of bread were fit to be eaten?

7 Work out

(a) $1\frac{3}{4} \times \frac{2}{3}$ (b) $2\frac{1}{2} \times \frac{3}{5}$ (c) $1\frac{2}{3} \times 2\frac{1}{4}$ (d) $3\frac{1}{4} \times 1\frac{1}{5}$

Changing fractions, decimals and percentages

Exercise 3M

1   Change the following to fractions, cancelling when possible.
(a) 0.03   (b) 0.15   (c) 32%   (d) 26%
(e) 0.94   (f) 3%   (g) 0.12   (h) 30%

2   Change the following to decimals.
(a) 17%   (b) $\frac{2}{5}$ (c) $\frac{3}{4}$ (d) 2%

(e) 48%   (f) 60%   (g) $\frac{9}{25}$ (h) $\frac{13}{20}$

3   Charlie scored $\frac{16}{25}$ in a Science test and Holly scored 62%. Who scored the higher mark?

4   Change the following to percentages.
(a) 0.8   (b) 0.08   (c) $\frac{7}{20}$ (d) $\frac{1}{4}$

(e) 0.36   (f) $\frac{19}{25}$ (g) $\frac{1}{3}$ (h) 0.2

Exercise 3E

1   Which is larger? $\boxed{\frac{17}{50}}$ or $\boxed{35\%}$

2   Write in order of size, smallest first.
(a) 30%, $\frac{9}{20}$, 0.28   (b) $\frac{7}{50}$, 0.2, 23%   (c) 0.38, $\frac{8}{25}$, 35%

3   0.2 of this pie graph is yellow. What *fraction* of
the pie graph is *not* yellow?

4   Use a calculator to change the following fractions to decimals.
(a) $\frac{6}{7}$ (b) $\frac{2}{3}$ (c) $\frac{5}{9}$ (d) $\frac{3}{11}$

5   Which of the following numbers are larger than 0.7?

$\boxed{\frac{36}{50}}$ $\boxed{0.08}$ $\boxed{\frac{17}{25}}$ $\boxed{69\%}$ $\boxed{\frac{3}{4}}$

6   Write in order of size, largest first.

$\boxed{82\%}$ $\boxed{\frac{17}{20}}$ $\boxed{0.8}$ $\boxed{0.09}$ $\boxed{\frac{3}{5}}$ $\boxed{\frac{30}{40}}$ $\boxed{73\%}$

4.6 Handling data

In section 4.6 you will:

- use two-way tables
- use grouped data
- use pie charts
- use scattergraphs

Two-way tables

Exercise IM

1

JANUARY	Max. Temperature	Hours of sunshine	Rainfall in mm
Vancouver	42	2	8
Rio de Janeiro	84	7	2
London	45	2	2

The table gives the expected weather in January for Vancouver,
Rio de Janeiro and London.

(a) Which city expects the most rainfall?

(b) Which city expects the most sunshine?

(c) What is the expected maximum temperature in London?

2 Jane, John and Joan all work in a restaurant. The tips they receive one week are recorded
below.

	Jane	John	Joan
Under £3	8	12	6
£3 to £5	17	14	20
Over £5	10	18	8

(a) How many tips between £3 and £5 did Joan receive?

(b) Who received the most tips this week?

3 The table shows the age at which one hundred mothers had their first child in 1950 and 2000.

	1950	2000
under 18	16	12
18 to 24	44	23
25 to 30	27	35
Over 30	13	30

How many mothers had their first child

(a) between the ages of 18 and 24 in 2000?

(b) between the ages of 25 and 30 in 1950?

(c) Write a sentence about any differences you notice between 1950 and 2000.

4 International dialling codes.

		To		
		France	Germany	UK	USA
	France	—	1949	1944	191
From	Germany	0033	—	0044	001
	UK	0033	0049	—	001
	USA	01133	01149	01144	—

What code would you need to dial

(a) from UK to Germany

(b) from France to the USA

(c) from the USA to UK?

5 How far is it from

(a) Berlin to Helsinki

(b) Amsterdam to Paris

(c) What would be the total distance of the round trip from Berlin to Paris on to Rome and back to Berlin?

Road distances in km

Amsterdam				
665	Berlin			
1205	505	Helsinki		
487	1047	1605	Paris	
1653	1476	2041	1399	Rome

Grouped data

Exercise 1E

1 A drug company claims that its new nutrient pill helps people to improve their memory.
As an experiment two randomly selected groups of people were given the same memory test.
Group A took the new pills for a month while group B took no pills.
Here are the results of the tests: (A high score indicates a good memory).

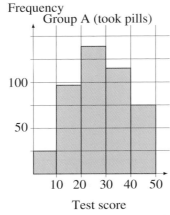

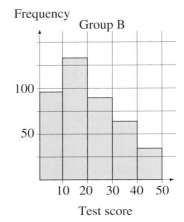

Does it appear that the new pills did in fact help to improve memory?

2 Here are the heights of the 21 members of a school swimming team
136.8, 146.2, 141.2, 147.2, 151.3, 145.0, 155.0,
149.9, 138.0, 146.8, 157.4, 143.1, 143.5, 147.2,
147.5, 158.6, 154.7, 144.6, 152.4, 144.0, 151.0.

(a) Put the heights into groups

class interval	frequency
$135 \leq h < 140$	
$140 \leq h < 145$	
$145 \leq h < 150$	

(b) Draw a frequency diagram like
those in question 1

↑ Frequency

135   140   height

3 Here is an age distribution pyramid
for the children at a Center Parcs resort.

(a) How many girls were there
aged 5–9?

(b) How many children were there
altogether in the 0–4 age range?

(c) How many girls were at the resort?

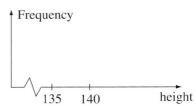

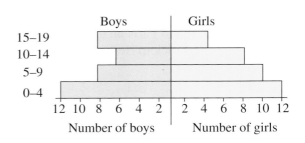

Exercise 3M

1. Here are the heights and masses of 9 people. Draw the axes shown and complete the scatter graph.

Name	Mass (kg)	Height (cm)
Alice	45	115
Fred	60	160
Jack	65	155
John	55	125
Percy	75	160
Hugh	75	170
Mabel	65	140
Diana	85	180
Cyril	52	146

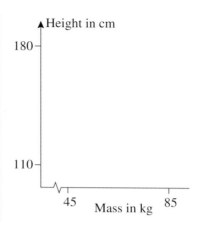

2. The scatter graph shows the number of hot drinks sold by a café and the outside temperature.

   (a) On how many days was it less than 12°C?

   (b) How many hot drinks were sold when it was 35°C?

   (c) On how many days were 40 or more hot drinks sold?

   (d) Fill the blank with either 'increases' or 'decreases': As temperature *increases* the number of drinks sold _____.

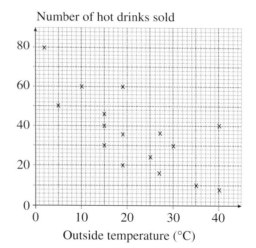

3. The graph shows the scores in a spelling test and the shoe sizes of 14 children.

   (a) How many take size 6 or less?

   (b) The pass mark is 4 or more. How many people failed?

   (c) Is there a connection between a person's shoe size and test score?

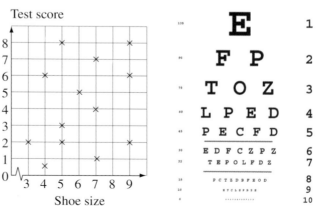

4. Decide on two pieces of data to get from each person in the class (agree this with your teacher). Draw a scatter graph to show this information. Can you see a connection between the two pieces of data?

Scatter graphs using a spreadsheet on a computer

Exercise 3E

1 Task: To plot a scatter graph showing the marks of 10 students in Maths and Science.

Enter the headings: *Maths* in A1, *Science* in B1
Enter the data as shown.

Now highlight all the cells from A2 to B11.
[Click on A1 and drag across and down to B11.]

Click on the ▭ chart wizard on the toolbar.

Select XY (Scatter) and select the picture which looks like a scatter graph.

	A	B
1	Maths	Science
2	23	30
3	45	41
4	73	67
5	35	74
6	67	77
7	44	50
8	32	41
9	66	55
10	84	70
11	36	32

Follow the on-screen prompts.

On 'Titles' enter: Chart title: Maths/Science results
                    Value (X) axis: Maths
                    Value (Y) axis: Science

Experiment with 'Axes', 'Gridlines', 'Legend' and 'Data Labels'.

2 Enter the data below on a spreadsheet and print a scatter graph. What does each scatter graph show?

(a)
Height	Armspan
162	160
155	151
158	157
142	144
146	148
165	163
171	167
148	150
150	147

(b)
Temperature	Sales
23	7
18	14
7	23
20	9
4	30
12	19
15	15
18	15
10	20

3 If time, find other data and create more scatter graphs.

CHECK YOURSELF ON SECTIONS 4.5 AND 4.6

1 Adding and subtracting fractions

Work out

(a) $\frac{3}{7} - \frac{1}{5}$

(b) $\frac{2}{5} + \frac{3}{8}$

(c) $2\frac{1}{4} + 1\frac{2}{3}$

2 Multiplying fractions

Work out

(a) $\frac{5}{8}$ of 56

(b) $\frac{3}{4} \times \frac{2}{9}$

(c) $\frac{3}{5} \times 7$

3 Changing fractions, decimals and percentages

Copy and complete the table:

fraction	decimal	percentage
	0.09	
$\frac{15}{50}$		
		80%
		4%
$\frac{13}{25}$		
	0.44	

4 Using two-way tables

The table shows how many children are in years 7, 8 and 9 in Henton High School.

(a) How many children are there in Year 9?

(b) How many boys are there in Year 8?

(c) How many girls are there in total?

	Year 7	Year 8	Year 9
boys	102	119	97
girls	106	94	110

5 Using grouped data

Here are age distribution pyramids for the U.K., Kenya and Saudi Arabia. The bars represent the percentage of the population in the age group shown.

(a) For the U.K. about what percentage of the population are *male aged 20–24*?

(b) For Kenya about what percentage are *female aged 0–4*?

(c) What percentage of the population are *female aged 75 +*

  (i) for the U.K.?

  (ii) for Kenya?

(d) Look carefully at the charts for the U.K. and Kenya. Write a sentence to describe the main differences in the age distribution for the two countries.

(e) Look carefully at the charts for Kenya and Saudi Arabia. Do both countries have about half male and half female populations?

6 Using pie charts

Meg asked 40 people what their favourite fruit was.
The table shows the information. Work out the angle
for each sector and then draw a pie chart to show the results.

Fruit	Frequency
peach	3
apple	8
strawberry	13
banana	5
pear	7
orange	4

7   Using scattergraphs

The scatter graph shows the heights and masses of some people.

(a) How many people were more than 150 cm tall?

(b) How many people weighed 60 kg or less?

(c) Answer *true* or *false*: 'In general as height increases, mass increases'.

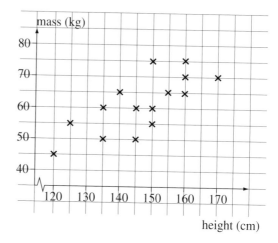

UNIT 4   MIXED REVIEW

Part one

1 These cards show the scores awarded by four judges in a diving contest.
   (a) Find the mean score.
   (b) Find the median score.
   (c) Write down the range of scores.

   | 6 | 3 | 7 | 4 |

2 Expand (multiply out)

   (a) $4(n + 3)$ (b) $m(n - 5)$ (c) $x(x + 2)$

3 Work out

   (a) $\frac{5}{7} - \frac{1}{4}$ (b) $\frac{3}{8} + \frac{3}{5}$ (c) $\frac{2}{3} + \frac{2}{9}$

4 Ben and Elaine each have 30 sweets.
   (a) Ben eats $\frac{2}{5}$ of his sweets. How many does he eat?
   (b) Elaine eats 5 of her sweet. What *fraction* of her sweets does she eat?

5 Martian creatures are either tripods or octopods. Tripods have three legs. Octopods have eight legs. The Martians, on a visit to Earth, have 60 legs between them. How many are tripods and how many are octopods? Find both possible solutions.

202

6   Solve these equations:

(a) $3x + 2 = 20$ (b) $6x - 1 = 29$ (c) $8 + 4x = 20$

7   The marks of 24 children in a test are shown.

32	15	43	20	47	55	63	51
47	22	49	58	37	12	68	26
35	38	31	19	26	52	49	19

Stem	Leaf
1	5
2	
3	2
4	3
5	
6	

Key
1 | 5 means 15

(a) Draw a stem and leaf diagram.
    The first three entries are shown.
(b) What is the range of the marks?
(c) What is the median mark?

8   Richard is three times as old as Frances. If Richard is also 30 years
    older than Frances, how old is Frances? (Hint: Let n be the age of
    Frances and form an equation)

9
x [rectangle]
$x + 4$

The area of this rectangle is 40 cm². Use trial
and improvement with a calculator to find the
value of x to 1 decimal place.

10 Some children collect 1500 sea shells. The shells weigh
    15.3 kg. Calculate the mean weight of a shell.

11 Work out

(a) $\frac{1}{4} \times \frac{3}{5}$ (b) $\frac{2}{3} \times 12$ (c) $\frac{3}{7} \times \frac{1}{6}$

12 This pie chart shows the energy resources available
    for a particular country.

(a) If $\frac{2}{9}$ of the resources are nuclear, what angle will
    be needed for nuclear in the pie chart?
(b) What angle will be needed for gas?

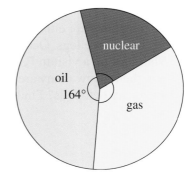

13 Copy the diagram.
Describe fully the following transformations:
(a) triangle 1 onto triangle 3
(b) triangle 1 onto triangle 5
(c) triangle 3 onto triangle 2

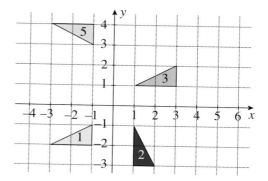

14 Solve these equations:

(a) $4(x + 1) = 20$ (b) $4(x - 2) = 20$ (c) $8(x + 5) = 56$

15 A dice was thrown 20 times. Here are the results.

Score on dice	1	2	3	4	5	6
Number of throws	3	1	5	5	2	4

Copy and complete : mean score $= \dfrac{(1 \times 3) + (2 \times 1) + (3 \times 5) + \ldots}{20}$

$$= \boxed{}$$

Part two

1 Put these numbers in order of size, starting with the smallest.

$0.4, \quad \dfrac{3}{5}, \quad \dfrac{1}{4}, \quad 45\%$

2 Solve these equations:

(a) $4n + 3 = 2n + 15$ (b) $5n - 1 = 2n + 17$ (c) $3(2n + 3) = 4n + 25$

3 David finds $\frac{5}{8}$ of his grandmother's favourite cake. He eats $\frac{1}{4}$ of this part of the cake.
What fraction of the original cake has he eaten?

4 (a) Copy the diagram onto squared paper.
(b) Use tracing paper to mark the centre of
the rotation which rotates shape A onto
shape B.
(c) Describe *fully* the rotation.

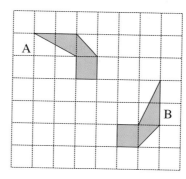

5 The scatter graphs show the sales of ice cream, soup and sandwiches on different days. Describe the connection, if any, between the sales of each product and the temperature.

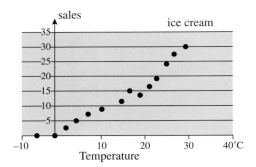

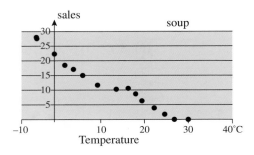

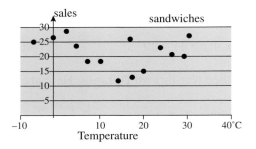

6 The total mass of five greyhounds is 76 kg. Calculate the mean mass of the dogs.

7 Expand and simplify

(a) $4(n + 2) + 3(2n + 5)$ (b) $4(2n + 5) - 3(n - 3)$

8 The pupils in a school were given a spelling test. Some of the results are given in the table

(a) Copy and complete the table with the missing entries.

(b) How many pupils passed the test in total?

	Passed	Failed	Total
Boys		311	589
Girls		257	
Total		568	914

9 A pie chart shows the contents of a Transport Museum.

(a) The sector for trams has an angle of 36°. What percentage of the whole pie chart is this sector?

(b) The sector for steam trains has an angle of 144°. What percentage of the whole pie chart is this sector?

10 Work out $\dfrac{1}{2} \times \dfrac{2}{3} \times \dfrac{3}{4} \times \dfrac{4}{5} \times \dfrac{5}{6} \times \dfrac{6}{7}$

11 Which is larger? $\frac{1}{2} + \frac{1}{5}$ or 0.8

12 The perimeter of this triangle is 38 cm. Form an equation involving x then use it to find the length of AC (all lengths are in cm).

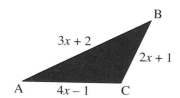

13 Find the missing numbers

(a)
```
    6  7  ☐
    3  ☐  2
+   ☐  1  9
───────────
☐   8  7  5
```

(b)
```
   ☐  0  7  3
   1  ☐  6  2
+  4  5  ☐  2
──────────────
   8  2  1  ☐
```

14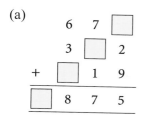

The coins in a box have the following values in pence.

5   1   2   10   50   20   5   5   1   1

100   2   10   5   5   2   2   2   200   50

For these coins find   (a) the mean value

                      (b) the median value

15 Kerry and Felix arrange a Charity concert. They charge £3.50 per person. The graph below shows the times at which people arrive at the concert.

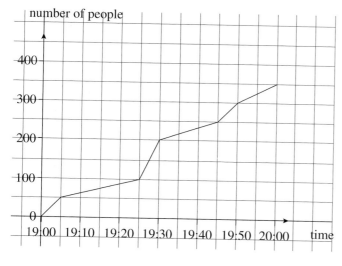

(a) How much money has been taken by 19:45?

(b) Kerry and Felix want to collect £700 for their Charity. The cost of the concert is £500. Do they collect enough money to meet their target?

Puzzles and Problems 4

1. The totals for the rows and columns are given. Find the values of the letters.

(a)

W	Y	X	Z	24
Y	Y	Y	Y	36
Z	Y	X	X	26
X	Z	Y	W	24
24	30	32	24	

(b)

E	D	E	C	E	45
A	B	D	C	E	41
E	C	E	C	E	41
D	A	C	C	A	33
E	E	D	C	C	43
42	41	47	35	38	

(c) Find P, Q, R, S and find the letter hidden by an ink blot.

S	Q	R	S	42
Q	Q	Q	Q	36
Q	Q	●	S	44
S	Q	P	R	41
44	36	41	42	

(d) This one is more difficult

A	B	B	A	38
A	A	B	B	38
A	B	A	B	38
B	B	A	B	49
27	49	38	49	

2. The symbols ɣ, ↑, !, ⊖, ⊥ each stand for one of the digits 1, 2, 3, 5 or 9 but not in that order. Use the clues below to work out what number each symbol stands for.

(a) ↑ × ↑ = ⊥

(b) ⊖ × ↑ = ↑

(c) ⊖ + ⊖ = ɣ

(d) ɣ + ↑ = !

3 The ten symbols below each stand for one of the digits 0, 1, 2, 3, 4, 5, 6, 7, 8 or 9 but not in that order.

♪ ▽▽ □ ⊙ ↑ ∗ ⧄ △ ⦶ ⊠

Use the clues below to work out what number each symbol stands for.

(a) ♪ + ♪ + ♪ + ♪ + ♪ = ▽▽

(b) ▽▽ + ⊠ = ▽▽

(c) ▽▽ + ♪ = ⊙

(d) ⦶ + ⦶ + ⦶ + ⦶ = ↑

(e) ∗ × ∗ = ⧄

(f) ⊙ – ⦶ = △

(g) ∗ + △ = □

4 Here is a 5 × 5 square cut into 8 smaller squares.

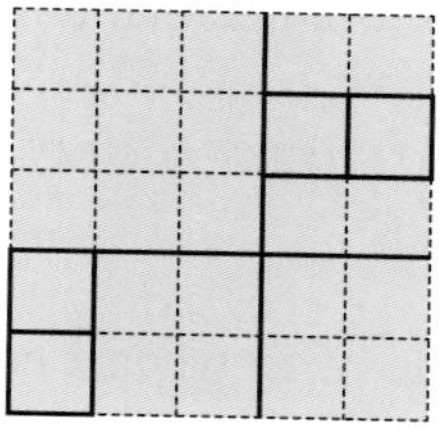

(a) Cut up a 7 × 7 square into 9 smaller squares.

(b) Cut up a 9 × 9 square into 10 smaller squares but you can use only one 3 × 3 square.

5

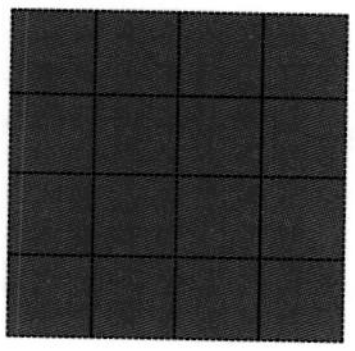

Fill up the square with the numbers 1, 2, 3, 4 so that each number appears only once in every row and column.

[You can have the same numbers in any diagonals.]

6 Fill up the square with the numbers 1, 2, 3, 4 so that each number appears only once in every row, column and *main* diagonal.

The main diagonals are marked: AC and BD. [You can repeat a number on a 'short' diagonal, as shown.]

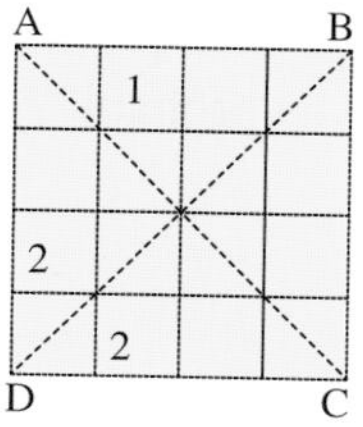

Mental Arithmetic Practice

Ideally a teacher will read out each question twice, with pupils' books closed.

- *Allow 5 seconds to answer each of*
  questions (1) *to* (6)

(1) What is half of the total of 18 and 22.

(2) Change one hundred and forty millimetres into centimetres.

(3) What is sixty-three divided by nine ?

(4) If $3n = 12$, write down the value for n.

(5) Write $\frac{14}{21}$ in its simplest form.

(6) Write four fifths as a decimal number.

- *Allow 10 seconds to answer each of*
  questions (7) *to* (20)

(7) What is the value of $5x$ when x equals six?

(8) A TV film starts at five minutes to seven. It lasts forty-five minutes. At what time does the film finish?

(9) What is one hundred and forty minus eighty?

(10) On a coach there are fifty pupils. Thirty of the pupils are girls. A pupil is chosen at random. What is the probability that a girl is chosen?

(11) What is 5% of 260?

(12) Ten per cent of a number is eight. What is the number?

(13) A pond is fifteen feet long. About how many metres is that?

(14) Write the number two and a half million in figures.

(15) If $x - 3 = 30$, work out the value of $2x$.

(16) Two angles in a triangle are 80° and 55°. How large is the other angle in the triangle?

(17) Estimate the value of fifty-two per cent of sixteen pounds ninety pence.

(18) How many halves are there altogether in four and a half?

(19) What is five hundred minus forty-five?

(20) n stands for number. Write an expression for the following: 'add six to n, then multiply the result by three'.

- *Allow 15 seconds to answer each of*
  questions (21) *to* (30)

(21) Pete and Bob share some money in the ratio of one to two. Pete's share is fifteen pounds. How much money is Bob's share?

(22) What is one quarter of two hundred thousand?

(23) Write two consecutive numbers that add up to thirty-five.

(24) What is the value of eleven squared plus three squared?

(25) Divide twenty-two pounds between four people. How much money does each person get?

(26) Work out an approximate answer for 41.22×9.87

(27) Find n if two time n minus one equals eleven.

(28) The marks for four pupils in a test are 1, 3, 4 and 4. What is the mean mark?

(29) Work out three plus four plus five, all squared.

(30) A man's heart beats 80 times in 1 minute. How many times does it beat in one hour?

A long time ago!   4

Perfect numbers

| 496 | What a perfect number! |

The factor pairs of 496 are 1, 496

2, 248

4, 124

8, 62

16, 31

Ignore the number (496) itself. Add up all the other factors.

$1 + 2 + 4 + 8 + 16 + 31 + 62 + 124 + 248 =$ (496)

> A number is perfect if it is equal to the sum of its factors (excluding itself).

The ancient Greeks looked very closely at perfect numbers to help them although there are not many perfect numbers which have been found.

Exercise

1   Find all the factors of 6 then show that 6 is a perfect number.

2   Find out if any of the numbers 24, 25, 26, 27, 28 or 29 are perfect by finding factors and adding them up.

Your answer to this question should be the number of days between a new full moon. Hundreds of years ago people felt that the *perfection* of the universe was shown by this period for the moon.

3   Find out if any of the numbers between 10 and 20 are perfect.

4   **RESEARCH:**

(a) The number 33550336 is a perfect number. Find at least two more perfect numbers.

(b) Find out what is meant by 'abundant' and 'deficient' numbers.

UNIT 5

5.1 Ratio and Proportion

In section 5.1 you will:

● use ratios

● tackle problems involving direct proportion

● use map scales

Reminder: we use ratio to compare parts of a whole.

In a mixed class of 32 children, 17 are girls.
There must be 15 boys.
The ratio girls:boys is 17:15

Reminder: ratios can sometimes be written in a simpler form.

The ratios 6:10 and 3:5 are the same (divide by 2)
The ratios 15:20:30 and 3:4:6 are the same (divide by 5)

Exercise 1M

In questions (1) to (4), make sure that your answers are in their simplest form.

(1) In a hall there are 45 chairs and 9 tables. Find the ratio of chairs to tables.

(2) In a class of 24 children, 8 are boys. Write down the ratio boys:girls.

(3) In a room there are 18 women and 16 men. Find the ratio of women to men.

(4) In an office there are twice as many men as women. Write down the ratio men:women.

(5) In a group of people, the ratio of red umbrellas to other colours is 1:5. If there are 4 red umbrellas, how many umbrellas of a different colour are there?

6 Write these ratios in a more simple form.
   (a) 15:10   (b) 15:25   (c) 20:80
   (d) 44:40   (e) 40:25   (f) 18:24

7 In a shop, the ratio of apples to pears is 5:2. If there are 200 pears, how many apples are there?

8 A factory produces mainly cars but also the occasional washing machine! The ratio of cars to washing machines is 5:1. One day 400 cars were made. How many washing machines were produced?

9 Write these ratios in a more simple form.
   (a) 9:6:12   (b) 40:5:15   (c) 12:10:8
   (d) 18:12:18   (e) 70:10:50   (f) 14:7:35

10 In a box, the ratio of apples to peaches to bananas is 3:1:2. If there are 8 peaches, how many apples are there and how many bananas are there?

11 In a firm, the ratio of women to men is 3:2. If there are 14 men, how many women are there?

12 On a farm, the ratio of cows to sheep to pigs is 3:4:5. If there are 35 pigs, how many sheep are there and how many cows are there?

13 On a Saturday the football results gave a ratio of home wins to away wins to draws of 6:2:1. If there were 10 away wins, how many home wins were there and how many draws were there?

14 Find the ratio (coloured area) : (uncoloured area) for each diagram.

(a) 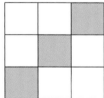   (b) 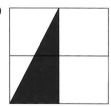   (c)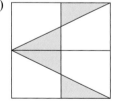

Ratio and sharing

Share £63 between Ann, Ben and Carol in the ratio 2:3:4. The ratio 2:3:4 means we are dividing into '2 + 3 + 4' = 9 shares. £63 is split into 9 shares so 1 share = £63 ÷ 9 = £7.

Ann gets 2 shares × £7 = £14

Ben gets 3 shares × £7 = £21

Carol gets 4 shares × £7 = £28

[Check: 14 + 21 + 28 = 63✓]

Exercise 1E

1. Will and Chloe share a prize of £60 in the ratio 3:1. How much does each person receive?

2. Alex and Debbie share a bag of 30 sweets in the ratio 3:2. How many sweets does each person get?

3. Share each quantity in the ratio given.

   (a) 54 cm, 4:5   (b) £99, 4:7   (c) 132 km, 6:5

   (d) £36, 2:3:4   (e) 200 kg, 5:2:3   (f) £2000, 1:9

4. Two hungry dogs share a meal weighing 650 g in the ratio 7:3. Find the larger share.

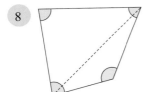

5. Kate and Connor share 72 marbles in the ratio 4:5. How many marbles does Connor get?

6. Find the largest share in each of these problems

   (a) £56, ratio 3:5

   (b) 90 kg, ratio 7:2

   (c) 240 m, ratio 3:4:3

7. The angles in a triangle are in the ratio 3:1:2. Find the size of the three angles.

8. The angles in a quadrilateral are in the ratio 2:2:3:2. Find the largest angle in the quadrilateral.

9. Find the smallest share in each of these problems

   (a) £60, ratio 1:11

   (b) 48 cm, ratio 2:1

   (c) 42 litres, ratio 2:3:2

10. Mrs. Turner gives Sam and Robyn £360 in the ratio 1:3. Mr. Harris gives Alana, Bill and Julie £320 in the ratio 2:1:5. A digital camera costs £197.50. Sam and Alana want to put their money together to buy the camera. They do not have enough money so Robyn gives them the rest of the money for the camera. How much money does Robyn have to give them?

11 In a kitchen, the ratio of forks to spoons is 7:9. If there are 45 spoons, how many forks are there?

12 Baldeep, Millie and Mike work for a number of hours in the ratio 7:3:2. Baldeep worked for 42 hours which was the most. How many hours did Millie and Mike work for in total?

13 Gary and Ning share some sweets in the ratio 5:3. If Ning gets 21 sweets, how many sweets do they share out in total?

14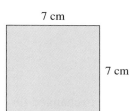

Two squares are shown.

(a) Write down the ratio of the lengths of their sides.

(b) Work out the ratio of their areas.

Direct proportion

If 10 calculators cost £63.50, find the cost of 3.

Find the cost of 1 calculator and then find the cost of 3.

10 calculators cost £63.50

1 calculator costs £63.50 ÷ 10 = £6.35

3 calculators cost £6.35 × 3 = £19.05

Exercise 2M

You may use a calculator.

1 Find the cost of 4 cakes if 7 cakes cost £10.50.

2 Magazines cost £20 for 8. Find the cost of 3 magazines.

3 If 5 hammers cost £23, find the cost of 7.

4 11 discs cost £13.20. Find the cost of 4 discs.

5  During a snowstorm there are 474 cars in a 3 mile traffic jam. About how many cars are there in an 8 mile jam?

6 A worker takes 8 minutes to make 2 circuit boards. How long would it take to make 9 circuit boards?

7   The total weight of 8 tiles is 1720 g. How much do 17 tiles weigh?

8   A machine can fill 3000 bottles in 15 minutes. How many bottles will it fill in 2 minutes?

9   If 4 grapefruit can be bought for £2.96, how many can be bought for £8.14?

10    Carl and Simone jet ski 25 km in 30 minutes. How long will they take to jet ski 40 km at the same speed?

11   £15 can be exchanged for 18 euros. How many euros can be exchanged for £37.50?

12   A car travels 280 km on 35 litres of petrol. How much petrol is needed for a journey of 440 km?

13   Usually it takes 10 hours for 4 men to build a wall. How many men are needed to build a wall twice as big in 10 hours?

14

christmas	decorations
baubles	£10.20 for 12
candles	£18.60 for 20
angels	£8 for 5

The prices of some Christmas decorations are shown opposite. Jim needs to buy 8 baubles and 12 candles. He also wants to buy as many angels as possible with the rest of his money. He has £20 to spend. How many angels can he buy with his left-over money?

Map scales

On a map of scale 1:2 000 000, Swansea and Cardiff appear 3 cm apart.

What is the actual distance between the towns?

1 cm on map = 2000 000 cm on land.

3 cm on map = 3 × 2000 000 cm on land.

6 000 000 cm = 60 000 m

          = 60 km

Swansea is 60 km from Cardiff.

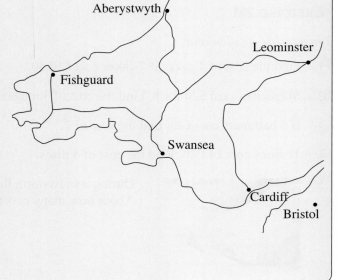

Exercise 2E

1. On a map whose scale is 1:1000, the distance between two houses is 3 cm. Find the actual distance between the two houses, giving your answer in metres.

2. The distance on a map between two points is 8 cm. Find the actual distance in metres between the two points, given that the scale of the map is 1:100.

3. The scale of a certain map is 1:10 000. What is the actual distance in metres between two churches which are 4 cm apart on the map?

4. On a map whose scale is 1:100 000, the distance between two villages is 7 cm. What is the actual distance in kilometres between the two villages?

5. The distance on a map between two towns is 9 cm. Find the actual distance in kilometres between the two towns, given that the scale of the map is 1:1 000 000.

6. Find the actual distance in metres between two towers which are 5 cm apart on a map whose scale is 1:10 000.

7. A river is 5 cm long on a map whose scale is 1:20 000. Find the actual length of the river.

8. The distance on a map between two buildings in Miami is 3 cm. The scale of the map is 1:50000. What is the actual distance between the two buildings in kilometres?

9. Two places are separated by a distance of 20 cm on a map having a scale of 1:6000. How far apart in reality are the two places?

10. The scale of a map is 1:200 000. What is the actual distance between two villages given that they are 8.5 cm apart on the map?

11. If two towns are 5.4 cm apart on a map and the scale of the map is 1:3 000 000, what is the actual distance between the two towns?

12. Andrew finds that the distance between two cities on a map whose scale is 1:5 000 000 is 12 cm. What is the actual distance in kilometres between the two cities?

13. If the distance between two places on a map is 10 cm, find the actual distance in kilometres between the two places, given that the scale of the map is 1:10 000.

14. Sandra has two maps. There are train stations in Manley and Cowton. Map A has a scale of 1:20 000 and shows that Sandra is 17.5 cm from Manley. Map B has a scale of 1:50 000 and shows that Sandra is 6 cm from Cowton. Which train station should Sandra head for if she wants to walk the least distance? *Explain your answer.*

5.2 Negative numbers review

In section 5.2 you will:

- add and subtract negative numbers

- multiply and divide negative numbers

Adding and subtracting

Reminder:
$$-3 - (-1)$$
$$= -3 + 1$$
$$= -2$$

$$4 - (+7)$$
$$= 4 - 7$$
$$= -3$$

$$6 + (-7)$$
$$= 6 - 7$$
$$= -1$$

$$-3 + (-2)$$
$$= -3 - 2$$
$$= -5$$

Exercise 1M

1 Work out

(a) $5 + (-6)$ (b) $2 - (-4)$ (c) $1 - (-4)$ (d) $-4 - 2$

(e) $8 - (+5)$ (f) $-1 + (-3)$ (g) $-5 - (-3)$ (h) $2 + (-6)$

(i) $-3 - (-6)$ (j) $6 - (+8)$ (k) $-4 + (-1)$ (l) $-7 - (-4)$

2 Copy and complete this addition square.

+	−3			−5
−2		−3		
		5		
−4	2			
				2

3 Find the value of each expression below if $m = -4$

$$n = 5$$
$$p = -6$$

(a) $m + n$ (b) $m - p$ (c) $n - m$ (d) $m + p$ (e) $n - p + m$

4 A golfer has the following scores at 6 holes.

$-1, +1, +1, 0, -2, -1$

What is the total score for this golfer?

5 Copy and complete each number chain.

(a)

(b)
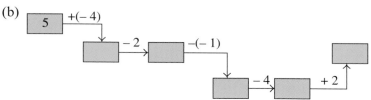

(c)

Multiplying and dividing

Reminder: $4 \times (-3) = -12$ $-2 \times 8 = -16$ $-4 \times (-4) = 16$

$20 \div (-5) = -4$ $-24 \div 4 = -6$ $-40 \div (-5) = 8$

Exercise 1E

1 Answer true or false.

(a) $4 \times (-5) = -20$ (b) $-3 \times (-6) = -18$ (c) $-2 \times (-4) = 8$

(d) $-5 \times 2 = -10$ (e) $4 \times (-8) = 32$ (f) $-3 \times (-5) = 15$

2 Copy and complete this multiplication square.

$\times$		-5	6	
-3				
		-20		-28
8				
-9	18			

3 Find the value of each expression below if $w = -3$, $x = -7$, $y = 0$

(a) wx (b) $4x$ (c) $6w$ (d) w^2 (e) $3w + x$

(f) $2x - w$ (g) xy (h) x^2 (i) $w + 3x$ (j) wxy

4　The midnight temperatures during one week on a mountain road are shown below:

$-6°C, -3°C, -5°C, -1°C, -6°C, -8°C, -6°C$

Find the mean average temperature.

5　Find the missing numbers

(a) $5 \times \boxed{} = -50$

(b) $30 \div (-5) = \boxed{}$

(c) $\boxed{} \times (-6) = 42$

(d) $-36 \div 9 = \boxed{}$

(e) $-60 \div \boxed{} = -6$

(f) $\boxed{} \div (-3) = -2$

(g) $-54 \div (-6) = \boxed{}$

(h) $-4 \times \boxed{} = 28$

(i) $48 \div \boxed{} = -6$

5.3 Sequences – the nth term

In section 5.3 you will:

● find the nth term of arithmetic sequences

(a) For the sequence 4, 8, 12, 16, 20,….. the rule is 'add 4'.

Here is the *mapping diagram* for the sequence.

Term number (n)		Term
1	$\longrightarrow$	4
2	$\longrightarrow$	8
3	$\longrightarrow$	12
4	$\longrightarrow$	16
⋮		⋮
10	$\longrightarrow$	40
⋮		⋮
n	$\longrightarrow$	$4n$

The terms are found by multiplying the term number by 4.

So the 10th number is 40, the 20th term is 80.

A *general* term in the sequence is the nth term, where n stands for any number.

The nth term of this sequence is $4n$.

(b) Here is a more difficult sequence: 4, 7, 10, 13,…..

The rule is 'add 3' so, in the mapping diagram, we have written a column for 3 times the term number [i.e. $3n$].

Term number (n)		$3n$		Term
1	$\longrightarrow$	3	$\longrightarrow$	4
2	$\longrightarrow$	6	$\longrightarrow$	7
3	$\longrightarrow$	9	$\longrightarrow$	10
4	$\longrightarrow$	12	$\longrightarrow$	13

We see that each term is 1 more than $3n$.

So, the 10th term is $(3 \times 10) + 1 = 31$

the 15th term is $(3 \times 15) + 1 = 46$

the nth term is $(3 \times n) + 1 = 3n + 1$

Exercise 1M

1 Copy and complete these mapping diagrams.

(a)

Term number (n)		Term
1	$\longrightarrow$	6
2	$\longrightarrow$	12
3	$\longrightarrow$	18
4	$\longrightarrow$	24
⋮		⋮
12	$\longrightarrow$	☐
⋮		⋮
n	$\longrightarrow$	☐

(b)

Term number (n)		Term
1	$\longrightarrow$	8
2	$\longrightarrow$	16
3	$\longrightarrow$	24
4	$\longrightarrow$	32
⋮		⋮
8	$\longrightarrow$	☐
⋮		⋮
n	$\longrightarrow$	☐

(c)

Term number (n)		Term
1	$\longrightarrow$	10
2	$\longrightarrow$	20
3	$\longrightarrow$	30
⋮		⋮
15	$\longrightarrow$	☐
⋮		⋮
n		☐

2 Copy and complete these mapping diagrams. Notice that an extra column has been written.

(a)

Term number (n)		$4n$		Term
1	$\longrightarrow$	4	$\longrightarrow$	5
2	$\longrightarrow$	8	$\longrightarrow$	9
3	$\longrightarrow$	12	$\longrightarrow$	13
4	$\longrightarrow$	16	$\longrightarrow$	17
⋮		⋮		⋮
20	$\longrightarrow$	☐	$\longrightarrow$	☐
⋮		⋮		⋮
n	$\longrightarrow$	$4n$	$\longrightarrow$	☐

(b)

Term number (n)		$5n$		Term
1	$\longrightarrow$	5	$\longrightarrow$	4
2	$\longrightarrow$	10	$\longrightarrow$	9
3	$\longrightarrow$	15	$\longrightarrow$	14
4	$\longrightarrow$	20	$\longrightarrow$	19
⋮		⋮		⋮
12	$\longrightarrow$	☐	$\longrightarrow$	☐
⋮		⋮		⋮
n	$\longrightarrow$	☐	$\longrightarrow$	☐

(c)

Term number (n)		$2n$		Term
1	$\longrightarrow$	2	$\longrightarrow$	3
2	$\longrightarrow$	4	$\longrightarrow$	5
3	$\longrightarrow$	6	$\longrightarrow$	7
4	$\longrightarrow$	8	$\longrightarrow$	9
⋮		⋮		⋮
10	$\longrightarrow$	☐	$\longrightarrow$	☐
⋮		⋮		⋮
n	$\longrightarrow$	☐	$\longrightarrow$	☐

(d)

Term number (n)		$5n$		Term
1	$\longrightarrow$	5	$\longrightarrow$	7
2	$\longrightarrow$	10	$\longrightarrow$	12
3	$\longrightarrow$	15	$\longrightarrow$	17
4	$\longrightarrow$	20	$\longrightarrow$	22
⋮		⋮		⋮
20	$\longrightarrow$	☐	$\longrightarrow$	☐
⋮		⋮		⋮
n	$\longrightarrow$	☐	$\longrightarrow$	☐

3 Here you are given the *n*th term. Copy and complete the diagrams.

(a)

Term number (*n*)	7*n*	Term
1 ⟶	7 ⟶	8
2 ⟶	☐ ⟶	☐
3 ⟶	☐ ⟶	☐
4 ⟶	☐ ⟶	☐
⋮	⋮	⋮
n ⟶	7*n* ⟶	7*n* + 1

(b)

Term number (*n*)	3*n*	Term
1 ⟶	3 ⟶	1
2 ⟶	☐ ⟶	☐
3 ⟶	☐ ⟶	☐
4 ⟶	☐ ⟶	☐
⋮	⋮	⋮
n ⟶	3*n* ⟶	3*n* − 2

(c)

Term number (*n*)	5*n*	Term
1 ⟶	5 ⟶	☐
2 ⟶	☐ ⟶	☐
3 ⟶	☐ ⟶	☐
8 ⟶	☐ ⟶	☐
⋮		
n ⟶	5*n* ⟶	5*n* + 1

(d)

Term number (*n*)	10*n*	Term
1 ⟶	☐ ⟶	☐
2 ⟶	☐ ⟶	☐
5 ⟶	☐ ⟶	☐
10 ⟶	☐ ⟶	☐
⋮		
n ⟶	10*n* ⟶	10*n* + 1

Exercise 1E

1 Copy and complete:

(a) 5, 9, 13, 17, . . .　　　n^{th} term = 4*n* + ☐

(b) 3, 5, 7, 9, . . .　　　n^{th} term = 2*n* + ☐

(c) 2, 7, 12, 17, . . .　　　n^{th} term = 5*n* − ☐

(d) 4, 11, 18, 25, . . .　　　n^{th} term = 7*n* − ☐

(e) 7, 10, 13, 16, . . .　　　n^{th} term = 3*n* + ☐

2 Groups of people form a circle.

After 1 minute there are 6 people.

After 2 minutes there are 11 people.

After 3 minutes there are 16 people.

After 4 minutes there are 21 people.

(a) How many people do you expect in the circle after 5 minutes ?

(b) Which of the following is true?

'After *n* minutes there will be (5*n* + 4) people' *or*

'After *n* minutes there will be (5*n* + 1) people'

3   Write down each sequence and select the correct expression for the nth term from the list given.

(a) $3, 6, 9, 12, \ldots$
(b) $5, 10, 15, 20, \ldots$
(c) $1^2, 2^2, 3^2, 4^2, \ldots$
(d) $7, 14, 21, 28, \ldots$
(e) $2, 3, 4, 5, 6, \ldots$
(f) $5, 8, 11, 14, 17, \ldots$
(g) $1, 3, 5, 7, 9, \ldots$

$3n$ $n + 1$

$7n$ $2n - 1$

n^2 $5n$ $3n + 2$

4   This table can seat 6 people.

The diagrams below show how many people can be seated when tables are joined together.

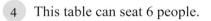

$n = 1$ $n = 2$ $n = 3$

(a) Draw the diagram for 4 tables.

(b) Write down how many people sit at 1 table, 2 tables, 3 tables and 4 tables.

(c) How many people would sit at 5 tables?

(d) Copy and fill in the empty box:

'The number of people sitting at n tables is $4n + \square$'

(e) *Discuss* with your teacher *why* the rule in part (d) works.

5

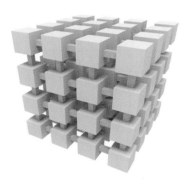

A mesh is made from cubes as shown. Several different sizes are made. The number of cubes used each time is shown below:

$1, 8, 27, 64, 125, \ldots$

Which of the rules below works for this sequence?

$n + 7$ $n^2 + 4$ n^3 $n^2 - 1$

Finding the nth term

In an *arithmetic* sequence the difference between each pair of terms is always the same number.

3, 11, 19, 27, 35, . . .

the difference between each pair of terms is 8

each number is called a term

The nth term is always of the form $an + b$
where a is the *difference* between each pair of terms.

The difference here is 8 so $a = 8$.

Put the sequence in a table and write a column for $8n$.

We can see that the term is always 5 less than $8n$ so $b = -5$.

The nth term is $8n - 5$.

n	$8n$	term
1	8	3
2	16	11
3	24	19
4	32	27

Exercise 2M

1. Look at the sequence 5, 9, 13, 17, . . .
   The difference between terms is 4.
   Copy the table, which has a column for $4n$.
   Copy and complete: 'The nth term of the sequence is $4n + \boxed{}$.'

n	$4n$	term
1	4	5
2	8	9
3	12	13
4	16	17

2. Look at the sequence and the table underneath. Find the nth term in each case.

   (a) Sequence 7, 10, 13, 16, . . .

n	$3n$	term
1	3	7
2	6	10
3	9	13
4	12	16

   nth term = $\boxed{}$

   (b) Sequence 4, 9, 14, 19, . . .

n	$5n$	term
1	5	4
2	10	9
3	15	14
4	20	19

   nth term = $\boxed{}$

3 In the sequence 6, 10, 14, 18, . . .
the difference between terms is 4.
Copy and complete the table and write
an expression for the *n*th term of the sequence.

n		term
1	□	6
2	□	10
3	□	14
4	□	18

4 Look at the sequence 5, 8, 11, 14, . . .

Write down the difference between terms.

Make a table like the one in question (3) and use it to find an expression for the *n*th term.

5 Write down each sequence in a table and then find the *n*th term.
(a) 8, 10, 12, 14, 16, . . .
(b) 3, 7, 11, 15, . . .
(c) 8, 13, 18, 23, . . .

6 Make a table for each sequence and write the *n*th term.
(a) 11, 19, 27, 35, . . .
(b) $2\frac{1}{2}, 4\frac{1}{2}, 6\frac{1}{2}, 8\frac{1}{2}, \ldots$
(c) −7, −4, −1, 2, 5, . . .

7 Here is a sequence of shapes made from sticks

Shape number: *n* = 1   *n* = 2   *n* = 3
Number of sticks: 4   7   10

The number of sticks makes the sequence 4, 7, 10, 13, . . .

Make a table for the sequence and find the *n*th term.

Exercise 2E

In questions ① to ⑥ you are given a sequence of shapes made from sticks or dots. If you need to, make a table to help you find the *n*th term of the sequence.

1 Here is a sequence of triangles made from dots. Draw the next diagram in the sequence. How many dots are there in the *n*th term?

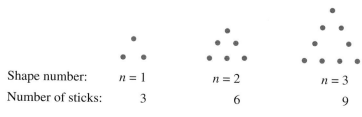

Shape number: *n* = 1   *n* = 2   *n* = 3
Number of sticks: 3   6   9

2   Here is a sequence of 'steps' made from sticks. Draw the next diagram in the sequence. How many sticks are there in the *n*th term?

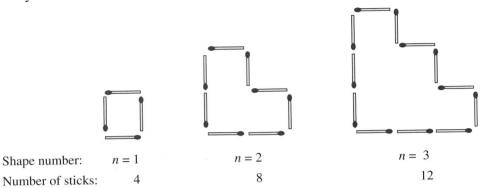

Shape number: *n* = 1   *n* = 2   *n* = 3

Number of sticks: 4   8   12

3   Louise makes a pattern of triangles from stricks.

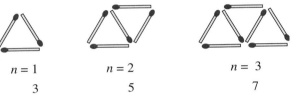

Shape number: *n* = 1   *n* = 2   *n* = 3

Number of sticks: 3   5   7

Draw shape number 4 and shape number 5.

How many sticks are there in the *n*th term?

4   Here is a sequence of houses made from sticks

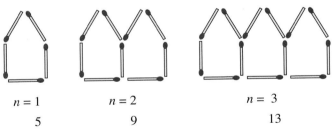

Shape number: *n* = 1   *n* = 2   *n* = 3

Number of sticks: 5   9   13

Draw shape number 4. How many sticks are there in the *n*th term?

5   Paul makes a pattern of squares from dots.

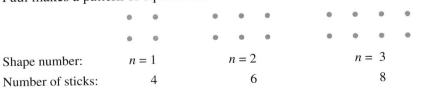

Shape number: *n* = 1   *n* = 2   *n* = 3

Number of sticks: 4   6   8

Draw shape number 4 and shape number 5.

How many dots are there in the *n*th term?

6 Here is another sequence made from dots.

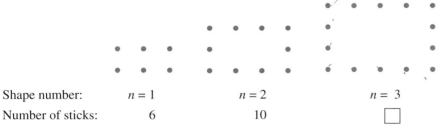

Shape number: $n = 1$ $n = 2$ $n = 3$
Number of sticks: 6   10   ☐

Draw shape numbers 4 and 5. How many dots are there in the nth term?

CHECK YOURSELF ON SECTIONS 5.1, 5.2 AND 5.3

1   Using ratios

(a) In a cinema there are 45 adults and 27 children. Write down the ratio of adults to children in its simplest form.

(b) The ratio of red cubes to white cubes is 1:26. Another solid is made using the same ratio of cubes. How many white cubes are used if 6 red cubes are used?

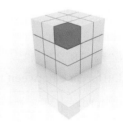

(c) £360 is shared in the ratio 4:2:3. How much is the largest share?

2   Tackling problems involving direct proportion

(a) Find the cost of 2 footballs if 7 footballs cost £37.80.

(b) Some hikers take 6 hours to walk 21 km. At the same pace of walking, how long would it take them to travel 35 km?

3 Using map scales

(a) The distance on a map between two houses is 4 cm. The scale of the map is 1:50 000. What is the actual distance in kilometres between the two houses?

(b) On a map whose scale is 1:20 000, the length of a field is 3 cm. What is the actual length of the field in metres?

4 Adding and subtracting negative numbers

Work out

(a) $3 + (-5)$ (b) $2 - (-4)$ (c) $-4 - (-2)$ (d) $-3 - 2$ (e) $-6 + 2$

5 Multiplying and dividing negative numbers

Work out

(a) -3×2 (b) $-6 \times (-7)$ (c) $-45 \div (-9)$ (d) $27 \div (-3)$ (e) $4 \times (-11)$

6 Finding the nth term of arithmetic sequences

(a) Look at the sequence and the table. Find an expression for the nth term.

8, 13, 18, 23, . . .

Difference between terms = 5

n^{th} term = [   ]

n	$5n$	term
1	5	8
2	10	13
3	15	18
4	20	23

(b) Look at the sequence 2, 9, 16, 23, . . .

Write down the difference between terms. Use this to find an expression for the nth term .

5.4 Enlargement

In section 5.4 you will:

- enlarge shapes
- use centres of enlargement

● The original picture here has been enlarged by a scale factor of 2.

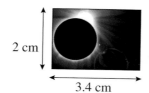

2 cm

3.4 cm

4 cm

6.8 cm

Notice that both the height *and* the width have been doubled.

● For an enlargement the original and the enlargement must be exactly the same shape. All angles in both shapes are preserved.

●

A

B

Length of A = 2 × length of B

Width of A = 2 × width of B

∴ A *is* an enlargement of B

Exercise IM

Look at each pair of diagrams and decide whether or not one diagram is an enlargement of the other. For each question write the scale factor of the enlargement or write 'not an enlargement'.

1

2

3

4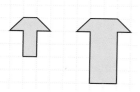

5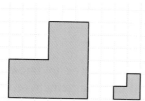

6

Enlarge the shapes in questions 7 to 12 by the scale factor given. Make sure you leave room on your page for the enlargement.

7

× 2

8

× 3

9

× 2

228

10 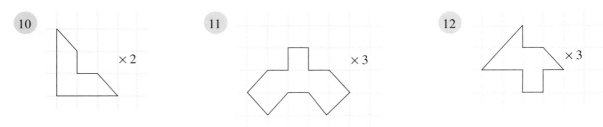 × 2

11 × 3

12 × 3

13 This picture is to be enlarged to fit the frame. Find the height of the frame.

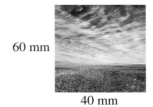

60 mm

40 mm

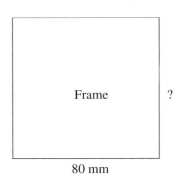

Frame ?

80 mm

14 Here are some letters of the alphabet.
  (a) Enlarge them by a scale factor of 2.
  (b) Draw your own initials and enlarge them by a scale factor of 2.

Exercise IE

Look at each pair of diagrams and decide whether or not one diagram is an enlargement of the other. For each question write the scale factor of the enlargement or write 'not an enlargement'.

1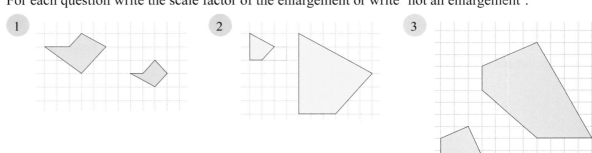

2

3

4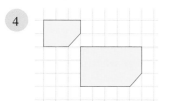

5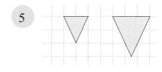

6

7 This is a challenge! Draw an enlargement of this picture with scale factor 2. Shade in the numbers with different colours.

8 A photograph measuring 5 cm by 3.5 cm is enlarged so that it fits exactly into a frame measuring 20 cm by x cm. Calculate the value of x.

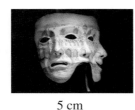

3.5 cm

5 cm

x

20 cm

9 A photograph measuring 6 cm by 4 cm is reduced to fit frame A and another copy of the photograph is enlarged to fit frame B.

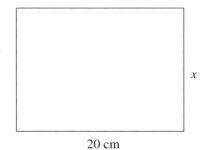

reduced

enlarged

x A

1.5 cm

4 cm

6 cm

B

12 cm

y

Calculate the value of x and the value of y.

Centre of enlargement

(a) Draw an enlargement of triangle 1 with scale factor 3 and centre of enlargement O.

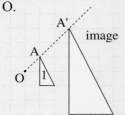

image

(b) Draw an enlargement of shape P with scale factor 2 and centre of enlargement O.

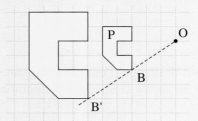

Notice that OA' = 3 × OA.

Notice that OB' = 2 × OB.

In both diagrams, just one point on the image has been found by using a construction line or by counting squares. When one point is known the rest of the diagram can easily be drawn, since the size and shape of the image is known.

Exercise 2M

In questions ① to ⑥ copy the diagram and then draw an enlargement using the scale factor and centre of enlargement given.

Leave room for enlargement!

1

O
scale factor 2

2

O
scale factor 3

3

O   scale factor 2

4

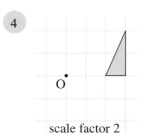

O
scale factor 2

5

O
scale factor 3

6

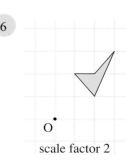

O
scale factor 2

7 Copy the diagram. Draw an enlargement of the triangle with scale factor 2 and centre of enlargement (0, 0).

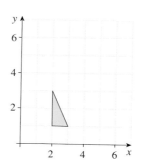

8 For (a), (b) and (c) draw a grid similar to the one in question 7. Draw an enlargement of each shape.

Shape	Centre of enlargement	Scale factor
(a) (1, 1) (2, 1) (2, 2) (1, 2)	(0, 0)	3
(b) (2, 1) (4, 2) (2, 2)	(0, 0)	2
(c) (4, 5) (6, 5) (6, 6) (4, 6)	(8, 8)	2

Finding the centre of enlargement

A mathematical enlargement always has a *centre of enlargement* as well as a scale factor. The centre of enlargement is found by drawing lines through corresponding points on the object and image and finding where they intersect. For greater accuracy it is better to count squares between points because it is difficult to draw construction lines accurately over a long distance.

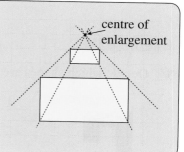

Exercise 2E

Draw the shapes and then draw lines through corresponding points to find the centre of enlargement. Don't draw the shapes too near the edge of the page!

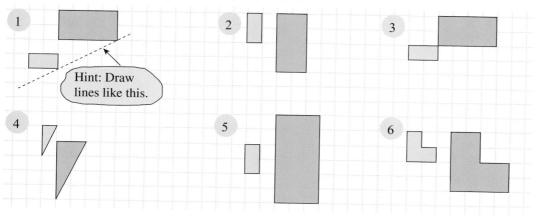

Hint: Draw lines like this.

5.5 Congruent shapes, tessellation

In section 5.5 you will:

- use congruent shapes
- draw tessellations

Congruent shapes are exactly the same in shape and size. Shapes are congruent if one shape can be fitted exactly over the other.

P and Q are congruent   R and S are not congruent

Exercise IM

1. Decide which shapes are congruent pairs. [You can use tracing paper]

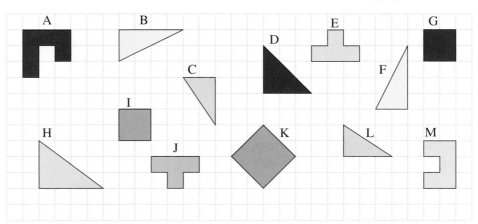

2. Copy the diagram and colour in congruent shapes with the same colour.

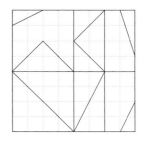

3 Two congruent right angled triangles are joined together along equal sides

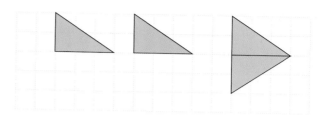

(a) How many shapes are possible?

(b) How many shapes are possible if the congruent triangles are equilateral?

4

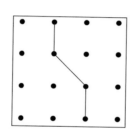

You are told that triangles DBC and CFA are congruent. Copy and complete:

(a) side AF = side ☐

(b) side CF = side ☐

(c) angle CFA = angle ☐

(d) angle ☐ = angle CDB.

5

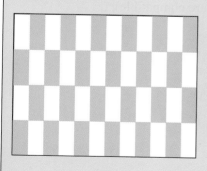

Use square dotty paper or squared paper.
Draw 4 × 4 grids as shown.
The 4 × 4 grids are divided into two congruent shapes.
Divide 4 × 4 grids into two congruent shapes in as many different ways as possible.

Tessellation

In tessellation we study the different ways we can regularly tile any flat surface, no matter how large. The examples below show tessellation using quadrilaterals:

(Rectangles)

(Kites)

Any quadrilateral could be drawn on card and used to make a tessellation.

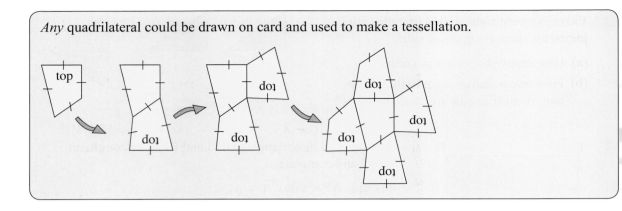

- Interesting tessellations may be formed using sets of different shapes, provided the lengths of their sides are compatible

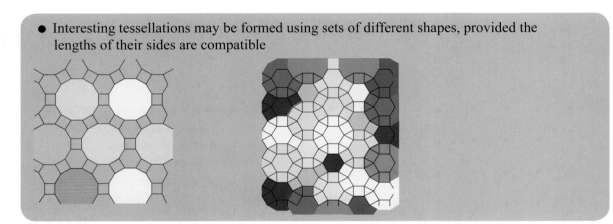

Exercise 2M

1   Draw and cut out a template on card for each of the shapes below:
    (You can trace the shapes below to save time. All their sides are compatible).

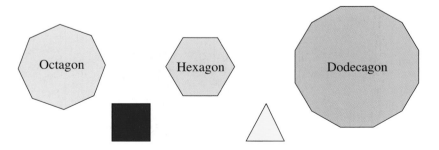

2   Either (i) draw a tessellation on plain paper or (ii) draw a tessellation directly onto tracing paper, using:

(a) only hexagons

(b) only octagons and squares

(c) only dodecagons and equilateral triangles.

(d) only hexagons, squares and equilateral triangles.

(e) only dodecagons, hexagons and squares.

(f) only squares and equilateral triangles.

3   For each tessellation in 2 , colour the pattern in an interesting way.

CHECK YOURSELF ON SECTIONS 5.4 AND 5.5

1   Enlarging shapes

(a) Enlarge this shape by a scale factor 2.

(b) Is shape B an enlargement of shape A?

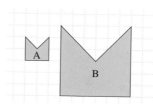

2   Using centres of enlargement

(a) Copy this diagram and then draw an enlargement using scale factor 2 and the centre of enlargement O.

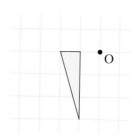

236

(b) Copy this diagram and then draw lines through corresponding points to show the centre of enlargement.

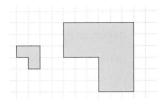

3   Using congruent shapes

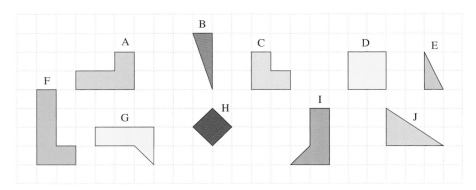

(a) Which shape is congruent to shape I?

(b) Which shape is congruent to shape B?

4   Drawing tessellations

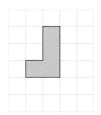 Draw a tessellation using this shape *at least* 8 times.

5.6 Drawing graphs review

In section 5.6 you will:

- draw graphs
- find the equation of a line

Drawing graphs

Draw the graph of $y = 2x + 3$
for x-values from 0 to 4.

> Remember this is done by
> first completing a table of values

$2x + 3$ means  $x \rightarrow \boxed{\times 2} \rightarrow \boxed{+3}$

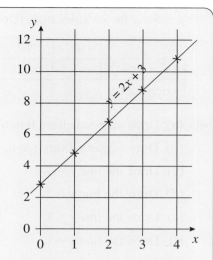

x	0	1	2	3	4
y	3	5	7	9	11
Coordinates	(0, 3)	(1, 5)	(2, 7)	(3, 9)	(4, 11)

Lines parallel to the axes

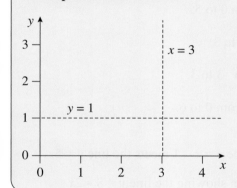

A line parallel to the y-axis has an equation

$x =$ 'a number'

A line parallel to the x-axis has an equation

$y =$ 'a number'

Exercise 1M

For each question, copy and complete the table then draw the graph using the scales given.

1. $y = x + 3$ for x-values from 0 to 5

x	0	1	2	3	4	5
y			5			
coordinates			(2, 5)			

(x-axis: use 1 cm for 1 unit
y-axis: use 1 cm for 1 unit)

2. $y = 2x + 2$ for x-values from 0 to 5
$2x + 2$ means $x \rightarrow \boxed{\times 2} \rightarrow \boxed{+2}$

x	0	1	2	3	4	5
y				8		
coordinates				(3, 8)		

(x-axis: use 1 cm for 1 unit
y-axis: use 1 cm for 2 units)

3 $y = 5 - x$ for x-values from 0 to 5

x	0	1	2	3	4	5
y			3			
coordinates			(2, 3)			

(x-axis: use 1 cm for 1 unit
y-axis: use 1 cm for 1 unit)

4 (a) Draw an x-axis from 0 to 6.

(b) Draw a y-axis from 0 to 6.

(c) Draw the line $y = 4$.

(d) Draw the line $y = 2$.

(e) Draw the line $x = 3$.

(f) Draw the line $y = x$.

(g) Write down the co-ordinates of the point where the line $y = x$ meets the line $x = 3$.

5 Use a table of values to draw $y = 2x + 4$ for x-values from 0 to 5.

6 Use a table of values to draw $y = x^2$ for x-values from -3 to 3.

7 Use a table of values to draw $y = x^2 + 2$ for x-values from -3 to 3.

8 (a) Use a table of values to draw $y = x - 1$ for x-values from 0 to 6.

(b) Draw the line $y = 5$.

(c) Write down the coordinates of the point where the line $y = x - 1$ meets the line $y = 5$.

9

(a) Copy this diagram showing the line $y = 8 - 2x$.

(b) Draw the line $x = 1$.

(c) Draw the line $x = 3$.

(d) Write down the co-ordinates of the point where the line $y = 8 - 2x$ meets the line $x = 1$.

10 (a) Use a table of values to draw $y = x^2 + x$ for x-values from 0 to 4.

(b) Use the curve to find the value of y when $x = 2.5$.

Finding the equation of a line

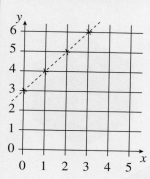

This line passes through:

$(0, 3), (1, 4), (2, 5), (3, 6)$

For each point the y coordinate is three more than the x coordinate. The equation of the line is $y = x + 3$

Exercise 1E

In questions ① to ⑩ you are given the coordinates of several points on a line. Find the equation of each line.

①

x	1	2	3	4	5
y	5	6	7	8	9

②

x	1	2	3	4	5	6
y	7	8	9	10	11	12

③

x	6	7	8	9	10
y	2	3	4	5	6

④

x	0	1	2	3	4	5
y	9	8	7	6	5	4

⑤

x	1	2	3	4	5
y	4	8	12	16	20

⑥

x	0	1	2	3	4
y	12	11	10	9	8

⑦

x	10	11	12	13	14
y	7	8	9	10	11

⑧

x	2	4	6	8	10
y	10	20	30	40	50

⑨

x	0	1	2	3	4
y	1	4	7	10	13

⑩

x	0	1	2	3	4
y	3	5	7	9	11

⑪

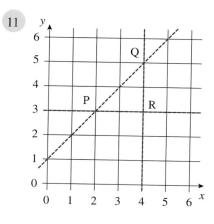

Find the equation of the line through

(a) P and Q

(b) P and R

(c) Q and R

240

Investigation – the painted cube

The diagrams below show 5 different sized cubes formed by unit cubes.

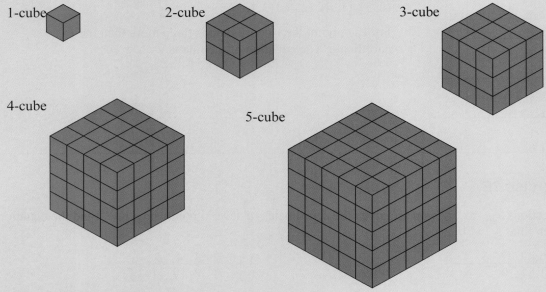

1-cube   2-cube   3-cube

4-cube   5-cube

(A) Copy and complete this table

Object	1-cube	2-cube	3-cube	4-cube	5-cube	6-cube	7-cube	8-cube
Number of cubes	1	8						

(B) The outside of each large cube is painted red. Some unit cubes will have 3 faces painted red, some will have 2 painted red, some will have only 1 painted red and some will stay completely unpainted.

Copy out and complete the table below showing the number of unit cubes with 3, 2, 1 or 0 faces painted red.

Object	Number of unit cubes	Number of red faces			
		3	2	1	0
2-cube	8	8 cubes	0	0	0
3-cube					
4-cube					
5-cube					

(C) Use your table to help you predict the number of unit cubes with 3, 2, 1, 0 faces coloured red for a 6-cube and for a 7-cube.

(D) How many unit cubes will have 1 red face for a 10-cube?

(E) How many unit cubes will have no red faces for a 20-cube?

5.7 Area review

In section 5.7 you will:

- use the areas of rectangles, triangles, trapeziums and parallelograms
- use the area of a circle

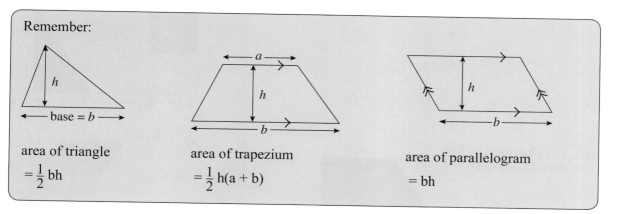

Remember:

area of triangle
$= \frac{1}{2} bh$

area of trapezium
$= \frac{1}{2} h(a + b)$

area of parallelogram
$= bh$

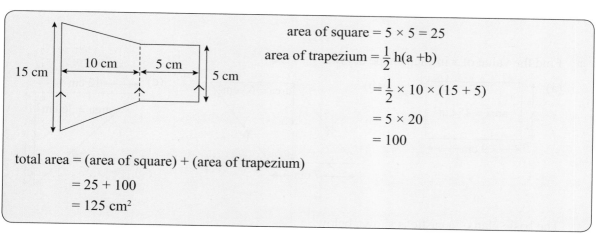

area of square $= 5 \times 5 = 25$

area of trapezium $= \frac{1}{2} h(a + b)$

$= \frac{1}{2} \times 10 \times (15 + 5)$

$= 5 \times 20$

$= 100$

total area $=$ (area of square) + (area of trapezium)

$= 25 + 100$

$= 125 \text{ cm}^2$

Exercise 1M

1   Calculate the area of each shape. The lengths are in cm.

(a)

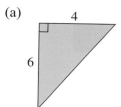

(b)

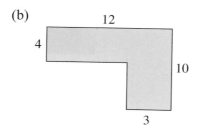

(c)

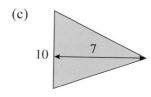

(d)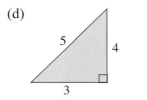

(e)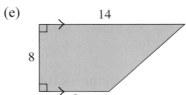

(f)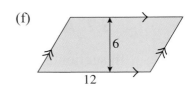

2 Work out the area of the lawn. The lengths are in metres.

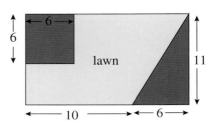

3 Which area is the odd one out?

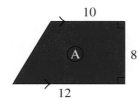

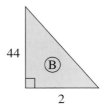

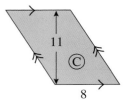

4 Find the value of x in each shape below.

(a)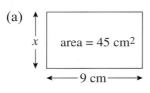

(b)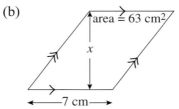

(c)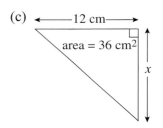

5 The basic plan of a castle is shown below.

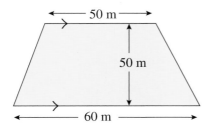

Work out the area of this plan.

6

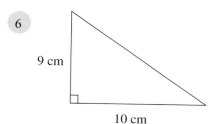

The area of the triangle is equal to the area of the parallelogram. What is the height of the parallelogram?

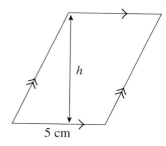

9 cm

10 cm

h

5 cm

7 A square has a perimeter of 36 cm. Calculate the area of the square.

8

Pete covers his entire roof with solar panels. Each panel measures 2 m by 1.5 m. Pete uses 30 panels. What is the total area of Pete's roof?

9 A brother and sister argue because they both want the larger bedroom. Look at the plan opposite. Which bedroom do they both want? Show your working out. (You may use a calculator)

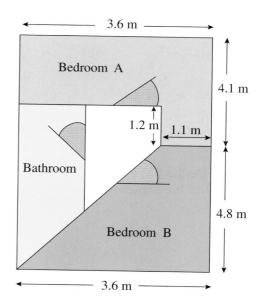

3.6 m

Bedroom A

4.1 m

1.2 m   1.1 m

Bathroom

4.8 m

Bedroom B

3.6 m

Remember :

r

area of a circle = πr²

This means π multiplied by (radius)²

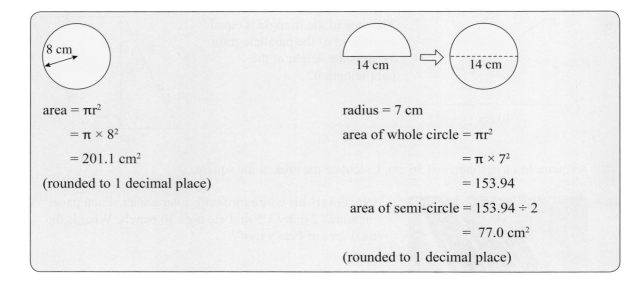

area = πr²

    = π × 8²

    = 201.1 cm²

(rounded to 1 decimal place)

radius = 7 cm

area of whole circle = πr²

                = π × 7²

                = 153.94

area of semi-circle = 153.94 ÷ 2

                    = 77.0 cm²

(rounded to 1 decimal place)

Exercise 1E

1. Calculate the area of each circle and give your answer correct to one decimal place.

(a)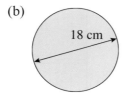

(b)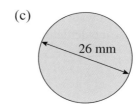

(c)

(d)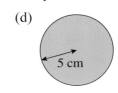

2. Find the area of the face of this clock if its diameter is 1.6 m. Give the answer to 1 decimal place.

3.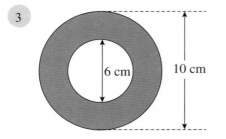

Find the purple area. Give the answer to 1 decimal place.

④ Calculate the area of each shape and give your answer correct to 1 decimal place.

(a)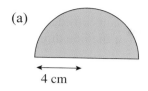

4 cm

(b)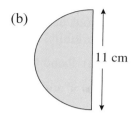

11 cm

(c)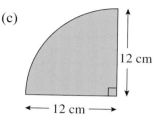

12 cm

12 cm

⑤

The end of each crayon is a circle with a radius of 4.5 mm. Find the total area of the ends of all 34 crayons. Give the answer to the nearest whole number.

⑥ Calculate the total area of this window, giving your answer to the nearest whole number.

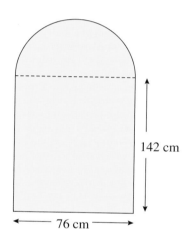

142 cm

76 cm

CHECK YOURSELF ON SECTIONS 5.6 AND 5.7

1   Drawing graphs

Copy and complete the table for $y = 2x - 1$ then draw the graph using 1 cm for 1 unit on each axis.

x	0	1	2	3	4
y					
coordinates					

2   Finding the equation of a line

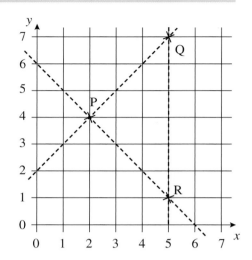

Look at the co-ordinates of points on each line carefully. Find the equation of the line through

(a) P and Q

(b) P and R

(c) Q and R

3   Using the areas of rectangles, triangles, trapeziums and parallelograms

Calculate the area of each shape. The lengths are in cm.

(a)
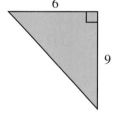
6

9

(b)
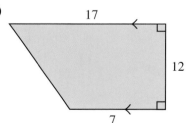
17

12

7

(c)
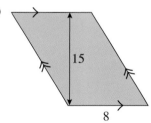
15

8

4   Using the area of a circle

Calculate the area of each shape, giving your answers to 1 decimal place.

(a)
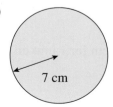
7 cm

(b)
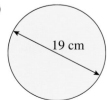
19 cm

(c)
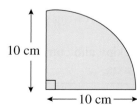
10 cm

10 cm

UNIT 5   MIXED REVIEW

Part one

1   Work out

(a) $(-2) + (-5)$ (b) $3 \times (-4)$ (c) $(-6)^2$ (d) $32 \div (-8)$

2   On a map of scale 1:20 000 a road is 2 cm long. How long is the actual road in metres?

3   The skateboard sequence was taken by a camera with a delay of 0.14 second between pictures. How long did the jump take?

4   £36 000 is shared between Ben and Lara in the ratio 5:4. How much money does Ben get?

5   Copy each sequence and find the missing terms.

(a) ☐   4   4.01   4.02   ☐

(b) ☐   ☐   5.05   5.1   ☐   5.2

6   Copy each shape and then enlarge it using the centre of enlargement and the scale factor shown.

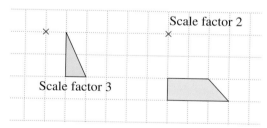

Scale factor 2

Scale factor 3

7   Maggie has the same number of 20p and 50p coins. The total value of the coins is £7. How many of each coin does she have?

8   Calculate the pink area.

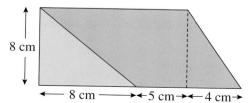

8 cm

8 cm   5 cm   4 cm

248

9 Draw the graph of $y = 3x + 1$ for values of x from 0 to 4.

$x \longrightarrow \boxed{\times 3} \longrightarrow \boxed{+1} \longrightarrow y$

x	0	1	2	3	4
y					

10 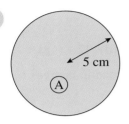 Which shape has the larger area and by how much?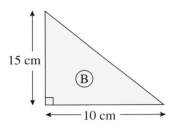

11 Find the missing numbers

(a) $6 \times \boxed{} = -30$ (b) $-48 \div \boxed{} = -8$ (c) $-7 - \boxed{} = -4$

12  The photo shows a mini chain reaction with dominoes. It takes 4.2 seconds to topple 21 dominoes.
How long will it take to topple a huge pattern with 63 000 dominoes in a line?

13 Draw a tessellation using this shape *at least* 8 times.

14 Write the ratio 12:21:18 in a more simple form.

15 Susie makes a pattern of rectangles from sticks.

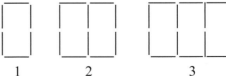

Shape-number, N	1	2	3
Number of sticks, S	6	10	14

Susie's rule is 'The number of sticks is four times the shape-number and then add 2.'

(a) Work out the number of sticks in shape-number 8.

(b) One of the shapes needs 50 sticks. What is its shape-number?

(c) Write a formula, without words, to work out the number of sticks for any shape-number.
Use S for the number of sticks and N for the shape-number. Write '$S = \ldots\ldots$'.

Part two

1 Copy and complete this addition square.

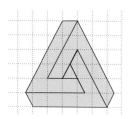

+		−3	
−2			−1
	−4	−1	
	−7		

2 Enlarge this shape on squared paper by a scale factor 2.

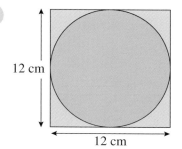

3

x	0	1	2	3	4	5
y	8	7	6	5	4	3

This table shows the coordinates of several points on a line. Write down the equation of this line using x and y.

4 Dawn has lots of 36p and 27p stamps and she wants to waste as little money as possible when posting 3 packets. Which stamps should she use if the required postage is:

(a) 80p   (b) 150p   (c) £2?

5 On a map of scale 1 : 100 000 000 the distance from London to Athens is 2.5 cm. What is the actual distance in kilometres between these two cities?

6 Calculate the blue area, giving the answer to 1 decimal place.

12 cm

12 cm

7 Look at these number cards: $\boxed{5}$ $\boxed{-2}$ $\boxed{0}$ $\boxed{7}$ $\boxed{-6}$ $\boxed{3}$ $\boxed{2}$ $\boxed{-4}$

(a) Fill in the missing number: $-2 + \boxed{?} = 5$

(b) Which card will give the *highest* possible answer here: $-2 \times \boxed{}$?

(c) Which card will give the *lowest* possible answer here: $-4 - \boxed{}$?

(d) Which card will give the *highest* possible answer here: $3 - \boxed{}$?

8 2, 6, 10, 14, 18, …

Which expression below gives the *n*th term for this sequence?

$\boxed{n + 4}$ $\boxed{4n - 2}$ $\boxed{2n + 4}$

9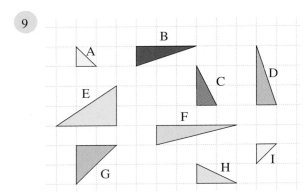

Which triangle is congruent to triangle B?

10 A 350 g packet of almonds costs £2.10. How much does it cost for each 100 g of almonds?

11

The thumbs on these handprints are in the ratio 9:7:5. If the largest thumb is 63 mm long, how long is the smallest thumb?

12 Part of a wall is painted yellow as shown. On average it takes Rio 12 minutes to paint 1 m² of the wall. How long does it take Rio to paint the yellow part of the wall?

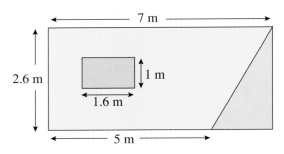

13 In this number wall each brick is made by adding the two bricks underneath it. Copy and complete the wall.

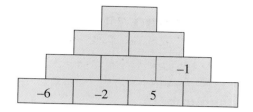

14 In a magic square each row, column and both main diagonals have the same total. Which of the following numbers should replace n in this magic square?

2   4   6

		7
4		14
		n

15 Photograph B is an enlargement of photograph A. Calculate the height of photograph B.

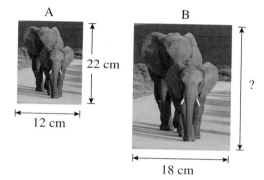

A

22 cm

12 cm

B

?

18 cm

Puzzles and Problems 5

Crossnumbers

Make two copies of the pattern below and complete the puzzles
using the clues given. To avoid confusion it is better not to write the
small reference numbers 1, 2–18 on your patterns.

1		2		3			4
				5			
	6		7			8	
9					10		
		11					12
				13	14		
15	16				17		
			18				

Part A [No calculators]

Across

1. 499 + 43

3. 216 × 7

5. 504 ÷ 9

6. 8214 − 3643

8. Half of 192

9. 20% of 365

10. Prime number between 30 and 36

11. 213 + 62 + 9

13. 406 ÷ 7

15. $0.7268 \times 10 \times 10 \times 10 \times 10$

17. 1000 − 731

18. $2 \times 10^2 + 11$

Down

1. 1% of 5700
2. 600 − 365
4. 6^3
7. 4488 ÷ 6
8. $30^2 + 3 \times 6$

9. 10 000 − 2003
11. $4 \times 4 \times 4 \times 4$
12. $58.93 \times (67 + 33)$
14. 1136 − 315
16. $11^2 - 10^2$

Part B [A calculator may be used. Write any decimal points on the lines between squares.]

Across

1. $9 \times 10 \times 11$

3. Ninety less than ten thousand

5. $\left(7\frac{1}{2}\right)^2$ to the nearest whole number

6. 140.52 ÷ 0.03

8. Last two digits of 99^2

9. $3^2 + 4^2 + 5^2 + 6^2$

10. Angle between the hands of a clock at 2.00 pm

11. Eight pounds and eight pence

13. Next prime number after 89

15. 11% of 213

17. 3.1 m plus 43 cm, in cm

18. Area of a square of side 15 cm.

Down

1. $\dfrac{5 \times 6 \times 7 \times 8}{2} - 11 \times 68$

2. 26% as a decimal

4. 0.1^2

7. Next in the sequence $102\frac{1}{2}$, 205, 410

8. 1 − 0.97

9. 52% of £158.50

11. 0.0854 ÷ (7 − 6.99)

12. $10^3 + 11^3$

14. $3 \times 5 \times 7^2$

16. Half of a third of 222

Mental Arithmetic Practice

Ideally a teacher will read out each question twice, with pupils' books closed.

Test 1

• *Allow 5 seconds to answer each of questions* 1 *to* 6

1. Write the number five hundred and sixty-seven to the nearest hundred.

2. What is five point two multiplied by one thousand?

3. Work out five per cent of four hundred.

4. Simplify the expression a × a × a.

5. What is the sum of 2.3, 2.7, 2.3 and 2.7?

6. What is one tenth of half a million?

• *Allow 10 seconds to answer each of questions* 7 *to* 20

7. What is the value of $2(x + 1)$ when x equals four?

8. Tim's height is one point seven metres. Greg's height is one hundredth of a metre more than Tim's height. What is Greg's height?

9. Twenty per cent of a number is eleven. What is the number?

10. Two angles in a triangle are each sixty-five degrees. What is the size of the third angle?

11 In a group of sixty-three children, twenty-eight are girls. How many are boys?

12 What is the area of a triangle with a base of 8 cm and a height of 7 cm?

13 The value of four x plus y is sixteen. Write the value of eight x plus two y.

14 Divide two by nought point one.

15 Michelle got thirty out of fifty on a test. What percentage did she get?

16 Work out one plus two plus three, all squared.

17 If '−4 less than x less than 0', write down one possible value of x.

18 How many eighths are there in one half?

19 Multiply six point nought two by one thousand.

20 Treble a number then subtract 1 gives the answer 65. What is the value of the number?

• *Allow* 15 *seconds to answer each of*

questions 21 *to* 30

21 What is the cost of two items at two pounds ninety-nine pence each?

22 Which is the smaller of these three numbers?

0.2 0.18 0.332

23 Work out an approximate answer for 497.3 ÷ 1.97

24 Each side of a square is thirty-two centimetres. What is the perimeter of the square?

25 Between which pair of whole numbers does the square root of thirty-three lie?

26 If 32 × 19 = 608, what is sixteen multiplied by nineteen?

27 A map has a scale of one to one thousand. What is the actual length of a path which is 8 cm long on the map? Give your final answer in metres.

28 What is the value of $x^2 - 6$ when x equals nought?

29 Which has the longer perimeter: a square of side 10 cm or an equilateral triangle of side 15 cm?

30 A film started at eight fifty p.m. and ended two and a quarter hours later. When did it finish?

A long time ago! 5

The Tower of Hanoi

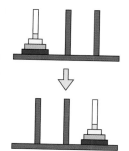

This puzzle was created by Eduard Lucas in the 19th century. The task is to move a pile of different sized discs from one post to another.

There are 3 posts. Only one disc may be moved at any time and must be moved directly onto another post. A larger disc may never be placed onto a smaller disc.

The aim is to move all the discs to another post using the least number of moves.

Exercise

1

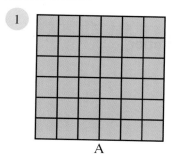
A

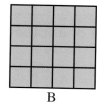
B

C

Cut out 3 squares as shown.

Use them in place of 3 discs.

Place C on top of B on top of A.

Place 3 crosses on a piece of paper in place of posts.

Move A, B and C from one post onto another post using the Tower of Hanoi rules above.

What are the least number of moves needed?

Discuss with a partner. Could they do any better than you?

2 Now repeat with 4 discs.

3 Try with just 2 discs.

4 One disc would need one move.

Look at your answers for 1 disc, 2 discs, 3 discs and 4 discs.

Can you see a pattern for the least number of moves so far?

If you can see a pattern, what will be the least number of moves needed for 5 discs?

Now move 5 discs for real.

5 What is the least number of moves needed for 7 discs?

6 **RESEARCH:**

Check whether your answer for 7 discs is correct.

UNIT 6

6.1 Percentages

In section 6.1 you will:

- express one number as a percentage of another number
- find a percentage of a number
- find percentage increases and decreases

Expressing one number as a percentage of another number

25 children are in a quiz. 9 are boys.

What percentage of the children in the quiz are boys?

9 out of 25 $= \dfrac{9}{25} = \dfrac{36}{100} = 36\%$

Exercise 1M

1. Tom has 20 pieces of fruit. 7 pieces of fruit are apples. What percentage of the fruit are the apples?

2. 50 children watch a school football match. 22 are girls. What percentage of the children are girls?

3. 500 people were asked what their favourite film was. 85 of them said 'Lord of the Rings'. What percentage of the people chose 'Lord of the Rings'?

4.  What percentage of these bags are red?

5   Danny plays 25 games of pool and wins 16 of them. What percentage of the games did he *not* win?

6   Mark spent $\frac{2}{5}$ of his money on a computer game and $\frac{3}{20}$ of his money on food. What percentage of his money has he got left?

7   Three tenths of Lorna's books were Science Fiction. What percentage of her books were *not* Science Fiction?

8   Change each of the following into a percentage then put them in order of size, starting with the smallest.

A. 7 out of 25	B. 13 out of 20	C. 18 out of 60	D. 50 out of 200

9   Tania scored 60 out of 150 in a test. What percentage did she score?

To change more 'tricky' numbers into a percentage of each other, write the two numbers as a fraction of each other then multiply by 100.

23 people are asked if they can drive a car. 14 of them replied with a 'yes'. What percentage of the people can drive?

$$14 \text{ out of } 23 = \frac{14}{23} \times 100 = 60.87 \text{ (using a calculator)}$$
$$= 60.9\% \text{ (to one decimal place)}$$

Exercise 1E

You may use a calculator. Give all answers to one decimal place.

1   There are 31 children in a class. 17 of them are girls. What percentage of the class are girls?

2   What percentage of the letters in the box are
(a) vowels?
(b) the letter R?

S	M	O	K	I	N	G	I	S
N	O	T	P	A	R	T	I	C
U	L	A	R	L	Y	G	O	O
D	F	O	R	Y	O	U	O	K

3   16 children were playing in the park. 9 of them were wearing sandals. What percentage of the children were *not* wearing sandals?

4
	Men	Women	Total
colour blind	55	37	92
not colour blind	473	394	867
Total	528	431	959

The table shows the results of a test for colour blindness conducted on 959 people.
(a) What percentage of the men were colour blind?
(b) What percentage of the colour blind people were women?

5   A breakfast cereal contains the following ingredients by weight: Toasted Oat Flakes 720 g, Raw Sugar 34 g, Oat Bran 76 g, Honey 26 g, Banana 57 g, Hazelnuts 12 g.
What percentage of the packet is Oat Bran?

6   Four friends create kebabs for a barbecue. They decide to work out which kebab has the lowest fat content.

Jack's kebab	43.1 g fat in a 122 g portion
Gabby's kebab	29.6 g fat in a 85 g portion
Tom's kebab	48.2 g fat in a 149 g portion
Kate's kebab	31.8 g fat in a 98 g portion

Which kebab has the lowest percentage of fat in it?

7
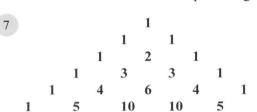

This triangle is known as Pascal's triangle. What percentage of the numbers are prime numbers? (remember: 1 is *not* prime)

8   The table gives details of the ages of children in a school with 884 pupils.
   (a) What percentage of the under-15's are boys?
   (b) What percentage of the pupils in the whole school were girls?
   (c) What percentage of the girls are 15 and over?

	Boys	Girls
Under 15	215	184
15 and over	223	262

'Simple' percentages in your head

Remember: Use multiples of 10% and 1%

10% of £30 $= \frac{1}{10}$ of 30 $= 3$ so 40% of £30 $= 3 \times 4 = £12$

1% of £900 $= \frac{1}{100}$ of 900 $= 9$ so 7% of £900 $= 9 \times 7 = £63$

Exercise 2M

Do not use a calculator.

1   Work out

   (a) 20% of £80   (b) 5% of £40   (c) 30% of £70

   (d) 70% of £20   (e) 90% of £120   (f) 5% of £50

2 Meryl and Lee are playing 'pick a stick'.
   There are 40 sticks. Lee ends up picking 35%
   of the sticks. Meryl gets the rest of the sticks.
   How many sticks does Meryl get?

3 Steve has 280 toy soldiers. He gives 20% of the soldiers to his younger sister.
   How many soldiers does he have left?

4 Work out
   (a) 3% of £400   (b) 2% of £6200   (c) 6% of £800
   (d) 11% of £200   (e) 9% of £2100   (f) 19% of £300

5 Which is larger? (15% of £80) or (4% of £300)

6 Find the odd one out
   (a) 6% of £400   (b) 16% of £200   (c) 5% of £480

7 Find   (a) 5% of £60   (b) $2\frac{1}{2}$% of £60   (c) $7\frac{1}{2}$% of £60

8 Work out $17\frac{1}{2}$% of £80.

Percentages of a number with a calculator

16% means $\frac{16}{100}$ or 0.16

Work out 16% of £440

Either   16% of £440   *or*   16% of £440

$= \frac{16}{100} \times \frac{440}{1}$ $= 0.16 \times 440$

$= £70.40$ $= £70.40$

Exercise 2E

You may use a calculator.

Work out

1   12% of £600   2   6% of £250   3   81% of £9

4   8% of £450   5   7% of £440   6   43% of £185

7   5% of £22   8   4% of £660   9   8% of £2555

10 85% of £400   11 6.5% of £200   12 7% of £6

13 29% of £2000   14 4.5% of £400   15 17% of £175

16　The price of a diving holiday is £860. During the next year the holiday price is 5% higher. How much is this higher price?

17　In a restaurant a service charge of 10% is added to the price of a meal. What is the service charge on a meal costing £28.50?

18　At a garage 140 cars were given a safety test and 65% of the cars passed the test.
(a) How many passed the test?
(b) How many failed the test?

19　Of the 980 children at a school 45% cycle to school, 15% go by bus and the rest walk.
(a) How many cycle to school?
(b) How many walk to school?

20　A lottery prize of £65 000 is divided between Steve, Pete and Phil so that Steve receives 22%, Pete receives 32% and Phil the rest. How much money does Phil receive?

In questions 21 to 30 , work out each percentage and give the answer correct to the nearest penny.

21　13% of £2.13

22　27% of £5.85

23　15.1% of £7.87

24　11% of £6.27

25　13% of £6.17

26　16% of £0.87

27　37% of £5.20

28　15% of £11.23

29　4% of £0.65

30　6.2% of £8.55

> **Example**
>
> Work out 8% of £11.99 to the nearest penny.
>
> $$\frac{8}{100} \times \frac{11.99}{1}$$
>
> $= 0.95\vert92$
>
> $= £0.96$ to the nearest penny

Percentage increase of decrease

In 2009 the cost of taxing a car increased from £220 by 70%. What is the new cost?

70% of £220

$$= \frac{70}{100} \times \frac{220}{1} = £154$$

New cost of taxing car $= £220 + £154$

$$= £374$$

Exercise 3M

Do not use a calculator.

1. The price of a phone was £90. It is increased by 5%. What is the new price?

2. In a closing-down sale, a shop reduces all its prices by 20%.
   Find the sale price of a jacket which previously cost £60.

3. A marathon runner weighs 70 kg at the start of a race. During the race his weight is reduced by 5%. How much does he weigh at the end of the race?

4. (a) Increase £70 by 40%. (b) Decrease £320 by 15%.
   (c) Decrease £180 by 20% (d) Increase £120 by 35%.

5. A shop increases all its prices by 5%. What are the new prices of the items below?

A £20   B £90   C £65

6. Gemma has £3600. She spends 45% of her money. How much money does she have left?

7. A car costs £8600. During the first year it loses 15% of its value. How much is the car now worth?

8.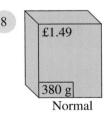

   £1.49 · 380 g · Normal

   £1.49 · 35% extra FREE! · g · Offer

   As part of a special promotion, the weight of Corn Flakes sold in a packet is increased by 35%, while the price remains the same. Calculate the weight of Corn Flakes in the special 'offer' size.

9. In ten years the population of a town is increased by 7% from its original number of 55400. What is the new population?

Exercise 3E

You may use a calculator.

1. A dog normally weighs 28 kg. After being put on a diet for three months its weight is reduced by 35%. How much does it weigh now?

2. The length of a new washing line is 21m. After being used it stretches by 3%. Find the new length.

3 A hen weighs 2.7 kg. After laying an egg her weight is reduced by 1%. How much does she weigh now?

4 A mouse weighs 630 g. While escaping from a cat it loses its tail and its weight is reduced by 4%. How much does it weigh now?

5 Cheryl weighs 56 kg. After a month of hard work in the gym and 'sensible' eating, her weight decreases by 6%. How much does she weigh now?

6 Find the new price of a necklace costing £85, after the price is reduced by 7%.

7

5 cm

8 cm

(a) Calculate the area of the rectangle shown.
(b) Calculate the new area when the length and width of the rectangle are each increased by 10%.

8

Coopers
£85
watch
20% discount
less a further £15

Which shop offers the best deal and how much money would you save if you bought the watch from this shop?

Tanners
£85
watch
35% discount

9 The island state of Gandia is divided between 3 tribes A, B and C as shown.

Tribe A subsequently starts a war and increases its land area by 15%. The area controlled by tribe B is reduced by 5%.

Draw a possible new map of the country and state the area now controlled by each tribe.

10 During the 2009 season the average home crowd watching Manchester United was 77600 and the average price paid for admission was £45.

For the 2010 season the average crowd was 3% less but the average admission price was increased by 8%. How much money was paid for admission for the 19 home games in the 2010 season? Give your answer correct to the nearest thousand pounds.

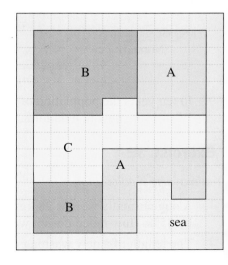

6.2 Probability

In section 6.2 you will:

- find the probability of events occurring or not occurring
- find experimental probabilities
- find probabilities involving two events

Events occurring or not occurring

- If the probability of an event occurring is p, then the probability of it not occurring is $1 - p$.
- Ten identical discs numbered 1, 2, 3, 4, 5, 6, 7, 8, 9, 10 are put into a bag. One disc is selected at random.

  In this example there are 10 possible equally likely outcomes of a trial.

  (a) The probability of selecting a '2' $= \frac{1}{10}$

  This may be written p(selecting a '2') $= \frac{1}{10}$

  (b) p (not selecting a 2) $= 1 - \frac{1}{10}$

  $= \frac{9}{10}$

  (c) p (selecting a number greater than 7) $= \frac{3}{10}$

  (d) p (not selecting a number greater than 7) $= 1 - \frac{3}{10} = \frac{7}{10}$

Exercise 1M

1   Seven discs numbered 3, 4, 5, 7, 9, 11, 12 are placed in a bag. One disc is selected at random. Find the probability that it is

(a) a 5   (b) not a 5

(c) an odd number   (d) an even number

2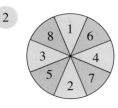

With this spinner find the probability of getting:

(a) a 7   (b) not a 7   (c) a prime number

(d) a number greater than 6

3 The probability of a drawing pin landing 'point up' is 0.61.

Find the probability of the drawing pin landing 'point down'.

4 A dice has its faces numbered 2, 3, 3, 3, 4, 7.
Find the probability of rolling
(a) a '7'
(b) an even number.

5 One card is selected at random from the nine cards shown.

Find the probability of selecting
(a) the King of diamonds
(b) a 9 or 10
(c) a picture card
(d) a card with a number less than 9

6 If Mala throws a 3 or a 5 on her next throw when playing 'Snakes and Ladders' she will slide down a snake on the board. What is the probability that she will avoid a snake on her next throw?

7 One card is picked at random from a pack of 52. Find the probability that it is
(a) a diamond
(b) not a diamond
(c) the King of hearts
(d) not the King of hearts

8 Nicole has 3 kings and 1 ace. She shuffles the cards and takes one without looking. Nicole asks two of her friends about the probability of getting an ace

Angie says:
'It is $\frac{1}{3}$ because there are 3 kings and 1 ace'.

Syline says
'It is $\frac{1}{4}$ because there are 4 cards and only 1 ace.'

Which of her friends is right?

9 A shopkeeper is keen to sell his stock of left-handed scissors. He has read that 9% of the population is left-handed. What is the probability that the next person to enter his shop is right-handed?

10 A South Seas diver collected 965 oysters. Just one of the oysters contained a pearl. One oyster is chosen at random. Find the probability that

(a) it contains a pearl

(b) it does not contain a pearl.

Exercise 1E

1

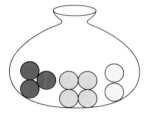

A bag contains 9 balls: 3 red, 4 blue and 2 yellow.

(a) Find the probability of selecting a red ball.

(b) The 2 yellow balls are replaced by 2 blue balls. Find the probability of selecting a blue ball.

2 The 26 letters of the alphabet are written on discs. The five discs with vowels are put in bag A and the other discs are put in bag B.

Find the probability of selecting

(a) an 'o' from bag A

(b) a 'z' from bag B

(c) a 'w' from bag A

3 A box contains 12 balls: 3 red, 2 yellow, 4 green and 3 white.

(a) Find the probability of selecting

(i) a red ball

(ii) a yellow ball

(b) The 3 white balls are replaced by 3 yellow balls. Find the probability of selecting

(i) a red ball

(ii) a yellow ball.

4 A field contains 10 cows, 5 horses and 1 lion. The lion is thought to be tame and half of the cows are mad.

One animal is chosen at random.

Find the probability that the animal:

(a) is mad

(b) enjoys eating grass

(c) might eat you.

5   Mo puts these numbered balls in a bag.

(a) He shakes the bag and takes one ball without looking. What is the probability of getting a '2'?

(b) Mo wants to put more balls in the bag so that the chance of getting a '4' is *twice* the chance of getting a '3'. What ball could he put in the bag?

6   A bag contains the balls shown. One ball is taken out at random. Find the probability that it is
(a) red   (b) not red   (c) blue
One more red ball and one more blue ball are added to the bag.
(d) Find the new probability of selecting a red ball from the bag.

7   Steve has taken a number of cards at random from a pack. The probability of picking a red card from Steve's cards is $\frac{3}{5}$.

(a) How many cards of each colour *could* there be in Steve's cards?

(b) Write down another possibility for the number of cards of each colour that are in Steve's cards.

8   Mark played a card game with Paul. The cards were dealt so that both players received two cards. Mark's cards were a five and a four. Paul's first card was a six.

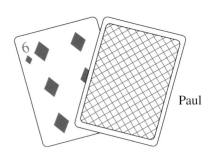

Mark   Paul

Find the probability that Paul's second card was

(a) a five

(b) a picture card [a King, Queen or Jack].

9   One ball is selected at random from a bag containing m white balls and n green balls. What is the probability of selecting a green ball?

Experimental probability

Experimental probability = $\dfrac{\text{number of trials in which event occurs}}{\text{total number of trials made}}$

Exercise 2M

Carry out experiments to work out the experimental probability of some of the following events.

Exercise 2E

You may use a calculator.

1   A bag contained coloured balls. Rajiv randomly selects a ball from the bag and
    then replaces it. Here are the results.

Colour	White	Green	Blue
Frequency	10	31	19

Estimate the probability that on his next draw he will select
(a) a white ball   (b) a green ball.

2   Dimpna and Jenny both did the 'dropping a drawing pin' experiment. Here are their results.

Dimpna

Trials	20
'Point up'	10

Jenny

Trials	150
'Point up'	61

Another drawing pin is dropped.
(a) For Dimpna, what is the probability of getting 'point up'?
(b) For Jenny, what is the probability of getting 'point up'?
(c) Whose result is likely to be more reliable? Why?

3   Roll a fair dice 60 times. How many 'ones' would you expect to roll?
    Compare your experimental result with the theoretical one.
    Suppose you do the experiment again (i.e. roll the dice another 60 times.)
    Would you expect to get the same result?

4 Sean collected the results of 40 Liverpool home games.
Estimate the probability that in their next home game:

(a) they will win

(b) they will lose.

Won	18
Lost	10
Drawn	12

For Liverpool's next 40 games, the results were:

Using all 80 results, estimate the probability of

(c) winning their next game.

(d) drawing their next game.

Won	23
Lost	11
Drawn	6

Would you expect these probabilities to be more accurate than those based on the first 40 matches? Why?

Two events: listing possible outcomes

When an experiment involves two events, it is usually helpful to make a list of all the possible outcomes. When there is a large number of outcomes, it is important to be systematic in making the list.

● Coins
Using H for 'head' and T for 'tail', two coins can land as:

H	H
H	T
T	H
T	T

The probability of tossing two tails $= \frac{1}{4}$

● Two dice
When a red dice is thrown with a white dice, the outcomes are (red dice first):
$(1, 1), (1, 2), (1, 3), (1, 4), (1, 5), (1, 6), (2, 1), (2, 2), (2, 3)...(6, 6)$.
The 36 equally likely outcomes can be shown on a grid.
Point A shows a 4 on the red dice and a 5 on the white dice. Point B shows a 2 on the red dice and a 4 on the white dice.

The probability of rolling
a four on the red dice and
a five on the white dice is $\frac{1}{36}$

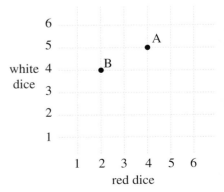

Exercise 3M

1. Roll a pair of dice 108 times and in a tally chart record the frequency of obtaining the totals from 2 to 12.

Total	Frequency
2	
3	
⋮	
⋮	
12	

2. (a) Work out the expected probability of getting a total of 5 when two dice are rolled together. Compare your answer with the experimental probability of getting a total of 5 obtained in the experiment in question ① .

   (b) Work out the expected probability of other totals and compare them with the experimental results.

3. The four cards shown are shuffled and placed face down on a table.

   Two cards are selected at random.

   (a) List all the possible pairs of cards which could be selected.
   (b) Find the probability that the total of the two cards is
      (i) 5
      (ii) 9

4. A red dice is thrown first and then a blue dice is thrown.
   (a) Find the probability that the score on the blue dice is the same as the score on the red dice.
   (b) Find the probability that the score on the blue dice is one more than the score on the red dice.

5.

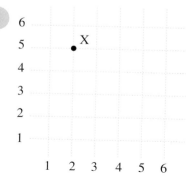

   Two dice are rolled together and the *difference* is found.

   In the grid the point X has a difference of 3 obtained by rolling a 2 and a 5.

   Find the expected probability of obtaining a difference of
   (a) 3
   (b) 0

Exericise 3E

1　The spinner shown has six equal sections on the
outside and three equal sections in the middle.
The spinner shows a '5' and an 'A'.

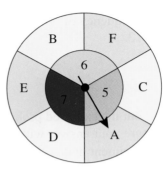

Find the probability of spinning

(a) a 'C'

(b) a '7'

2　A coin and a dice are tossed together.

(a) List all the possible outcomes.

(b) Find the probability of getting

(i) a head on the coin and a 6 on the dice

(ii) a tail on the coin and an even number on the dice.

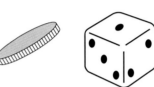

3　Two bags contain numbered discs as shown.
One disc is selected at random from each bag.
The numbers on the two discs are added together.

(a) Draw a grid to show all 28 possible outcomes.

(b) Find the probability that

(i) the total of the two numbers is 6

(ii) the total of the two numbers is less than 5.

4　A bag contains a 1p coin, a 10p coin and a 20p coin. Two coins are selected at random.

(a) List all the different ways in which two coins can be selected from the bag.

(b) Find the probability that the total value of the two coins selected is

(i) 11p

(ii) 30p

5　(a) List all the outcomes when three coins
are tossed together, for example: H T H

(b) Find the probability of getting

(i) exactly one head

(ii) three tails

CHECK YOURSELF ON SECTIONS 6.1 AND 6.2

1 Expressing one number as a percentage of another number

(a) John has 25 books. Nineteen of the books are about history. What percentage of the books are about history?

(b) A man earns £10400 and pays £1768 in tax. What percentage of his earnings does he pay in tax?

2 Finding a percentage of a number

Use a calculator to work out

(a) 35% of £15 (b) 16% of £213 (c) 5.4% of £1650

3 Finding percentage increases and decreases

(a) Ali earns £540 each week.
She gets a pay rise of 15%.
How much money does she earn now?

(b) (i) Calculate the area of this picture.
  (ii) Calculate the new area when the length of each side is decreased by 5%.

12 cm

12 cm

4 Finding the probability of events occurring or not occurring

(a) During the winter the probability of Amy's car starting in the morning is 0.9.
What is the probability that Amy's car will *not* start in the morning?

(b) A box contains 2 yellow balls, 3 blue balls and 3 pink balls.
Find the probability of
  (i) selecting a blue ball
  (ii) *not* selecting a pink ball
  (iii) The 2 yellow balls are replaced by 2 pink balls.
   Find the probability of *not* selecting a pink ball.

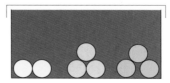

5   Finding experimental probabilities

Steve takes 25 penalties and scores 18 goals.

Estimate the probability that with his next penalty:

(a) he will score a goal

(b) he will *not* score a goal

(c) would you expect the probabilities to be more accurate
     if Steve took 100 penalties and these results were used?

6   Finding probabilities involving two events

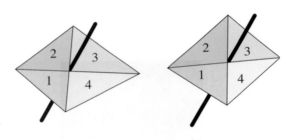

(a) Each spinner is used once.
     List all the possible outcomes.

eg.   Spinner A   Spinner B
         1   1
         1   2
         ⋮   ⋮

(There are 16 different outcomes)

(b) What is the probability of getting a total
     score of 3?

(c) Two coins are thrown. What is the
     probability that they both land on heads?

6.3 Measures

In section 6.3 you will:

- convert metric units
- use imperial units

Converting between metric units

Length	Mass	Volume
1 cm = 10 mm	1 kg = 1000 g	1 millilitre (ml) = 1 cm^3
1 m = 100 cm	1 tonne = 1000 kg	1 litre = 1000 ml

(a) 2.3 km = 2300 m
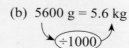

(b) 5600 g = 5.6 kg
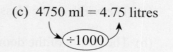

(c) 4750 ml = 4.75 litres

Exercise 1M

Copy and complete the following:

1   2.75 m = _____ cm

2   0.45 m = _____ cm

3   5 m = _____ cm

4   19 cm = _____ m

5   350 m = _____ km

6   15 cm = _____ m

7   60 mm = _____ cm

8   200 mm = _____ cm

9   5 mm = _____ cm

10   2500 m = _____ km

11   3 kg = _____ g

12   9.8 kg = _____ g

13   450 g = _____ kg

14   2 tonnes = _____ kg

15   3500 ml = _____ litres

16   An alligator is crossing a 5.8 metre road. The alligator has 94cm still to walk to get to the other side of the road. How far has the alligator walked across the road so far?

17   Ben weighs 52.4 kg. He puts on 1850 g weight during the next three weeks. How many kilograms does he now weigh?

18   A giant conveyer belt moves 100 kg of coal every minute. How many tonnes of coal will be moved in 1 hour?

274

19 Ellie walks 70 m in one minute. How many kilometres does she walk in half-an-hour?

20  A bottle of medicine contains 0.28 litres of cough mixture. How many 5 ml spoonfuls of medicine will the bottle provide?

21 A newspaper reported that a very rich American earned $30 every second of the day. How much did the rich American earn in one day?

22 Jack buys a 0.44 kg pack of bacon and 0.25 kg of butter. For breakfast he eats 75 g of bacon and 15 g of butter on his toast. How much bacon and how much butter does he have left?

23 Copy and complete each sentence.

(a) The width of the classroom is about ☐ m.

(b) The height of the door is about ☐ cm.

(c) A can of coke has a capacity of about ☐ ml.

(d) The width of a thumbnail is about ☐ mm.

24 A lorry weighs 2.6 tonnes. A load of 870 kg is put onto the lorry. What is the total weight (in tonnes) of the lorry and its load?

25 At noon on April 1st a giant egg-timer was started. It was due to stop 1020 seconds later. At what time did it stop?

Converting between metric and imperial units

1 m ≈ 3 feet   1 kg ≈ 2.2 pounds

8 km ≈ 5 miles   1 gallon ≈ 4.5 litres

1 litre is just less than 2 pints

1 foot = 12 inches   1 yard = 3 feet

1 stone = 14 pounds   1 pound = 16 ounces

Exercise 1E

Some, though not all, of the measurements on the next page are reasonable. Use your common sense to help you complete this table. Where the measurement given is obviously wrong write a more sensible number.

Object	Measurement	Object	Measurement
Pound coin		Football	
Tennis ball		Family car	
This book		Newborn baby	
Chair height		Bag of sugar	
Tennis court		Biro	
Car speed		Labrador	
Pile of pound coins		Badminton net	
12 year old boy		50 seater coach	

A bag of sugar weighs about 2 pounds

A one pound coin weighs about 200 g

A tennis court is about 20 yards long.

A 50-seater coach is about 15 metres long

A tennis ball has a diameter of about 3 inches

A normal family car weighs about 160 kg.

IF A FULL SIZE PLASTIC FOOTBALL WAS FILLED WITH WATER IT WOULD CONTAIN ABOUT 3 LITRES

A fully grown labrador weighs about 4 kg

At a speed of 75 m.p.h. a car travels about one kilometre in a minute.

An 'average' new-born baby weighs about six ounces.

A pile of 100 one pound coins would be about 2 metres high

A badminton net is about 3 feet high

This book is about 4 mm thick.

The height of the seat of a normal chair is about 18 inches.

An ordinary biro is about $2\frac{1}{2}$ inches long

An average 12 year old boy weighs about six stones

6.4 Algebra Review

In section 6.4 you will:

- collect like terms
- substitute numbers for letters
- multiply out single brackets
- solve linear equations

Collecting like terms and substituting numbers into expressions

$5 \times m = 5\,m$

$m \times m = m^2$

$\dfrac{m}{n} = m \div n$

If $m = 4$ and $n = 6$:

$m + 2n = 4 + (2 \times 6) = 4 + 12 = 16$

$\dfrac{n^2}{m} = \dfrac{6 \times 6}{4} = \dfrac{36}{4} = 9$

Like terms can be added:

$3a + 4b + 2a - 2b = 5a + 2b$

$7m + 3 + 2m = 9m + 3$

Exercise 1M

For questions ① to ⑥ answer true or false:

1. $3a + 5a + 3b - b = 8a + 3b$
2. $4x + 3y + 2x - 4x = 2x + 3y$
3. $9m - 3m + 5n + n = 6m + 6n$
4. $2p + 3q + 5q + 2 - 2q = 2p + 6q + 2$
5. $x + 3y + 4x + x + 5 = 6x + 8y$
6. $8a + 6 - 3a + 7 - a = 4a + 13$

For questions ⑦ to ⑱, use $m = 7$, $n = 3$ and $w = 4$ to find the value of each expression.

7. $4m + n$
8. nw
9. $2w + 5n$
10. w^2
11. $2m - 2n$
12. $\dfrac{2m - 2n}{w}$
13. $\dfrac{8n}{w}$
14. $4m - w + n$
15. $w^2 - n^2$
16. $m^2 - 5w$
17. $mn + mw$
18. $\dfrac{m - w}{n}$

19.

Write down an expression for the perimeter of this triangle. Collect like terms if possible.

$3a + 5$, $3a + 5$, $3a + 5$

20   Sammy has £36. He spends £*m* on a trip to the cinema. Write down an expression for the money he now has left.

21   Mia gets £*x* from her parents and £*y* from her grandparents. She spends £10. Write down an expression for the money she now has left.

22   If $V = IR$, find the value of V when $I = 20$ and $R = 4$.

23   If $p = 2a + 2b$, find the value of p when $a = 7$ and $b = 12$.

24   A box of matches costs 43p. Dean buys *n* boxes. Write down an expression for the cost of the *n* boxes.

25   Bella has £$(3m + 7n)$. She spends £$3n$ but her mother gives her £*m*. Write down an expression for the money she now has.

Exercise IE

In questions ① to ⑥ , use $a = 2$ and $b = 9$ to find the value of each expression.

1   $3(a + 1)$ 2 $7(b - 4)$ 3 $5(b - a)$

4   $4(a + b)$ 5 $2(4a + b)$ 6 $a(b + 3)$

7   Copy and match up pairs of expressions shown below. The first one is done for you.

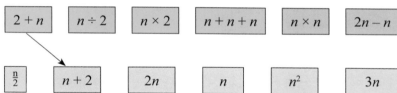

| $2 + n$ | $n \div 2$ | $n \times 2$ | $n + n + n$ | $n \times n$ | $2n - n$ |

| $\frac{n}{2}$ | $n + 2$ | $2n$ | n | n^2 | $3n$ |

8   If $v = u + at$, find the value of v when $u = 18$, $a = 10$ and $t = 6$.

9   If $m = 3(4n + 1)$, find the value of m if $n = 3$.

10   If $p = \frac{w}{5} - 6$, find the value of p if $w = 40$.

11   Frank has made a clock using *n* nuts.

   (a) His sister eats 8 nuts. Write down an expression for how many nuts are still in the clock.

   (b) Frank uses *m* nuts to make his clock look better. How many nuts are in the clock now?

   (c) Frank finishes his clock by using another *m* nuts. How many nuts are in the clock now?

12   The perimeter *p* of a shape is given by the formula

$$p = 3a + 7b + 4c - 2$$

Find the value of *p* when $a = 6$, $b = 4$ and $c = 1$.

13 Which of the cards below have a value *less than* 8 when $n = 4$?

$$2n - 1 \qquad \frac{40}{n} \qquad 2 + 3n \qquad (n - 1)^2$$

$$n^2 - 10 \qquad 5n - 11 \qquad 10 - n$$

14 If $x = 3p + 4$, find the value of x when $p = -2$.

15 Write down a story like question (11) which would give an expression of $m - n - 7$.

Multiplying out single brackets

Reminder: $\qquad 4(n + 2) = 4n + 8 \qquad\qquad\qquad 5(n - 3) = 5n - 15$

$\qquad\qquad\qquad\quad 4(2n + 3) = 8n + 12 \qquad\qquad\quad m(n - 2) = mn - 2m$

Exercise 2M

Multiply out

1 $3(n + 5)$ 2 $6(n - 2)$ 3 $8(n + 4)$

4 $5(n - 5)$ 5 $4(2n + 2)$ 6 $2(7n + 3)$

7 $4(3n - 4)$ 8 $6(4n - 1)$ 9 $7(2 + 6n)$

10 $4(3 + 9n)$ 11 $3(6n - 8)$ 12 $9(5n + 1)$

13 Each person is given £$(2n + 1)$. Write down an expression for the total amount of money these people are given. Multiply out your answer if you need to.

Expand (multiply out) the following expressions:

14 $m(n + 3)$ 15 $p(n + m)$ 16 $a(b - c)$

17 $n(w + y)$ 18 $y(m - 4)$ 19 $x(y + 6)$

20 $f(2n + 4)$ 21 $m(n + 7)$ 22 $4(3m + 5)$

23 $7(2w - 5)$ 24 $n(n - 4)$ 25 $w(w + n)$

Remove brackets and simplify

(a) $5(n + 1) + 3(2n + 4)$

$= 5n + 5 + 6n + 12$

$= 11n + 17$

(b) $2(3a + 4) - 3(a - 5)$

$= 6a + 8 - 3a + 15$

$= 3a + 23$

Exercise 2E

Remove the brackets and simplify.

1 $4(n + 2) + 3(n + 4)$

2 $5(n + 3) + 2(n + 2)$

3 $6(a + 3) + 4(a + 1)$

4 $3(a + 6) + 4(a + 5)$

5 $3(2m + 4) + 3(m + 6)$

6 $4(3n + 2) + 7(2n + 3)$

7 $5(3a + 2) + 4(5a + 6)$

8 $6(2y + 1) + 5(3y + 5)$

9 Find an expression for the total area of these two rectangles. Simplify your answer.

$n + 4$
6

4
$2n + 3$

In questions 10 to 19 remove the brackets and simplify.

10 $4(n + 3) + 5(n - 2)$

11 $3(2n + 1) - 4(n - 3)$

12 $5(a + 6) + 4(a - 3)$

13 $5(3m + 5) - 2(4m - 1)$

14 $6(3x + 5) - 3(4x - 2)$

15 $7(3a + 4) - 3(5a + 6)$

16 $5(4n + 2) + 2(2n - 3)$

17 $4(8n + 3) - 2(9n + 3)$

18 $4(6y + 9) - 3(4y - 1)$

19 $8(2x + 7) - 4(3x + 10)$

Solving linear equations

Remember: The main rule when solving equations is:

'Do the same thing to both sides'

Solve the equations. The circles show what is done to both sides of the equation.

(a) $3n + 2 = 20$

$\boxed{-2}\boxed{-2}$

$3n = 18$

$\boxed{\div 3}\boxed{\div 3}$

$n = 6$

(b) $2n - 7 = 21$

$\boxed{+7}\boxed{+7}$

$2n = 28$

$\boxed{\div 2}\boxed{\div 2}$

$n = 14$

(c) $3(2n - 4) = 18$

Remove brackets first

$6n - 12 = 18$

$\boxed{+12}\boxed{+12}$

$6n = 30$

$\boxed{\div 6}\boxed{\div 6}$

$n = 5$

Exercise 3M

Solve the equations.

1   $6 + n = 40$

2   $n - 5 = 10$

3   $n - 8 = 0$

4   $4n = 24$

5   $3n + 2 = 20$

6   $4n + 7 = 23$

7   $5n - 13 = 27$

8   $9n - 50 = 40$

9   $3n + 8 = 29$

10   $32 = 6n + 14$

11   $7n - 13 = 43$

12   $9 = 2n - 21$

13 
$$n + n + n = 18$$

and   Find the value of m

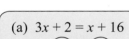
$$m + m + n = 26$$

Now solve these equations.

14   $3(n + 2) = 21$

15   $5(n - 3) = 25$

16   $8(n - 1) = 8$

17   $4(n - 6) = 12$

18   $7(n + 10) = 210$

19   $3(3n + 2) = 42$

20   $5(2n - 4) = 50$

21   $180 = 2(2n - 10)$

22   $20 = 4(2n - 7)$

23   If I double a number n and then subtract 5, the answer is 17. Write down an equation and solve it to find the value of n.

24   This triangle is isosceles. Write down an equation using x and then find the size of each angle in the triangle.

(a) $3x + 2 = x + 16$

$\quad$ $\bigcirc -x \quad \bigcirc -x$

$2x + 2 = 16$

$\quad$ $\bigcirc -2 \quad \bigcirc -2$

$2x = 14$

$\quad$ $\bigcirc \div 2 \quad \bigcirc \div 2$

$x = 7$

(b) $2(4x - 1) = 3(2x + 6)$

Remove brackets first

$8x - 2 = 6x + 18$

$\quad$ $\bigcirc -6x \quad \bigcirc -6x$

$2x - 2 = 18$

$\quad$ $\bigcirc +2 \quad \bigcirc +2$

$2x = 20$

$\quad$ $\bigcirc \div 2 \quad \bigcirc \div 2$

$x = 10$

Exercise 3E

Solve the equations.

1. $5x + 3 = 2x + 15$
2. $7x + 2 = 3x + 22$
3. $3x - 2 = x + 14$
4. $9x - 7 = 4x + 28$
5. $8x - 11 = 5x + 19$
6. $6x + 9 = 4x + 19$
7. $10x + 3 = 4x + 39$
8. $5x + 13 = 3x + 45$

9.  A hat costs £$(5n - 3)$ and jeans cost £$(3n + 17)$. If the hat and jeans cost the same amount of money, find the value of n then work out how much the hat costs?

Now solve these equations.

10. $3(x + 2) = 2(x + 7)$
11. $5(2x - 1) = 3(2x + 5)$
12. $6(x + 3) = 2(2x + 15)$
13. $4(2x - 5) = 5(x + 8)$
14. $2(3x + 2) = 4(x + 6)$
15. $6(3x - 2) = 4(4x + 3)$
16. $3(2x - 4) = 2(2x + 9)$
17. $4(3x + 2) = 5(2x + 4)$

18. If I subtract 2 from the number n and then multiply the result by 5, the answer is 20. Write down an equation and solve it to find the value of n.

19.  The perimeter of this rectangle is 32 cm. Find x and hence find the area of the rectangle.

$x - 2$

$4x + 3$

20. In this number wall the number in each brick is found by adding the numbers in the two bricks below. Find the value of n.

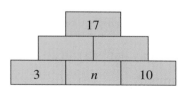

CHECK YOURSELF ON SECTION 6.3 AND 6.4

1   Converting metric units

Copy and complete the following:

(a) 6.7 kg = _____ g   (b) 5.89 litres = _____ ml   (c) 350 m = _____ km

(d) Pete and his 3 mates dig 2.4 tonnes of mud to clear a stream. If each person clears the same amount of mud, how many kilograms of mud does Pete clear?

2   Using imperial units

Answer true or false:

(a) A key measures about 3 inches.

(b) A teapot contains about 2 gallons when full.

(c) An average man will weigh about 13 pounds.

(d) A car is about 4 yards long.

3   Collecting like terms

(a) $3m + 6n - 4n + m = 4m + 2n$ True or false?

(b)

Write down an expression for the perimeter of this trapezium. Collect like terms if possible.

4   Substituting numbers for letters

(a) If $n = 7$, which of the expressions below has the largest value?

$8n$ $n^2 + 9$ $60 - n$ $(n + 1)^2$

(b) If $y = mx + c$, find the value of y when $m = 6$, $x = 7$ and $c = -10$.

5   Multiplying out single brackets

Multiply out   (a) $7(x + 4)$ (b) $6(2n - 1)$ (c) $m(m + n)$

Simplify   (d) $3(n + 5) + 8(n + 2)$ (e) $6(2x + 3) - 4(x - 2)$

6   Solving linear equations

Solve (a) $5x - 3 = 27$ (b) $3(2x + 5) = 33$ (c) $7x - 14 = 3x + 14$

Rafa concentrates better with a box on his head.
He is n years old.

(d) Write down an expression for how old he will be in 34 years time.

(e) Rafa works out that in 34 years he will be three times as old as he is now. Write down an equation using n.

(f) Solve the equation to find out how old he is now.

6.5 3-D Objects

In section 6.5 you will:

● draw 3-D objects on isometric paper

● solve problems with 3-D objects

● draw three different views of a 3-D object

Using isometric paper

A drawing of a solid is a 2-D representation of a 3-D object. Below are two pictures of the same object.

(a) On squared paper.

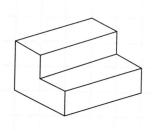

(b) On isometric dot paper.

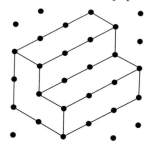

The dimensions of the object cannot be taken from the first picture but they can be taken from the second. Isometric paper can be used either as dots (as above) or as a grid of equilateral triangles. Either way, the paper must be the right way round (as shown here).

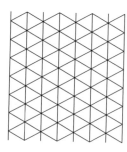

N.B. Most of the questions in this section are easier, and more fun to do, when you have an ample supply of 'unifix' or 'multilink' cubes.

284

Exercise 1M

1 On isometric paper make a copy of each object below. Underneath each drawing state the number of 'multilink' cubes needed to make the object. (Make sure you have the isometric paper the right way round!)

(a) 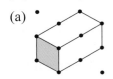 (b) 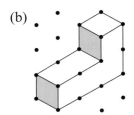 (c)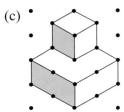

2 Using four cubes, you can make several different shapes. A and B are different shapes but C is the same as A.

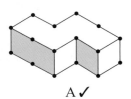 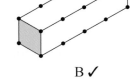 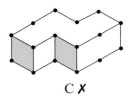

A ✓   B ✓   C ✗

Make as many different shapes as possible, using four cubes, and draw them all (including shapes A and B above) on isometric paper.

3 Make the object shown using cubes.
Now draw the object *from a different view*.

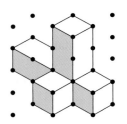

4   A 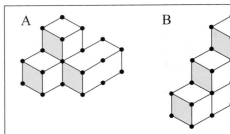   B   C    D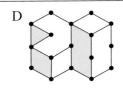

Build your own 3-D models of shapes A, B, C and D above. If possible use a different colour for each one.

Decide which of the shapes on the next page are the same as shape A.
Repeat for shapes B, C and D.
Which shape is neither A, B, C nor D?

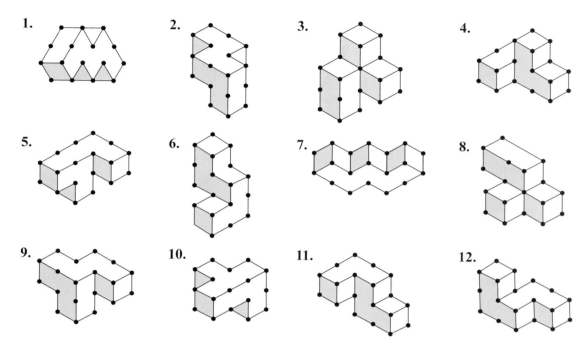

1. 2. 3. 4.

5. 6. 7. 8.

9. 10. 11. 12.

5   You need 18 cubes.
Make the two shapes below. Arrange them to make a 3 × 3 × 2 cuboid by adding a third shape, which you have to find. Draw the third shape on isometric paper.

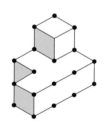   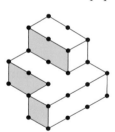

6   You need 27 small cubes for this question.
Make the four shapes below and arrange them into a 3 × 3 × 3 cube by adding a fifth shape, which you have to find. Draw the fifth shape on isometric paper. (The number next to each shape indicates the number of small cubes in that shape).

(a)

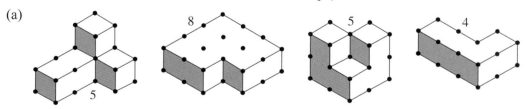

(b)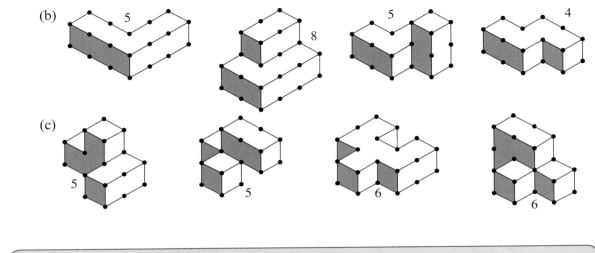

(c)

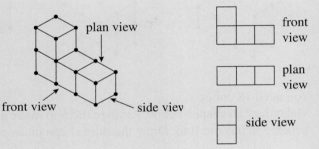

Three views of a shape

Here is a 3-D object made from centimetre cubes. We can draw 3 views of the object on squared paper.

plan view

front view

side view

front view

plan view

side view

Exercise 2M

In questions ① to ⑥ draw the plan view, the front view and the side view of the object

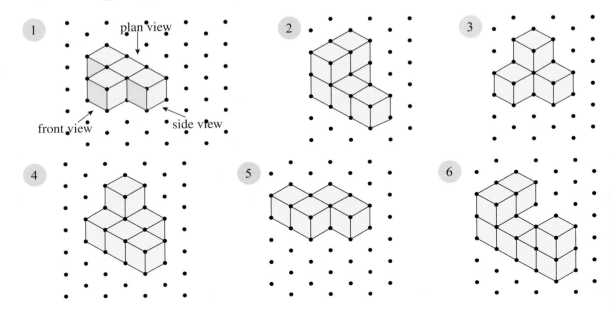

① plan view

front view   side view

②

③

④

⑤

⑥

In questions 7 to 10 you are given three views of a shape. Use the information to make the shape using centimetre cubes.

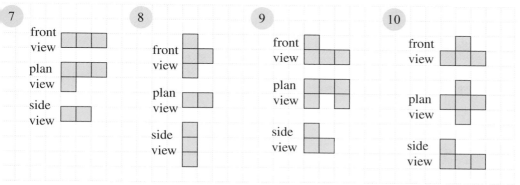

6.6 Bearings and scale drawing

In section 6.6 you will:

● use bearings

● make scale drawings

Bearings

Bearings are used by navigators on ships and aircraft and by people travelling in open country.
Bearings are measured from north in a *clockwise* direction.
A bearing is always given as a three-figure number.

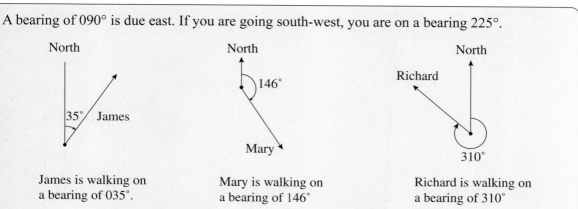

A bearing of 090° is due east. If you are going south-west, you are on a bearing 225°.

James is walking on a bearing of 035°.

Mary is walking on a bearing of 146°

Richard is walking on a bearing of 310°

Exercise 1M

1　Ten children on a treasure hunt start in the middle of a field and begin walking in the directions shown on the right. On what bearing is each child walking?

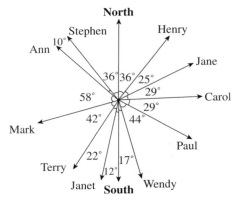

2　Ten pigeons are released and they fly in the directions shown below. On what bearing is each pigeon flying?

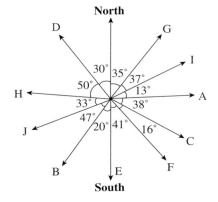

3　For each diagram, write down the bearing of C from D.

(a)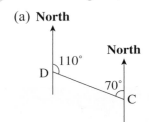

(b)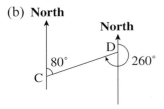

(c)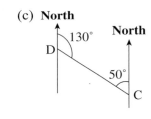

Exercise 1E

1　Use a protractor to measure the bearing on which each person is moving.

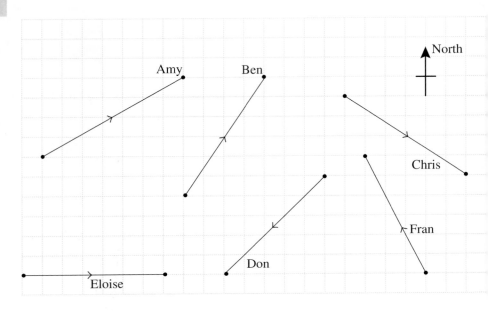

2 Measure the bearing of these journeys.

(a) A to B   (b) B to C

(c) A to C   (d) A to D

(e) C to D

3 Draw lines to show the following bearings.

(a) 040°   (b) 075°

(c) 120°   (d) 200°

(e) 300°

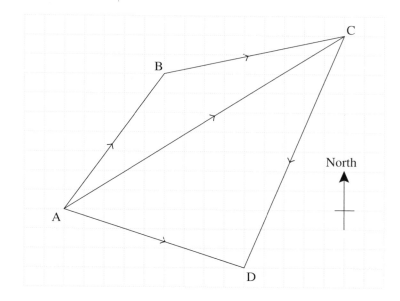

4 The map shows several features on and around an island. Axes are drawn to identify positions.
[eg The coordinates of the cave are (9, 3).]

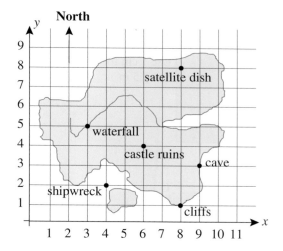

Four commandos, Piers, Quintin, Razak and Smudger, are in hiding on the island. Find the coordinates of the commandos, using the following information.

(a) The castle ruins are due south of Piers and the waterfall is due west of him.

(b) From Quintin, the bearing of the satellite dish is 045° and the shipwreck is due south of him.

(c) From Razak, the bearing of the waterfall is 315° and the bearing of the castle ruins is 045°.

(d) From Smudger, the bearing of the cave is 135° and the bearing of the waterfall is 225°.

(e) The leader of the commandos is hiding somewhere due north of the shipwreck in a hollow tree. From this tree, the castle ruins and the cliffs are both on the same bearing. Find the coordinates of this hollow tree.

290

Scale drawing

A rectangle has length 12 m and width 8 m.

Draw an accurate scale drawing of the rectangle using a scale of 1 cm for every 4 m.

Length 12 m will be $12 \div 4 = 3$ cm on the drawing.

Width 8 m will be $8 \div 4 = 2$ cm on the drawing.

Scale drawing:

3 cm

2 cm

Exercise 2M

Draw an accurate scale drawing of each shape below using the scale shown.

1

20 m

25 m

Use 1 cm for every 5 m.

2

30 m

A

50 m

B

Use 1 cm for every 10 m. Measure and write down the real length of AB (in metres).

3

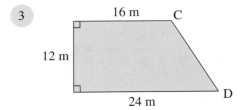

16 m   C

12 m

24 m

D

Use 1 cm for every 4 m. Measure and write down the real length of CD (in metres).

4

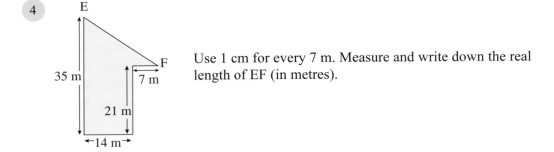

E

35 m

F

7 m

21 m

←14 m→

Use 1 cm for every 7 m. Measure and write down the real length of EF (in metres).

5

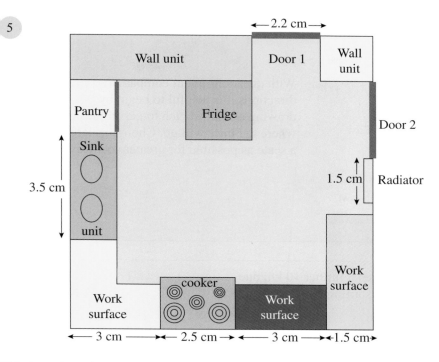

This is a plan of Mrs Smith's kitchen. It has been drawn to a scale of 1 cm for every 40 cm (often written as 1 : 40).

(a) In Mrs Smith's house, how wide is

    (i) the cooker   (ii) the sink unit   (iii) the radiator   (iv) door 1?

(b) If the work surface next to the radiator is 160 cm long what length would it be on the plan?

(c) If door 2 is 92 cm wide, what length should it be on the plan?

This is a plan of Mr Hazel's bathroom. It is drawn to a scale of 1 cm for every 50 cm (often written as 1 : 50).

(d) Measure the length and width of the floor on the plan.

(e) Calculate the real length and width of the bathroom.

(f) The door to the bedroom is 80 cm wide. How wide should it be on the plan? Measure and check your answer.

(g) The towel rail measures 1.4 cm on the plan. How long is the real one?

(h) Measure the length of the sliding door on the plan. How wide is the real one?

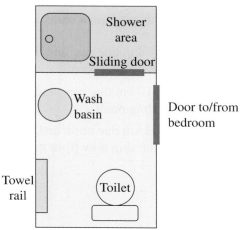

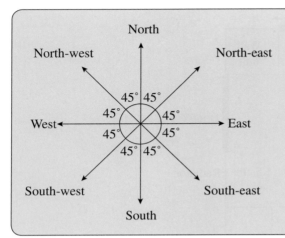

With questions about compass directions it is helpful to begin by drawing a small sketch to get an idea of where the lines will go. Choose as large a scale as possible for greater accuracy.

A ship sails 7 km north-east and then a further 10 km due south. How far is the ship from its starting point?

We will use a scale of 1 cm to 1 km.

(a) Mark a starting point S and draw a line at 45° to the lines on the page.

(b) Mark a point A, 7 cm from S.

(c) Draw a line vertically through A and mark a point F, 10 cm from A

(d) Measure the distance SF.
Answer: The ship is 7.1 km from its starting point.
(An answer between 7.0 km and 7.2 km would be acceptable.)

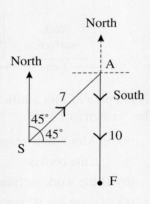

Exercise 2E

In questions (1) to (7) use a scale of 1 cm to represent 1 km.

1 A ship sails 7 km due east and then a further 5 km due south. Find the distance of the ship from its starting point.

2 A ship sails 10 km due west and then a further 4 km south-east. Find the distance of the ship from its starting point.

3 A ship sails 8 km due north and then a further 7 km on a bearing 080°. How far is the ship now from its starting point?

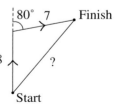

4 A ship sails 6 km on a bearing of 120° and then a further 4 km due south. How far is the ship from its starting point?

5 A ship sails 7 km on a bearing of 075° and then a further 5 km on a bearing of 130°.
   How far is the ship from its starting point?

6 A bird leaves its nest and flies around its
   territory in three stages.

   (a) Make a scale drawing to show the journey.

   (b) How far does the bird have to fly to return to
       its nest?

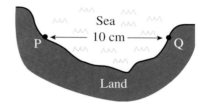

	Direction	Distance
1st stage	west	5 km
2nd stage	south-east	6 km
3rd stage	east	12 km

7 The diagram shows ports P and Q where P is
   10 km west of Q. An aircraft carrier A is 9 km
   north-east of P. An enemy submarine S is 4 km
   north-west of Q. The torpedoes on the submarine
   have a range of 4 km. Is the aircraft carrier in range
   of the torpedoes?

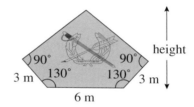

8 Here is a sketch of a company logo which is to be
   painted full size on the side of a ship.
   The designer needs to know the total height of the logo.
   Make a scale drawing of the logo with a scale of 1 cm
   to 1 m and find the height of the logo.

9 Draw a point F with a cross. Use a scale of 1 cm to 1 km to show
   the points G and H described below.

   Point G is 9 km from F on a bearing of 130° from F.
   Point H is 10 km from F on a bearing of 212° from F.
   What is the bearing of G from H?

10
   Make a scale drawing of a room in your house.
   Design a layout for the furniture you would like
   to have in the room.

6.7 Decimals Review

In section 6.7 you will:

- add, subtract and order decimals
- multiply and divide decimals

Adding, subtracting and ordering decimals

Remember: line up the decimal point

(a) $4.1 + 5 + 6.87$

$$
\begin{array}{r}
4.1 \\
5.0 \\
+\ 6.87 \\
\hline
15.97 \\
\scriptstyle 1
\end{array}
$$

(b) $14 - 8.6$

$$
\begin{array}{r}
{}^{0}1\overset{13}{4}.{}^{1}0 \\
-\ 8.6 \\
\hline
5.4
\end{array}
$$

Remember: For ordering, put in zeros first

(c) Write   3.6, 3.56, 3.62, 3.074 in ascending order.

These are   3.600, 3.560, 3.620, 3.074

In order: 3.074, 3.56, 3.6, 3.62

Exercise 1M

Work out

1   $4.2 + 9$

2   $4.19 - 3.68$

3   $7.3 - 5.12$

4   $6 + 3.18 + 2.6$

5   $13.7 + 6.49$

6   $18 - 4.7$

7   $23.6 - 5.28$

8   $14.2 + 5.17 + 7.5$

9   $5.2 + 8 - 2.37$

10   What is 0.001 less than 0.62?

11   Four people walk across a tightrope. The time taken for each person is shown below.

Maurice	78.4	seconds
Cheryl	79.2	seconds
Ashley	78.38	seconds
Deb	79.09	seconds

Write down the names in order of the time taken, starting with the quickest.

12 Write the number half way between 4.6 and 4.7.

13 The weights of five babies are shown below:

Ryan	Beth	Tania	David	Alex
3.94 kg	3.08 kg	3.6 kg	3.9 kg	3.07 kg

Write down the names in order of weight, starting with the heaviest.

14 Which is larger? 0.74 + 8 + 4.6 or 15.8 − 2.56

15

value of bike	cost of service
£0 – £150	£15.70
£151 – £300	£19.35
£301 – £500	£21.54
£501 – £1000	£25.60
over £1000	£32.45

Hayley's bike shop will service bikes (ie. make sure everything is working properly). The cost of the service depends on the value of the bike as shown in the table. Angus has three bikes serviced. The values of the bikes are £485, £1209 and £264.
How much does Angus pay to have all three bikes serviced?

Multiplying and dividing decimals

(a) 5 × 0.03
   (5 × 3 = 15)
   5 × 0.0<u>3</u> = 0.1<u>5</u>

(b) 0.8 × 0.4
   (8 × 4 = 32)
   0.<u>8</u> × 0.<u>4</u> = 0.3<u>2</u>

(c) 0.09 × 0.7
   (9 × 7 = 63)
   0.0<u>9</u> × 0.<u>7</u> = 0.06<u>3</u>

> Remember: To divide by any decimal number we transform the calculation into a division by a whole number

(d) 2.8 ÷ 0.4 = 28 ÷ 4 = 7   [Multiply 2.8 and 0.4 by 10]

(e) 1.8 ÷ 0.06 = 180 ÷ 6 = 30   [Multiply 1.8 and 0.06 by 100]

Exercise 1E

Work out

1 0.6 × 0.04

2 0.07 × 0.03

3 5 × 0.09

4 0.05 × 0.8

5 3.6 ÷ 0.04

6 0.065 ÷ 0.5

7 0.783 ÷ 0.03

8 0.1584 ÷ 0.06

9 Harry is on holiday and needs to change £80 into dollars. If £1 can be changed for $1.60, how many dollars will Harry get?

10 How many 0.2 m pieces of wood can be cut from a 3 metre length of wood?

11 Wire netting costs £0.88 per metre. What is the cost of 4.5 m of wire netting?

12

Mary buys some Pik'n Mix sweets at the cinema. The weight of the sweets is shown opposite. How much does Mary pay for her sweets if 1 kilogram costs £9.80?

13 Copy and complete the multiplication square.

×		0.6	0.07
0.4			
0.03	0.09		
	1.8		

14 (a) Find the area of this rectangle.

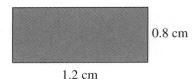

0.8 cm

1.2 cm

(b) Find the length of this rectangle.

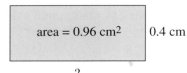

area = 0.96 cm^2 0.4 cm

?

15 (a) Make up your own story question which uses the numbers 3.6 and 0.45 to give an answer of 8.

(b) Now make up a story question which uses the numbers 0.45 and 8 to give an answer of 3.6.

(c) Try and make up more questions using just these 3 numbers.

6.8 Volume

In section 6.8 you will:

● find and use volumes of cuboids

Volume is a measure of how much physical space an object takes up.

Blocks A and B are each made from eight cubes, measuring 1 cm × 1 cm × 1 cm. They each have a volume of 8 cubic cm, which is written 8 cm³.

Rectangular blocks like these are called *cuboids*. A cube, like block B, is a special kind of cuboid.

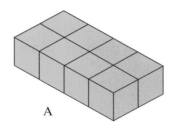

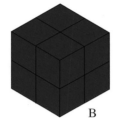

● The volume of a cuboid is given by the formula,

Volume = (length) × (width) × (height)

(a) Find the volume of the cuboid

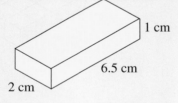

Volume = 2 × 6.5 × 1

= 13 cm³

(b) Find the volume of the cuboid

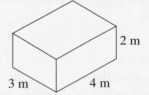

Volume = 3 × 4 × 2

= 24 m³   (note the units)

Exercise 1M

In questions **1** to **6** work out the volume of each cuboid. Give your answer in the correct units.

1

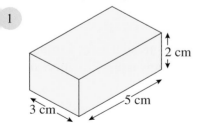

2

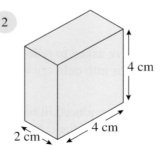

3

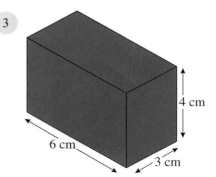

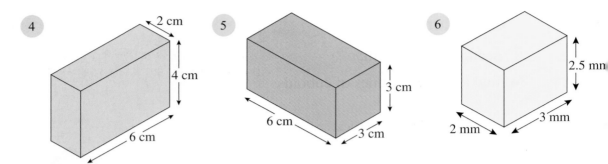

4 2 cm, 4 cm, 6 cm

5 3 cm, 6 cm, 3 cm

6 2.5 mm, 2 mm, 3 mm

In questions **7** to **12** write down the volume of the object. All the objects are made from centimetre cubes.

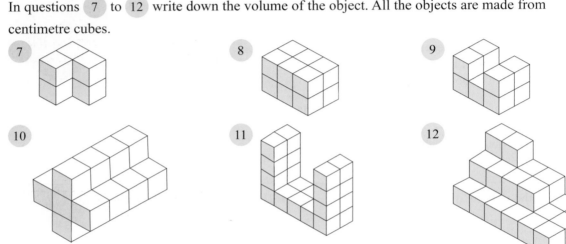

7

8

9

10

11

12

13 (a) Draw a sketch of a 4 m by 4 m by 2 m cuboid.
  (b) Calculate the volume of the cuboid.
  (c) Calculate the total surface area of the cuboid.

14 Calculate the volume of each girder by splitting them into cuboids. All lengths are in cm.

  (a) 1, 9, 2, 8, 5

  (b) 4, 6, 10, 5, 4, 3

15

Farmers were asked to redesign their melons so that they could fit more melons into delivery boxes. They grew melons as cubes of side 16 cm.

The melons are placed in boxes each of which is in the shape of a cube. Each side of the cube is 1.28 m. How many melons will fit into one of these boxes?

Exercise 1E

1

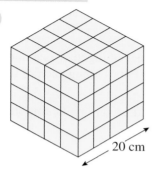

20 cm

The large cube is cut into lots of identical small cubes as shown. Calculate the volume of each small cube.

2

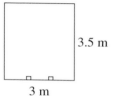

3.5 m

3 m

A mine shaft 400 m long is dug with the cross-section shown. Calculate the volume of earth which must be removed to make way for the shaft.

3 The diagram shows an empty swimming pool.
Water is pumped into the pool at a rate of 2 m³ per minute.
How long will it take to fill the pool?

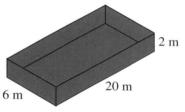

2 m

6 m   20 m

4 The shapes below are nets for closed boxes. Work out the volume of the box in each case, giving your answer in cubic cm.

(a)

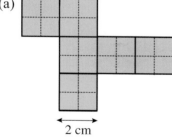

2 cm

(b)

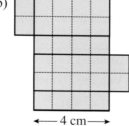

←— 4 cm —→

(c)

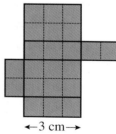

←3 cm→

5 In a storm 2 cm of rain fell in 1 hour. Calculate the volume of water, in cm³, which fell on the roof of the garage shown.

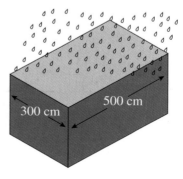

500 cm

300 cm

300

6   The inside of a spaceship orbiting the earth is a cuboid measuring 200 cm by 300 cm by
    200 cm. Unfortunately air is leaking from the spaceship at a rate of 1000 cm³ /sec.
    How long will it take for all the air to leak out?

7   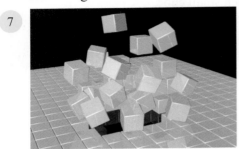 Gold cubes of side 3 cm are placed together in a flat
    square. The flat square has 30 cubes along each of its
    sides.

    What is the volume of the gold used to make this shape?

8   Find the length x.

(a)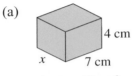
    4 cm
    x 7 cm
    volume = 70 cm³

(b)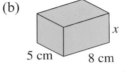
    x
    5 cm   8 cm
    volume = 120 cm³

(c)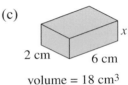
    x
    2 cm   6 cm
    volume = 18 cm³

(d)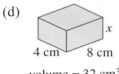
    x
    4 cm   8 cm
    volume = 32 cm³

(e)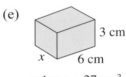
    3 cm
    x 6 cm
    volume = 27 cm³

(f)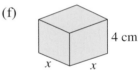
    4 cm
    x x
    volume = 100 cm³

9   The diagram shows an object of volume 7 cm³.
    Use isometric paper to draw the following objects:
    (a) a cuboid with volume 45 cm³
    (b) a T-shaped object with volume 15 cm³
    (c) an L-shaped object with volume 20 cm³
    (d) any object with a volume of 23 cm³.

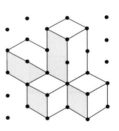

10 Sketch a cuboid a cm by b cm by c cm.
    (a) Write an expression for the volume of the cuboid.
    (b) Write an expression for the total surface area of the cuboid.

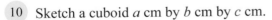

CHECK YOURSELF ON SECTIONS 6.6, 6.7 AND 6.8

1 Using bearings

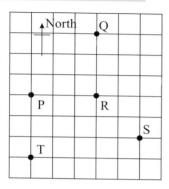

State the bearings of (a) Q from P

(b) R from P

(c) S from R

(d) R from Q

(e) P from R

(f) T from R

2 Making scale drawings

(a)

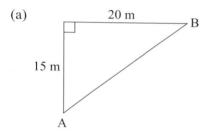

Draw an accurate scale drawing of this triangle using a scale of 1 cm for every 5 m. Measure and write down the real length of AB (in metres).

(b) A plane flies 70 km on a bearing of 040° and then a further 50 km south. Make a scale drawing using a scale of 1 cm for every 10 km. Find the distance of the plane from its starting point.

3 Adding, subtracting and dividing decimals

Work out   (a) $6.19 + 4.7 + 8$ (b) $14.2 - 6.87$

(c) Write these decimals in order of size, starting with the smallest:

0.74   0.704   0.074   0.407   0.04

4 Multiplying and dividing decimals

Work out   (a) 0.09×0.6 (b) $4.2 \div 0.06$ (c) $7.44 \div 0.3$

(d) Potatoes cost £0.86 per kilogram. Work out the cost of 3.5 kg of potatoes.

5   Finding and using volumes of cuboids

Find the volume of each solid.

(a)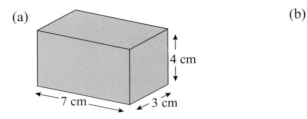

4 cm

7 cm   3 cm

(b)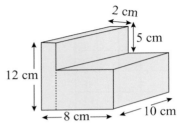

2 cm

5 cm

12 cm

8 cm   10 cm

(c)

The internal dimensions of the container with this lorry are 7 m by 3 m by 3 m. How many times would the lorry need to be fully loaded to transport 504 m³ of cargo?

UNIT 6   MIXED REVIEW

Part one

1   A survey of 400 people reveals that 28% of people like 'Minty Fresh' toothpaste. Work out the number of people who liked 'Minty Fresh.'

2   Ten discs numbered 1, 3, 3, 3, 4, 7, 8, 9, 11, 11 are placed in a bag. One disc is selected at random.

Find the probability that it is

(a) an even number

(b) a three

(c) less than 6.

3   Write each sentence with the number you think is most likely.

(a) The width of an adult hand is ☐. (4 inches, 4 cm, 0.5 m)

(b) The classroom door is ☐ high. (80 cm, 2 m, 3 feet)

(c) An adult man weighs about ☐. (75 g, 750 kg, 75 kg)

4. The model is made from matchboxes.

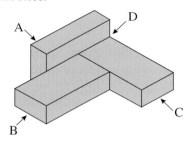

From which direction (A, B, C, or D) are these views taken?

(a)

(b)

(c)

(d)

5. When playing Monopoly, Philip knows that the probability of throwing a 'double' with two dice is $\frac{1}{6}$. What is the probability that he does *not* throw a double with his next throw?

6. Find the value of each expression when $n = 3$.

   (a) $n^2 - n$ (b) $4n + 2$ (c) $(5 - n)^2$ (d) $\frac{6}{n}$

7. Rewrite the expressions using algebra:
   (a) add four to m
   (b) subtract p from six
   (c) triple t then take away two

8. A dog weighs 25 kg. After a strict diet, the weight of the dog decreases by 8%. How much does the dog weigh now?

9.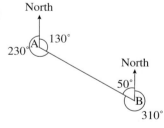

   Write down the bearing of A *from* B.

10. For one unit of electricity, which costs 12p, you can either watch 18 episodes of 'EastEnders' or heat water for 36 cups of tea.
    How much will it cost in electricity for Mr and Mrs Jones to watch 54 episodes of EastEnders and each drinking a cup of tea while doing so?

11 Solve the equations

(a) $5(2n - 3) = 25$ (b) $32 = 17 + 5n$ (c) $8n - 1 = 3n + 29$

12 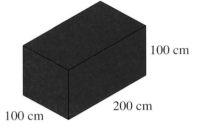 Carrots cost 75p per kilogram. Some carrots weigh the amount shown opposite. How much will these carrots cost?

13 How many times can the small box be filled from the large container which is full of fertilizer?

20 cm

10 cm 10 cm

100 cm

100 cm

200 cm

14 A spoon contains 20 ml of cough mixture. How many spoons can be filled from a one litre bottle of cough mixture?

15 13 out of 80 cars failed their annual MOT test. What percentage of the cars failed?

Part two

1 Karen is going to play a game called 'Lucky Dip.' There are three bags labelled A, B and C. Each bag contains red or green balls. You win if you draw out a red ball from a bag.

Bag A   Bag B   Bag C

(a) Write down the probability of winning from bag A, from bag B, and from bag C.

(b) What is the probability of *not* winning from bag A?

2 Sam thinks of a number. He multiplies it by 3, adds 4 and then doubles the result. The answer is 50. Form an equation and then solve it to find the number.

3 Asif is working on the top floor of a very tall office building. He walks up 826 steps from the ground floor to his office. Each step is 24 cm.

(a) How high does he climb in cm?

(b) Change the height into km, correct to one decimal place.

4 Multiply out these brackets.

   (a) $4(n + 6)$ (b) $5(3y - 7)$ (c) $m(m - p)$

5

Garden monster

Fang, with 27,000 teeth and weighing in at 21.7 g and 5in long, beat 30 contenders for the heavyweight title of the slug world. The event at a Bristol garden centre raised several hundred pounds for charity. Fang, a common black slug, was entered by Betty Baptiste, 60.

   (a) How many kg does Fang weigh?

   (b) Is Fang more or less than 20 cm long?

6 Anna has n marbles in a bag.

   (a) She takes 3 marbles from the bag. Write an expression for the number of marbles now in the bag.

   (b) Steve has four bags, each containing n marbles. Write an expression for the number of marbles there are altogether in the four bags.

   (c) In a game Steve wins 10 more marbles. Write an expression for the number of marbles which he has now.

7 Draw this shape, on squared paper, as viewed from

   (a) A

   (b) B

   (c) C

   (d) D

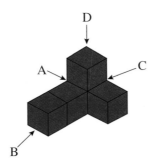

8 The cooks at McDonalds use 4000 ml of oil in 5 days. How many days will a 200 litre tank of oil last?

9 One card is picked at random from a pack of 52.
Find the probability that it is

   (a) the Queen of diamonds

   (b) a ten

   (c) a diamond.

10 Four people are putting their suitcases on a plane. Each person is only allowed to take 22 kg on the plane.

(a) Whose luggage is too heavy and by how much?

	Weight of suitcases
Yasmin	7.83 kg, 12.14 kg
Eric	9.46 kg, 13.78 kg
Marie	6.19 kg, 8.37 kg, 5.2 kg
Matt	5.87 kg, 9.26 kg, 7.49 kg

(b) People can pay money to put extra weight on the plane. The costs are shown in the table opposite.
How much extra will each of the people you chose in part (a) need to pay?

extra weight	cost
0.01 kg to 0.5 kg	£13.68
0.51 kg to 1.5 kg	£29.17
1.51 kg to 3 kg	£42.13
3.01 kg to 5 kg	£57.45

11

3 cm

4 cm

5 cm

(a) Calculate the volume of this cuboid.

(b) Calculate the volume of the cuboid when each of the dimensions is increased by 10%.

12 A bucket weighs 1.2 kg when it is empty, and 6.6 kg when it is full of water. What will it weigh when it is half full?

13

x

$x + 30°$

The diagram shows two angles in an isosceles triangle. Form an equation involving x and solve it to find the angles of the triangle.

14 For his prize-winning three dimensional puzzle of planet earth the inventor received £10000 plus 3% of the profits made by the distributor. In ten years the distributor's profit was £8 795 400. How much did the inventor receive altogether?

15 The symbols $\bigcirc$, $\triangle$, $\square$, $*$ represent numbers.
Use the clues in (a), (b) and (c) to answer part (d)

(a) $\bigcirc + \triangle = *$

(b) $\bigcirc = \triangle + \square$

(c) $\bigcirc + \bigcirc + \triangle = * + \square + \square + \square$

(d) $\triangle =$ how many $\square$ s?

Answers to 'check yourself' questions

Page 12   sections 1.1 and 1.2

1. (a) 5   (b) 512   (c) 6   (d) $-6, -2, \boxed{2}, 6, \boxed{10}$

2. (a) multiply by 4   (b) add 6   (c) subtract 3

(d) 9, 26, 77, 230   **3.** (a) $2\frac{1}{3}$ (b) $5\frac{5}{6}$

(c) $\frac{19}{5}$ (d) $\frac{11}{4}$ **4.** (a) $\frac{17}{30}$ (b) $\frac{5}{24}$

(c) $4\frac{1}{6}$ **5.** (a) 28   (b) $\frac{3}{10}$ (c) $\frac{3}{14}$

Page 26   sections 1.3 and 1.4

1. (a) 1, 28, 2, 14, 4, 7   (b) 60   (c) 15, 30, 45, 60, 75, 90

(d) 20, 40, 60, 80, 100, 120   (e) 60   **2.** (a) 20   (b) 121

3. (a) $126 = 2 \times 3 \times 3 \times 7$ (b) $150 = 2 \times 3 \times 5 \times 5$

4. (a) 2^5 larger by 5   (b) 625   (c) 47

5. (a) -6 (b) 1   (c) 7   (d) -5 (e) -2 (f) -3

6. (a) 28   (b) -10 (c) -5

(d) A = -16, B = -2, c = 24, D = -8, E = -4, F = -40

Page 33   section 1.5

1. (a) 28 cm^2 (b) 67 cm^2 (c) 100 cm^2 (d) 36 cm^2

2. (a) 90 cm^2 (b) 120 cm^2 (c) 96 minutes

Page 59   sections 2.1 and 2.2

1. (a) 6.2   (b) 23.85   (c) 0.36   (d) 0.2   (e) 10.05

(f) 10.76   (g) 118.03   **2.** (a) 800   (b) 200   (c) 36

(d) 2400   **3.** (a) $2m + 3n + 4$ (b) $x + 3y$ (c) $5p - 4$

(d) A & C   **4.** (a) mp (b) $3n - 5$ (c) $70 + 4q$

5. (a) $n \times 4, 2n + 2n, 5n - n$ (b) false

(c) No   (d) $5n + 14$

Page 29   sections 2.3 and 2.4

1.

$\frac{3}{5}$	$\frac{7}{20}$	$\frac{3}{100}$	$\frac{3}{8}$	$\frac{3}{25}$	$\frac{4}{5}$
0.6	0.36	0.03	0.375	0.12	0.8

2. (a) $0.\dot{8}$ (b) $0.\dot{4}\dot{5}$ **3.** (a) 0.34

(b) 44%   (c) True   (d) Roy by 2%

4. a = 112°, b = 68°, c = 73°, d = 46°, e = 134°

5. $a + b + c = 180°$ (angles on a straight line)
So angles in a triangle add up to 180°

6. a = 63°, b = 82°   **7.** a = 119°, b = 58°, c = 49°, d = 73°

Page 86   sections 2.5 and 2.6

1. (a) 5.6 cm   (b) 37.8°

2. (a) circle, centre P radius 4 cm

4. (a) 59.7 cm   (b) 232.5 cm

5. (a) 227.0 cm^2 (b) 907.9 cm^2 (c) 4

Page 105   section 3.1

1. (a) 3068   (b) 2812   (c) 27   (d) 0.79

(e) 2.18   (f) 0.12   **2.** (a) 0.05   (b) 1.35

(c) Snail A   **3.** (a) 0.03   (b) 0.048   (c) 0.084

(d) £2.67   **4.** (a) 70   (b) 140   (c) 0.64   (d) 8

Page 118   sections 3.2 and 3.3

1. (a) 17   (b) 36   (c) 14

(d) 6.41   (e) 0.72   (f) 6.67

2. (a) $\frac{17}{40}$ (b) $\frac{5}{14}$ (c) $1\frac{1}{3}$

3. (a) 17.89   (b) 115.84   (c) 0.92

4. (a) -126 (b) 14   (c) 16

5. (a) $m = 15$ (b) $y = 80$ (c) £1500

6. (a) 1   (b) 27   (c) -9 (d) 33

Page 135   sections 3.4 and 3.5

1. (a) $x = 4$ (b) $y = 3$ (c) $x = -2$ (d) line A $(x = 4)$

2. y: 4, 3, 2, 1, 0   coordinates: (0, 4), (1, 3), (2, 2), (3, 1), (4, 0)

3. (a) 7 km per litre   (b) 14 m.p.g.   (c) 4 gallons

4. (a) $y = x + 6$ (b) A: $x + y = 3$, B: $y = x + 1$

[Answers to 5 and 6 are in main answers book]

Page 162   Sections 4.1 and 4.2

1. (a) 9   (b) 6   (c) 7   (d) 7   (e) 2 and 6

2. one sentence using Class 8B mean = 6 and
Class 8C mean = 7, one sentence using
Class 8B range = 7 and Class 8C range = 6.

3. (a) 5   (b) 4   **4.** (a)

Stem	Leaf
1	9
2	7 9
3	4 7 7 8 9
4	1 3 3 5 7 8 8 9
5	1 2 6
6	1 2 4 7 8
7	7

Key
eg. 3|7 means 37

(b) range = 40, median = 55

Page 184   sections 4.3 and 4.4

1. (a) AB – Two taps are on, BC – one tap is on,

   CD – Simon gets into bath, DE – Simon lies in bath,

   EF – Simon gets out of bath,

   FG – Simon is out of bath looking for shampoo,

   GH – Simon gets into bath, HI – Simon lies in bath,

   IJ – Simon gets out of bath, JK – bath is emptied

   (b) In main answer book   (c) 15:15

2. (a) $5x - 20$ (b) $12x + 6$ (c) $n^2 - 8n$ (d) $11x + 26$

   (e) $14x + 19$ 3. (a) $n = 6$ (b) $x = 6$ (c) $n = 5$

4. (a) $n = 6$ (b) $x = 5$ (c) $x = 4$ 5. (a) 4.2 cm   (b) 6.8 cm

6. (a) 19°   (b) 5   (c) $x = 7$, BC = 33 cm

Page 199   sections 4.5 and 4.6

1. (a) $\frac{8}{35}$ (b) $\frac{31}{40}$ (c) $3\frac{11}{12}$

2. (a) 35   (b) $\frac{1}{6}$ (c) $4\frac{1}{5}$

3. (a) $\frac{9}{100}$, 9%   (b) 0.3, 30%

   (c) $\frac{4}{5}$, 0.8   (d) $\frac{1}{25}$, 0.04

   (e) 0.52, 52%   (f) $\frac{11}{25}$, 44%

4. (a) 207   (b) 119   (c) 310

5. (a) 4 – 5%   (b) about 11%

   (c) 5%, 0.5%   (d) more old people in UK

   (e) Saudi Arabia more males than females

6. peach 27°, apple 72°, strawberry 117°, banana 45°,
   pear 63°, orange 36°

7. (a) 5   (b) 8   (c) true

Page 225   sections 5.1, 5.2 and 5.3

1. (a) 5:3   (b) 156   (c) £160   2. (a) £10.80

   (b) 10 hours   3. (a) 2 km   (b) 600 m   4. (a) −2

   (b) 6   (c) −2   (d) −5   (e) −4

5. (a) −6   (b) 42   (c) 5

   (d) −9   (e) −44   6. (a) n^{th} term = $5n + 3$

   (b) difference = 7, n^{th} term = $7n - 5$

Page 235   sections 5.4 and 5.5

1. (a) enlargement   (b) yes   2. (a) enlargement

3. (a) G   (b) no shape is congruent to shape B

Page 245   sections 5.6 and 5.7

1. y: −1, 1, 3, 5, 7, coordinates: (0, −1), (1, 1), (2, 3), (3, 5), (4, 7)

2. (a) $y = x + 2$ (b) $x + y = 6$ or $y = 6 - x$ (c) $x = 5$

3. (a) 27 cm²   (b) 144 cm²   (c) 120 cm²

4. (a) 153.9 cm²   (b) 283.5 cm²   (c) 78.5 cm²

Page 271   sections 6.1 and 6.2

1. (a) 76%   (b) 17%   2. (a) £5.25   (b) £34.08

   (c) £89.10   3. (a) £621   (b) (i) 144 cm²   (ii) 129.96 cm²

4. (a) 0.1   (b) (i) $\frac{3}{8}$ (ii) $\frac{5}{8}$ (iii) $\frac{3}{8}$

5. (a) $\frac{18}{25} = 0.72$ (b) $\frac{7}{25} = 0.28$ (c) yes

6. (a) (1, 1), (1, 2), (1, 3), (1, 4), (2, 1), (2, 2), (2, 3), (2, 4), (3, 1),
   (3, 2), (3, 3), (3, 4), (4, 1), (4, 2), (4, 3), (4, 4)

   (b) $\frac{2}{16} = \frac{1}{8}$ (c) $\frac{1}{4}$

Page 282   sections 6.3 and 6.4

1. (a) 6700 g   (b) 5890 ml   (c) 0.35 km   (d) 600 kg

2. (a) true   (b) false   (c) false   (d) true

3. (a) true   (b) $6w + 2n + 2$

4. (a) $(n + 1)^2$ (b) y = 32

5. (a) $7x + 28$ (b) $12n - 6$ (c) $m^2 + mn$

   (d) $11n + 31$ (e) $8x + 26$ 6. (a) 6

   (b) 3   (c) 7   (d) $n + 34$

   (e) $n + 34 = 3n$ (f) $n = 17$

Page 301   sections 6.6, 6.7 and 6.8

1. (a) 045°   (b) 090°   (c) 135°   (d) 180°

   (e) 270°   (f) 225°   2. (a) 25 m   (b) ≈45 km

3. (a) 18.89   (b) 7.33   (c) 0.04, 0.074, 0.407, 0.704, 0.74

4. (a) 0.054   (b) 70   (c) 24.8   (d) £3.01

5. (a) 84 cm³   (b) 660 cm³   (c) 8

INDEX

Algebra — 51, 113, 171, 276
Alternate angles — 66
Angles — 66
Approximating — 46
Area — 27, 83, 241
Arithmatic without a calculator — 96
Averages — 147, 151

Bearings — 287
Binary numbers — 93
Brackets — 109, 171, 278

Calculator — 106
Centre of enlargement — 230
Centre of rotation — 156, 158
Checking answers — 46
Circles — 79
Circumference — 80
Collecting terms — 51, 276
Comparing sets of data — 150
Congruent shapes — 232
Construction — 74, 76
Coordinates — 132, 142
Corresponding angles — 66
Cube numbers — 16

Data collection — 192
Data in groups — 151, 192
Decimals — 97, 99, 294
Decimal places — 44

Enlargement — 226
Equations — 175, 279
Estimation — 46
Expressions — 53, 116
Eye of Horus — 42

Factors — 13
Fibonacci sequence — 146
Formulas — 113
Fractions, decimals, percentages — 60, 189
Fractions — 4, 185

Games — 50, 118
Geometrical reasoning — 66
Graphs — 120, 236

History of mathematics — 42, 93, 146, 209, 255
Horizontal lines — 120

Improper fractions — 4
Investigations — 18, 19, 56, 240
Isometric drawing — 283

Locus — 75

Map scales — 214
Mean — 147
Measures — 273

Median — 147
Mental arithmetic — 40, 94, 144, 208, 253
Metric units — 273
Metric and imperial units — 274
Mixed review — 34, 87, 137, 201, 247, 302
Mode — 147
Multiples — 13

Negative numbers — 20, 216
n^{th} term of sequence — 218

Order of operations — 106

Parallelogram — 30
Parallel lines — 66
Percentages — 62, 256
Perfect numbers — 209
Pi — 80
Pie charts — 193
Powers — 16
Prime factors — 15
Prime numbers — 13
Probability — 263
Problem solving — 180
Properties of numbers — 13
Proportion — 213
Puzzles — 39, 91, 142, 206, 252

Quadrilateral angles — 69

Range — 147
Ratio — 210
Real-life graphs — 125, 165
Recurring decimals — 61
Reflection — 129
Rotation — 156
Rounding — 44

Scale drawing — 290
Scale reading — 98
Scatter graphs — 196
Sequences — 1, 218
Spreadsheet on a computer — 198
Square numbers — 13
Straight line graphs — 120, 236
Substitution — 113, 276
Stem and leaf — 153

Tessellation — 233
Three dimensional objects — 283
Tower of Hanoi — 255
Transformations — 159
Trapezium — 30
Travel graphs — 166
Trial and improvement — 178
Two-way tables — 190

Vertical lines — 120
Volume — 297